Introduction to
SOIL
MICROBIOLOGY

Introduction to
SOIL
MICROBIOLOGY

MARTIN ALEXANDER
Associate Professor of Soil Science
Cornell University

JOHN WILEY & SONS, INC.
New York and London

Preface

Soil microbiology is not a new discipline, yet its entire history covers no more than a period of some eighty years. In the awakening era of microbiology, the study of soil organisms soon became an area of interest to a large number of the early bacteriologists, and the pioneering investigations of Winogradsky, Omeliansky, and Beijerinck still stand as major contributions to our knowledge of the bacterial population. At the same time, it became apparent to soil scientists that the surface crust of the earth is not merely a static physicochemical matrix upon which green plants grow but it is also a biological system in a continuous dynamic equilibrium.

The last few years have seen numerous significant contributions in and from soil microbiology. In the realm of applied science, the studies leading to the isolation of the chemotherapeutic antibiotics, the large-scale utilization of legume inoculation, and the investigations on the influence of the microflora on the effectiveness and persistence of agricultural pesticides can be cited. There has also been considerable emphasis on the interrelationships between saprophytes and pathogens in the soil as related to plant disease. In the realm of pure science, information on the ecology, function, and biochemistry of the microflora has grown considerably so that a clear picture of soil biology is beginning to emerge.

The present publication is not a definitive monograph but rather an introduction to soil microbiology. The innumerable developments in recent years make a complete review impossible within the scope of a single volume. Some of the more detailed points have been omitted for the sake of brevity, yet, where conflicts still exist, the contrasting viewpoints are presented. I have taken it upon myself in certain problematic areas, however, to weigh the evidence and present the stronger case. Time may change these views, but it is in the very nature of science to be in a continual state of flux and for the errors of one generation to be mended by the next.

Soil microbiology is not a pure discipline. Its parentage may be traced through bacteriology, mycology, and soil science; biochemistry and plant pathology have also made their mark, especially in recent years. Any approach to soil microbiology consequently must consider the variety of individuals and disciplines that have created the mold. The approach herein is to use microbiology, soil science, and biochemistry as partners. Where possible, each transformation is viewed as a reaction of importance to soil and to crop production, as a biological process brought about by specific microorganisms whose habitat is the earth's crust, and as a sequence of enzymatic steps.

Because these three disciplines are woven together into the fabric of soil microbiology, the reader should be familiar to some extent with basic principles of soil science, microbiology, and the chemistry of biological systems. In the framework of agriculture, the microflora is of significance because it has both a beneficial and a detrimental influence upon man's ability to feed himself. For the microbial inhabitant, the soil functions as a unique ecosystem to which the organism must become adapted and from which it must obtain sustenance. But in the last analysis the microbiologist can find definitive answers as to how these processes are brought about only through biochemical inquiries.

The presentation is made in essentially three general divisions. Initially there is a discussion of the major groups of microorganisms, particularly their description, taxonomy, abundance, and their significance and function. Then the major transformations carried out by the microflora are reviewed, including the reactions centered upon carbon, nitrogen, phosphorus, sulfur, iron, and manganese. These are presented in terms of agronomic importance, the specific organisms concerned, and the biochemical pathways involved. Lastly, ecological interrelationships affecting the microflora, soil-borne pathogens, and higher plants are discussed.

References are of great value not only to the research worker but to the advanced student as well. The blind acceptance of secondary sources when the primary material is readily accessible is not the hallmark of the serious student. Where available, reviews are cited at the end of each chapter so that the finer points of each topic may be sought out. Pertinent original citations are likewise included since these permit student and researcher alike to examine the original source, observe the techniques utilized, and draw their own conclusions. Emphasis is given to the more recent papers, but certain of the classical works are included, particularly where the studies have been of such a nature as to define a unique approach. Absence of citations reflects not the lack of quality of an investigation but only the lack of adequate space between the covers of any single book.

As an introduction to soil microbiology, many things will be left unsaid. It is hoped that a groundwork will be laid herein for a more full inquiry on the part of the reader. If this goal is reached even in part, the book will have served its purpose.

Two systems of abbreviation are used in the tabular presentation of large populations. One uses the negative exponent of the base 10, the second utilizes the positive exponent. The latter system has been adopted in this book.

I express my thanks to the following publishers and journals for the approval to use copyrighted materials: Academic Press (Ch. 10, fig. 3); *Acta Chemica Scandinavica* (Ch. 19, fig. 2); *Acta Microbiologica Polonica* (Ch. 6, fig. 2); *Annals of Botany* (Ch. 5, fig. 2); Cambridge University Press (Ch. 6, fig. 3; Ch. 14, fig. 1; Ch. 17, fig. 2); *Canadian Journal of Microbiology* (Ch. 9, fig. 2; Ch. 10, fig. 2; Ch. 11, fig. 3); The Iowa State University Press (Ch. 4, fig. 3); *Journal of General and Applied Microbiology* (Ch. 5, fig. 1); Macmillan and Company (Ch. 11, fig. 2; Ch. 22, fig. 2; Ch. 23, fig. 1; Ch. 23, fig. 2); Martinus Nijhoff (Ch. 17, fig. 1); *Ohio Journal of Science* (Ch. 4, fig. 2); Oliver and Boyd (Ch. 6, fig. 1); Springer-Verlag (Ch. 22, fig. 1); The University of Chicago Press (Ch. 2, fig. 3); *Van Zee Tot Land* (Ch. 15, fig. 1); The Williams and Wilkins Company (Ch. 7, fig. 2; Ch. 16, fig. 2; Ch. 21, fig. 2; Ch. 22, fig. 3; Ch. 23, fig. 4).

MARTIN ALEXANDER

Ithaca, New York
April, 1961

Contents

ix

MINERAL TRANSFORMATIONS

ECOLOGICAL INTERRELATIONSHIPS

MICROBIAL ECOLOGY

1

The Soil Environment

In an introduction to the microbiology of soil, it is essential to consider carefully the nature of the environment in which the microorganisms find themselves. The forces which play a role in the dynamics of soil populations and the effect of the population upon its environment are governed to a very great extent by the physical and chemical properties of the soil. It is to these, therefore, that attention must first be drawn.

The term *soil* refers to the outer, loose material of the earth's surface, a layer distinctly different from the underlying bedrock. A number of features characterize this region of the earth's crust. Agriculturally, it is the region supporting plant life and from which plants obtain their mechanical support and many of their nutrients. Chemically, the soil contains a multitude of organic substances not found in the underlying strata. For the microbiologist, the soil environment is unique in several ways: it contains a vast population of bacteria, actinomycetes, fungi, algae, and protozoa; it is one of the most dynamic sites of biological interactions in nature; and it is the region in which occur many of the biochemical reactions concerned in the destruction of organic matter, in the weathering of rocks, and in the nutrition of agricultural crops.

General Description of Soil

The soil is composed of five major components—mineral matter, water, air, organic matter, and a living population. The quantity of these constituents is not the same in all soils but varies with the local-

3

ity. Of the inanimate portion, the amount of mineral and organic matter is relatively fixed at a single site; the proportion of air and water, however, fluctuates. Air and water together account for approximately half the soil's volume, the volume so occupied representing the *pore space*. The mineral fraction, contributing generally slightly less than half the volume, originates from the disintegration and decomposition of rocks, but the fraction has become, during the course of time, modified from the rocks from which it was derived. Organic matter usually contributes some 3 to 6 per cent of the total. The living portion of the soil body—including various small animals and microorganisms—makes up appreciably less than 1 per cent of the total volume, yet it is undoubtedly essential for crop production and soil fertility.

The inorganic portion of soil, because of its influence upon nutrient availability, aeration, and water retention, has a marked effect upon the microbial population. In the mineral fraction are found particles of a variety of sizes, ranging from those visible to the unaided eye to clay particles seen only under the microscope. The various structural units are classified on the basis of their dimensions. At the largest extreme are stones and gravel, materials whose diameter exceeds 2.0 mm. Somewhat smaller are the sand particles which have a diameter of 0.05 to 2.0 mm. Structures whose diameter falls between 0.002 and 0.05 mm are classified as silt, and those with a diameter less than 0.002 mm (2μ) are considered to be clay particles.

The individual particle types differ from one another in other ways in addition to their dimensions. Thus, many more individual structural units are present in one gram of pure clay than in a gram of silt, and more particles are found in a gram of silt than in a like quantity of sand. More important, however, is the far greater surface area exposed per unit of mass of clay than for the larger particles (table 1). Because the chemical properties and activities of the particles are directly related to their surface area, the status of clay as a reactive constituent in the soil body assumes prominence. In turn, the clay fraction is the most influential in terms of microbiological effects. The clay minerals contain silicon, oxygen, and aluminum; also, iron, magnesium, potassium, calcium, sodium, and other elements may be found to varying degrees. Three of the major clay minerals in soils of the United States are kaolinite, montmorillonite, and illite. Subsequent discussion will reveal, in part, the unique biological role of these and other clay minerals.

TABLE 1

Size and Surface Area of Soil Particles

(Millar, Turk, and Foth, 1958)

Particle Type	Diameter	No. of Particles/g [*]	Surface Area
	mm		sq cm/g
Fine gravel	2.00–1.00	90	11.3
Coarse sand	1.00–0.50	722	22.7
Medium sand	0.50–0.25	5,780	45.4
Fine sand	0.25–0.10	46,200	90.7
Very fine sand	0.10–0.05	722,000	227
Silt	0.05–0.002	5,780,000	454
Clay	<0.002	90,300,000	11,300

[*] Assumed to have spherical shapes. Calculated on the basis of maximum diameter of the particle type.

By comparison, silts exert a lesser influence on the physical, chemical, and biological properties of soil. The sand particle, a comparatively large unit exposing a small surface area, is of still lesser consequence. Sand, however, does affect the movement of water and air.

For the purposes of description, textural classes have been established. *Texture* is determined on the basis of the soil's content of sand, silt, and clay, and the name of the textural class is ascertained from the triangle shown in figure 1. To obtain the class name, a line originating at the point corresponding to the percentage of silt is drawn inward and parallel to the left side of the triangle. From the point corresponding to the percentage of clay, a second line is drawn parallel to the base of the triangle. The class name is given by the segment in which the two lines intersect.

The diagram, it will be noted, introduces a new term, *loam*. A loam is a soil not dominated by any of the particle sizes. It may be further noted that considerable emphasis in the textural triangle is placed upon clay content; thus, a soil with less than 40 per cent clay may be classified as a sandy clay. This emphasis is a necessary outcome of the great reactivity of clays. Often, the adjectives light and heavy are used in technical or common parlance. Soils dominated by large particles exhibit a coarse texture and are termed light. Heavy

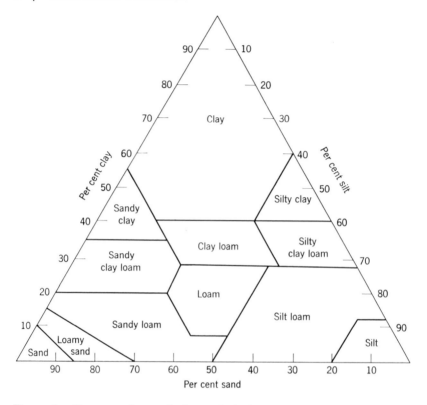

Figure 1. The textural triangle from which the names of textural classes are obtained.

soils, by contrast, have a fine texture and are dominated by small particles. It should be borne in mind that textural designations serve a far greater purpose than simple nomenclatural subdivisions because the ease with which a soil is worked, its aeration, and moisture rela-tionships—hence its biological activity—are governed to a great extent by texture.

A vertical section cut into the soil reveals that it possesses a dis-tinct *profile*, certain features distinguishing the thin, outer mantle of the earth. In the profile are several horizontal layers known as *hori-zons*. Even the most casual examination of the layers reveals appre-ciable differences in structure, texture, and color. These horizons are used in the classification of soils.

As a rule, three major layers make up the profile, the A, B, and C horizons. These in turn are often subdivided by the use of appropriate subscripts, such as A_1, A_2, and A_3. A typical profile may contain (a) a shallow or thick surface zone of decaying organic debris, (b) an underlying horizon from which certain inorganic constituents have been removed during the long period of soil formation, (c) a horizon at greater depth in which is deposited some of the constituents from the upper layers, and (d) a bottom layer similar to the original material from which the soil had developed. The organic debris layer is the A_0 horizon. The A horizon, the surface soil, designates the stratum subjected to marked leaching. It is also the layer of greatest biological concern as roots, small animals, and microorganisms are here most dense. In this zone, the concentration of organic matter is highest; hence it is the dominant reservoir of microbial food. The B horizon, the subsoil underlying the A horizon, has little organic matter, few plant roots, and a sparse microflora. In it, iron and aluminum compounds often accumulate. The A and B horizons together represent the true soil. At the very bottom of the profile is the C horizon, the layer containing the parent material of the soil proper. In this stratum, organic matter is present in very small quantities, and little life is noted.

No single description adequately characterizes the nature of soil profiles as individual profiles and horizons differ from one another in their thickness, chemical constitution, aeration, color, texture, and water relations. It is not surprising, therefore, that they support microbial populations differing in size and in activity. The attention of the microbiologist is usually drawn to the surface soil because here the population is most dense and the nutrient supply greatest; likewise, the beneficial or detrimental effects of the microflora on higher plants are most pronounced in the A horizon. On the other hand, the subsoil modifies the characteristics of the surface layer as a habitat for both macro- and microorganisms.

Differences among Soils

There are several broad soil belts on the earth's surface. Large areas of the Northern Hemisphere contain *podzolic* soils, a group developed in temperate, humid climates in forest areas. These soils usually are poor in organic matter and tend to be acidic. Podzolization, the formation of the podzolic type of soil, is of considerable interest to the microbiologist since the process is associated with the decomposition of organic matter accumulated at the soil surface and with the downward movement of organic substances formed or released by the subterranean micro-inhabitants. *Chernozemic* soils occupy vast areas of land in temperate regions and smaller areas in the tropics. They commonly have a thick A_1 horizon which often is particularly rich in organic matter. In tropical or semitropical zones are found *latosolic* soils; in these, the horizons are usually not distinct. Latosolic soils are frequently red or yellow in color because of the prominence of iron oxides. In other regions are found *desertic* soils which, as the name suggests, are formed in conditions of low rainfall. They contain little organic matter, a result of the sparse vegetation in the arid areas. In the *tundra,* the temperatures are low and the cool climate limits the activity and development of higher plants as well as microorganisms. Several representative profiles are shown in figure 2.

The broad soil belts delineated above have been investigated intensively and a classification system established. A review of the classification scheme currently used in soil science is beyond the scope of the present discussion, but the reader can obtain further information from the references cited at the end of the chapter.

The subdivisions within the profile and the common classification schemes are applied to *mineral soils,* whose dominant solid matter is inorganic. *Organic soils*—including the mucks and peats—are widespread and frequently are highly fertile in terms of crop-producing capacity. Organic soils generally have 60 to 95 per cent organic matter and, therefore, only a small proportion of mineral constituents. As a result, their chemical and physical properties do not resemble those of the mineral soils. Mucks and peats are formed in bogs and marshes wherein conditions for the microbiological decomposition of organic matter are poor, and large quantities of carbonaceous substances accumulate. With time, the accumulated residues assume the brown or black coloration typical of organic soils. Because of the way in which mucks and peats are formed, they do not have the usual type of profile. Unfortunately, organic soils have not received their deserved attention so that much of the chemical and microbiological literature is concerned specifically with mineral soils.

Local differences are found among soils. In moving from one area to the next, the depth, color, pH, and chemical composition of the various horizons are found to be dissimilar. The variations may often be traced to the nature of the rock material from which the soil developed, climatic factors, the type of vegetation, and topography. In-

Figure 2. Profiles of three great soil groups. Left: latosol; center: chernozem; right: podzol. (Courtesy of W. M. Johnson.)

deed, it is common to find a single farm situated on several soil types. The differences may be small or they may be appreciable. Physical, chemical, and biological variations need not be measured in miles, however, as many differences can be found within a small area. Thus, a poorly drained area a short distance from a well-drained site possesses a somewhat altered microbial population. In later chapters, it will be demonstrated that these differences can be measured even in centimeters; e.g., the microorganisms immediately surrounding the root surface are not the same as those just one centimeter away from the plant tissue. For the microbiologist, therefore, the soil type is of great consequence as is the microscopic environment within any one soil.

Some Physical Considerations

Solid materials occupy only about half the soil's volume. The remainder is composed of pores filled with air and water, both essential for life. The amount of pore space is dependent upon the texture, structure, and organic matter content. In clay soils, the pores are generally small. In sandy areas, on the other hand, the pores are large, but the total quantity of pore space is less than in soils rich in fine particles. The size of individual pores and the total pore space affect the movement and retention of water. In sandy soils, water moves rapidly through the large pores, but little is retained. The numerous micropores of heavier soils, on the other hand, contribute to the greater water retention.

The porosity of heavy soils is affected by the state of aggregation. *Aggregates* are large structural units composed of clay and silt particles. In contrast with sand, silt, and clay, aggregates are temporary structures whose stability varies with land management practices, meteorological conditions, microbial activity, and other factors. They range in size from large bodies which are easily broken apart to small granules of firm consistency. In addition to their effects upon water and air movement—which in turn regulate the activities of the microflora—aggregates are of interest microbiologically since the cell material and excretions of bacteria, fungi, and actinomycetes are factors affecting the formation and stability of the granules.

The water relationships of soil and the biological effects of moisture have received much study. In certain regions or during certain parts of the year, the soil is quite wet, and too much water is present for optimum biological action. At other times, the moisture level is low, and microorganisms suffer. Because soil water is derived from atmospheric precipitation, the supply is quite variable, and marked fluctuations in the soil water content are the rule in nature.

Part of the water moves with the pull of gravity, this being called *free* or *gravitational water*. Such water is situated within the larger soil pores that are often filled with air; as a result, gravitational water directly affects aeration. In addition, some water is retained against the gravitational pull; the retention against gravity results from the attraction between the water and other soil constituents. Not all of the water in soil is biologically available, and only part of that portion held against gravitational attraction can be used by living systems. Apparently, the non-biological constituents of soil compete well with microorganisms for water, an indication of the great binding power of the inanimate materials.

The soil solution contains a number of inorganic salts, but except in arid regions, the solution is quite dilute. The liquid phase is of importance to the subterranean flora because it contains several required nutrients. As needed food materials are found in the soil solution, the downward movement of water removes from the zone of microbial accessibility substances essential for proliferation. Nitrogen, potassium, magnesium, sulfur, and calcium but little phosphorus or organic matter are lost through leaching in this way. The rate and magnitude of such losses are regulated by the quantity of precipitation, the presence and type of vegetation, and the soil texture.

Aeration and moisture are directly related because that portion of the pore space not containing water is filled with gas. Air moves into those pores which are free of water; water in turn displaces the air. The gas found in the profile may be said to constitute the soil atmosphere. This subterranean atmosphere is not identical with that in the air above the earth or that at a point several inches from the soil surface. Commonly, the CO_2 concentration exceeds the atmospheric level by a factor of ten-fold to one-hundred-fold, but O_2 is less plentiful. The difference in the composition of the above-ground and below-ground atmospheres arises from the respiration of microorganisms and plant roots, living organisms consuming O_2 and releasing CO_2. Diffusion of the gases tends to right somewhat the concentration gradient so that the content of O_2 and CO_2 is governed by both the diffusion rate and by the rate of respiration. As a rule, the O_2 content declines and the CO_2 level in the gas phase increases with depth.

Changes in the soil atmosphere alter the size and functions of the microflora as both CO_2 and O_2 are necessary for growth. It is of interest, therefore, to speculate on the possibility of attaining a well-aerated (or more appropriately, oxygenated) soil. A well-aerated soil, from the microbiological viewpoint, is one in which microbial processes requiring O_2 proceed at a rapid rate. However, it is unlikely that soil ever becomes sufficiently aerated to satisfy all of its inhabitants because of the problems of gas movement into the small pores and microenvironments in which the organisms are situated. Hence, a soil that is sufficiently well aerated for the growth of higher plants does not necessarily contain an optimum concentration of O_2 for the microflora.

Improper aeration, the opposite extreme, is associated with poor drainage and waterlogging. Since small pores have a greater tenacity for water than the larger pores, the aeration status of heavy soils, which are dominated by micropores, is often poor; that is, a large part of the volume is occupied by liquid rather than by gas. In conditions where the O_2 supply is inadequate, the rates of many microbial transformations are reduced, and some processes may be eliminated. In O_2-deficient habitats, new microbiological processes may come into play, some of which may be deleterious to plant development; for example, N_2 or CH_4 is evolved, organic inhibitors appear, and sulfide, ferrous, and manganous ions accumulate during periods of O_2 deficiencies.

Some Chemical Considerations

Microorganisms obtain many of their nutrients from the inanimate portion of soil so that some consideration needs to be given to the chemical composition of the environment. Certain species get carbon or nitrogen from the atmosphere as CO_2, CH_4, or N_2, but the bulk of these two elements as well as the remaining microbial foods are derived from solid or liquid phases of the soil.

A chemical analysis of two representative podzolic soils is given in table 2. It will be noted from these data that considerable differences exist between the two soils. In general, the chemical composition of soils varies to a great extent, but certain elements are always abundant. Except for the organic soils, whose constitution is entirely different, the dominant substance is silicon dioxide. It often accounts for 70 to 90 per cent of the total mass. Aluminum and iron oxides are

TABLE 2

Chemical Composition of Two Podzolic Soils

(Marbut, 1935)

Hori-zon	Depth	Per Cent of Various Constituents									
		SiO_2	TiO_2	Fe_2O_3	Al_2O_3	MnO	CaO	MgO	K_2O	Na_2O	P_2O_5
	in.										
		Becket Fine Sandy Loam									
A_1	0–6	52.95	0.66	1.08	7.04	0.01	0.90	0.15	2.06	0.40	0.13
A_2	6–11	83.32	0.90	1.69	6.73	0.01	0.54	0.18	2.89	0.46	0.04
B_1	11–13	69.60	0.79	3.99	9.61	0.01	0.65	0.33	3.41	0.46	0.08
B_2	13–24	72.67	0.70	3.58	10.32	0.02	0.62	0.41	3.45	0.67	0.08
C	24–36	77.86	0.53	3.15	10.00	0.03	0.54	0.48	3.79	0.55	0.08
		Miami Silt Loam									
A_1	0–2	71.82	0.57	2.91	9.06	0.13	0.81	0.62	2.02	1.06	0.13
A_2	2–5	77.08	0.65	3.08	9.50	0.14	0.63	0.64	2.03	1.02	0.10
A_3	5–12	77.35	0.65	3.22	10.09	0.12	0.53	0.62	2.19	1.16	0.08
B_1	16–32	69.52	0.65	5.92	14.06	0.08	0.70	1.20	2.38	0.97	0.09
B_2	32–36	65.64	0.60	5.60	14.73	0.13	1.57	1.97	2.64	1.39	0.12
C	>36	47.93	0.39	3.34	8.56	0.07	13.59	6.05	1.93	0.85	0.09

likewise abundant, contributing approximately 4 to 12 and 1 to 5 per cent, respectively. Lesser quantities of calcium, magnesium, potassium, titanium, manganese, sodium, nitrogen, phosphorus, and sulfur are found. The organic matter content of mineral soils is variable, the range extending from 0.50 to 10 per cent of the total weight. The nitrogen content is usually approximately one-twentieth the organic matter level, i.e., 0.025 to 0.50 per cent. Except for carbon and potassium, the major elements needed for the synthesis of protoplasm are present to the extent of less than 1 per cent of the soil weight.

It is evident from table 2 that depth affects the chemical composition. Generally, the surface soil is richer in silicon dioxide than the subsoil, a result of the downward movement and deposition in the B horizon of other constituents during the long periods required for the formation of a soil. Organic matter and nitrogen are likewise most conspicuous in the surface layer. Conversely, the concentration of calcium and magnesium is frequently less in the A than in the lower horizons.

The statement that a soil has 3.1 per cent organic matter or 0.14 per cent nitrogen does not mean that these quantities are readily available to microorganisms. Only a small portion of the total organic carbon or nitrogen is utilized by the microflora each year; the rest remains as a slowly available reservoir. Therefore, the level of organic matter or nitrogen reflects more a potential than an actual supply. It is the available nutrient—a common term but one that has frequently eluded chemical characterization—which is of immediate significance to the microscopic inhabitants. By contrast, elements found in lower concentrations than carbon and nitrogen may be present in amounts sufficient to satisfy fully the biological requirement for them. For example, the need for magnesium, sulfur, and potassium is small, and the supply probably exceeds the demand in most circumstances. The same is usually true for those inorganic nutrients which are required in minute amounts. Trace nutrients include zinc, copper, molybdenum, and cobalt. Because of such considerations of food supply and food demand and the meager information on nutrient availability in soil, elemental analyses have only a limited value. Nevertheless, other means are available to determine which substances limit the population of microorganisms.

A factor that must be considered in a discussion of the nutrient supply is the remarkable ability of soils to retain ions. Cations (positively charged ions) such as NH_4^+, K^+, Ca^{++}, and Mg^{++} are removed from solution by clay minerals, which, because they possess a negative electrical charge, attract positively charged ions. Soil organic matter also retains cations, and its ability to remove charged ions from solution must be considered with that of the clay. In fact, on a weight basis, organic colloids are more active than clays in ion exchange. This retention of positive ions leads to an important soil characteristic, that of *cation exchange*. In cation exchange, one positively charged ion about the clay complex is replaced and released by another type of ion. Cations may be listed in order of their usual replacing capacity. In descending order, they are H^+, Ca^{++}, Mg^{++}, K^+, NH_4^+, and Na^+. Ionic exchange, through its effects upon nutrient availability and acidity, has a considerable bearing upon biological transformations.

An important characteristic of soil is its *cation exchange capacity*, which, as the name suggests, is a measure of the capacity of the clay and organic colloids to remove positive ions from solution. The data are usually expressed in terms of milliequivalents of ions removed per 100 g of soil. The exchange capacity varies with the amount and type of clay and organic matter. Because soils of heavy texture are richer in both clay and organic matter, they tend to have higher cation exchange capacities than light soils; therefore they may remove more of those nutrients that exist in the cationic form.

A number of the inorganic substances assimilated by microorganisms are anionic. These negatively charged ions are represented by bicarbonate, nitrate, phosphate, sulfate, and molybdate. Anion exchange, however, is never appreciable in soil; hence, it is of little importance biologically. Thus, ammonium is readily removed from the soil solution whereas nitrate, its oxidized counterpart, is not strongly adsorbed by the colloidal complex.

The Organic Fraction

The *organic fraction* of soil, often termed *humus,* is a product of the synthetic and decomposing activities of the microflora. Since it contains the organic carbon and nitrogen needed for microbial development, it is the dominant food reservoir. Because humus is both a product of microbial metabolism and an important food source, the organic fraction is of especial interest to the microbiologist.

When plant or animal remains fall upon or are incorporated into the soil, they are subjected to decomposition. From the original residues, a variety of products are formed. As the original material and the initial products undergo further decomposition, they are converted to brown or black organic complexes. At this stage, there no longer remains any trace of the original material. The native organic fraction originates from two sources: the original plant debris entering the soil and the microorganisms within the soil body. The latter work upon the former and synthesize microbial protoplasm and new compounds which become part of the organic fraction.

Humus exists in a dynamic state. It is under continual attack, yet it is being reformed by the subterranean population from the remains of the land's vegetation. The decomposition leads to a loss of some of the carbonaceous materials; at the same time, new microbial tissue is generated. The rate of carbon loss can be related to the structure and fertility of a soil; it also reflects the level of biological activity.

In undisturbed land, the organic matter content remains relatively constant. Modification of the habitat by cropping or by altering the aeration changes the level of humus as the original equilibrium between the rate of carbon addition and the rate of its volatilization is upset. The large amount of organic matter in peat soils, for example, is associated with a slow decomposition of vegetative remains in poorly drained, poorly oxygenated circumstances. When the area is drained, the O_2 level rises, and the accumulated carbonaceous matter is decomposed and volatilized as CO_2.

Chemists have been attempting to unravel the details of humus composition since the earliest days of soil science, but much is still to be discovered. It has been pointed out above that the organic fraction is derived from (a) plant constituents which are modified by the microflora and (b) constituents of microbial cells and products of

TABLE 3

Several Constituents of the Organic Molecules Found in Humus

I. Amino acids	VII. Pentose sugars
Glutamic acid	Xylose
Alanine	Arabinose
Valine	Ribose
Proline	VIII. Hexose sugars
Cystine	Glucose
Phenylalanine	Galactose
II. Purines	Mannose
Guanine	IX. Sugar alcohols
Adenine	Inositol
III. Pyrimidines	Mannitol
Cytosine	X. Methyl sugars
Thymine	Rhamnose
Uracil	Fucose
IV. Aromatic molecules	2-O-methyl-D-xylose
V. Uronic acids	2-O-methyl-D-arabinose
Glucuronic acid	XI. Aliphatic acids
Galacturonic acid	Acetic acid
VI. Amino sugars	Formic acid
Glucosamine	Lactic acid
N-acetylglucosamine	Succinic acid

microbial metabolism which are relatively resistant to decay and there-fore persist for some time after death of the organism. In terms of specific elements, the organic fraction contains compounds of carbon, hydrogen, oxygen, nitrogen, phosphorus, sulfur, and small amounts of other elements. Only a small portion of the total is soluble in water, but much can be brought into solution by alkali. In terms of types of compounds, humus contains a number of polymerized substances; aromatic molecules, polysaccharides of several kinds, bound amino acids, polymers of uronic acids, and phosphorus-containing compounds can be demonstrated (table 3). It must be emphasized, nevertheless, that no definite composition can be assigned to the organic fraction. Variations in its constitution are observed not only in different locali-ties—a natural consequence of differences in temperature, rainfall, and mineral matter—but also within individual fields. Humus should be considered as a portion of the soil which is composed of a hetero-geneous group of substances, most having an unknown parentage and an unknown chemical structure.

Summary

The physical and chemical characteristics of soil determine the nature of the environment in which microorganisms are found. These environmental characteristics in turn affect the composition of the microscopic population both qualitatively and quantitatively. It is from the soil that the water, air, and the inorganic and organic nu-trients are obtained; likewise, the soil serves as a buffer to the drastic changes that occur above the ground. The microbiologist often con-siders the soil as a vast, dynamic medium for the subterranean in-habitants as well as a site in which substances not available to higher plants are made available through microbial agencies.

In the succeeding chapters, emphasis will be placed upon the biological transformations occurring within the soil. It is essential, however, that the reader keep in mind the fact that the microscopic inhabitants do not exist in an isolated state but rather that they are just a part of a highly complex environment regulated by natural forces and, to a lesser extent, by man's activities. An appreciation of soil microbiology can only be gained by viewing the soil system as a dynamic whole, as a natural environment in which microorganisms play an essential and often poorly understood role.

REFERENCES

Baver, L. D. 1956. *Soil physics.* John Wiley and Sons, New York.

Bear, F. E., ed. 1955. *Chemistry of the soil.* Reinhold Publishing Corp., New York.

Black, C. A. 1957. *Soil-plant relationships.* John Wiley and Sons, New York.

Buckman, H. O., and N. C. Brady. 1960. *The nature and properties of soils.* The Macmillan Co., New York.

Marbut, C. F. 1935. Soils of the United States. In O. E. Baker, ed., *Atlas of American agriculture,* Government Printing Office, Washington.

Millar, C. E., L. M. Turk, and H. D. Foth. 1958. *Fundamentals of soil science.* John Wiley and Sons, New York.

Russell, E. W. 1950. *Soil conditions and plant growth.* Longmans, Green and Co., London.

Thompson, L. M. 1957. *Soils and soil fertility.* McGraw-Hill Book Co., New York.

2

Bacteria

The microbial population of the soil is made up of five major groups, the bacteria, actinomycetes, fungi, algae, and protozoa. In its early history, soil microbiology was considered to be synonymous with soil bacteriology since the other four groups were viewed as aliens of no consequence, but it soon became evident that this view was shortsighted and that the others were of great ecological, biochemical, and agricultural significance. Nevertheless, bacteria are the most abundant group, usually more numerous than the other four combined.

The number of bacterial cells in the soil is always great, but the individuals are small, rarely more than several microns in length. Because of the minute size of the bacteria and the large cells or extensive filaments of the other four groups, the bacteria probably account for appreciably less than half of the total microbiological tissue present in soil. No procedure for estimating microbial mass or numbers gives an indication of the importance of each taxonomic type. In adequately aerated soils, the bacteria and fungi dominate whereas bacteria alone account for almost all the biological and chemical changes in environments containing little or no O_2. Although transformations similar to those of the bacteria are carried out by the other groups, the bacteria stand out because of their capacity for rapid growth and vigorous decomposition of a variety of natural substrates.

An ecological differentiation of soil microorganisms in general and bacteria in particular was proposed by Winogradsky (29). This classification places the bacteria into two broad divisions, the *autochthonous* or indigenous species and the *zymogenous* or fermentation-producing organisms. The autochthonous population consists of the

19

numerous indigenous bacteria whose abundance is not subject to marked fluctuations. Their nutrient supply is derived from the soil organic fraction, and no external nutrients or energy sources are required; hence, their numbers remain relatively constant. Zymogenous organisms, those most active in chemical transformations, are usually scarce, but they flourish when organic nutrients are added. The actively fermenting species therefore need foods provided from without for their growth, but the supply is readily exhausted; thus, the zymogenous bacteria respond rapidly to soil amendment, become and remain numerous as long as the nutrients are available, then decline once their food source is depleted.

Winogradsky's ecological scheme is only one means of classifying the bacteria in natural environments. Bacteria are also divided on a systematic or taxonomic basis by the system proposed in *Bergey's manual of determinative bacteriology*. Other schemes provide for physiological differentiation using a variety of nutritional and metabolic characteristics including the nature of the energy source, the carbohydrates used for growth, the capacity to utilize N_2 as nitrogen source, etc. The ability to grow in the absence of O_2 is an important biochemical trait which has led to three separate and distinct categories: *aerobes*, which must have access to O_2; *anaerobes*, which grow

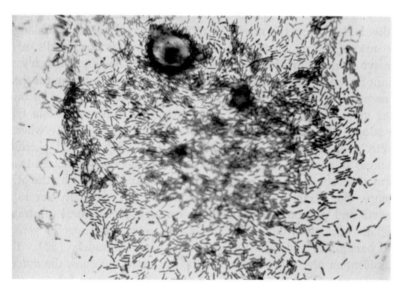

Figure 1. Rod-shaped bacteria developing in soil. (Courtesy of S. Ishizawa.)

only in the absence of O_2; and *facultative anaerobes*, developing either in the absence or presence of the gas.

Cell structure also serves as a means of bacterial characterization. Three morphological types are known, the *bacilli* or rod-shaped bacteria, which are the most numerous (figure 1), the *cocci* or spherical-shaped cells, and the *spirilla* or spirals. The latter are not common in soil. Some of the bacilli persist in unfavorable conditions by the formation of endospores that function as part of the normal life cycle of the bacterium. These endospores often endure in adverse environments because of their great resistance to both prolonged desiccation and to high temperatures. Spore-forming genera are present among the aerobic and anaerobic bacteria. The endospore can persist in a dormant state long after the lack of food or water has led to the death of vegetative cells. When conditions conducive to vegetative growth return, the spore germinates and a new organism emerges.

Distribution and Abundance

A determination of the numbers of viable bacteria in pure culture is a relatively simple procedure by plate counting or other means. The situation is far more difficult in a highly heterogeneous biological system such as the soil, where conventional microbiological techniques only estimate a portion of the total number of bacteria. No one medium is adequate nutritionally for all the species present since the growth requirements for many strains are unknown, and the observed count represents only a fraction of the total. A second limitation arises from the fact that bacteria frequently occur in the soil as colonies, and these may not disintegrate when the soil dilutions are shaken so that estimates tend to be low.

The standard methods of examining soils for viable counts often give variable numbers, and the errors in sampling and in sample preparation are frequently far greater than the variations inherent in the counting procedure itself. This limitation can be minimized by the use of many composites prepared from numerous borings made in the field. It is far better to use many subsamples than numerous replicate plates per dilution since the variation among duplicate soil samples is far greater than the variation between replicate plates or replicate dilutions (10). Not uncommon is the observation of greater variation between estimates made at the same time in different areas of a field than between counts made at a single location at various times of the year. The uninitiated must always bear in mind the vast population that exists in this highly heterogeneous environment. The presence of a single rootlet or particle of plant debris may cause a microecological effect of magnitude sufficient to change the population ten- or a hundred-fold. The microflora should be viewed, therefore, in microecological rather than in gross terms, for apparently minor deviations in moisture, organic matter, or pH may have drastic influences at points one centimeter apart, no less one meter or one mile apart.

Various procedures have been proposed for the direct microscopic examination of bacteria in soil. Conn (4) suggested a technique involving suspending the soil aliquot in 0.015 per cent gelatin, spreading the preparation over a calibrated area of a microscope slide, staining with phenolic rose bengal, and examining under the oil immersion objective. This microscopic procedure is not appropriate for investigations of the chemical activities of bacteria, but it is well suited for quantitative studies and for observation of the major morphological types. A more refined microscopic technique has been described which entails the incorporation of weighed amounts of soil in melted agar and the addition of drops of the agar infusion to a calibrated hemocytometer. The suspension is stained and then examined microscopically (12). If the amount of soil, the volume of gelatin or agar, and the area over which the smear is spread are known, then the bacterial numbers can be determined quantitatively.

A procedure developed independently by Rossi and Cholodny and commonly known as the Rossi-Cholodny buried slide or contact slide method has been used extensively for qualitative studies. A microscope slide is buried in the soil, and after appropriate periods the slide is removed, the larger debris carefully dislodged, and the microbial film adhering to and developing upon the glass surface stained with phenolic rose bengal. The Rossi-Cholodny slide is an excellent ecological tool as it allows microorganisms to develop in the physical posture typifying their normal position and associative relationships with their neighbors. Recognition of broad morphological categories and the effect of soil treatments is possible, but the chief advantage of this technique is as a means of assessing associations and interrelations between microorganisms and inert soil particles, plant roots, and other organisms.

The abundance of many bacterial, algal, and protozoan types cannot be estimated by the methods described above; for example, some organisms never produce recognizable colonies on agar media. For these, the dilution or most probable number technique is used, a method of estimating microbial density without direct enumeration. Following the inoculation of known volumes of a ten-fold soil dilution series into flasks of nutrient media adapted to the specific organism under study, growth will commence providing the inoculum contains one or more cells. Thus, if growth occurs in the culture prepared from the 10^5 but not the 10^6 dilution, the population of that microbial type is taken as between 10^5 and 10^6. Quantification is achieved by inoculating five or more replicate flasks of medium with each dilution, recording the number of flasks showing turbidity or growth at each dilution, and making use of appropriate most probable number tables. The dilution method is far less precise than plating, but it gives data not obtainable by use of agar media and has even permitted the enumeration of nitrifying bacteria as well as parasitic strains of certain plant pathogens whose abundance in soil could not be estimated readily by conventional means (3, 17).

Estimates of bacterial numbers vary according to the means of determination. Plate counts usually give values ranging from several hundred thousand up to one hundred million bacteria per gram of dry soil, the abundance being a reflection of the many environmental forces acting upon these minute inhabitants. Plating, however, probably underestimates the true bacterial population density as many soil bacteria fail to develop upon conventional media. Estimates by direct microscopy provide values of the order of 10^8 to 10^9 bacteria per gram of dry soil. The viable counting techniques thus give no more than 10 per cent and occasionally even less than 1 per cent of these values; a range of 1 to 10 per cent approximates the percentage of the total count that is observed by cultural means. It is noteworthy that there is no correlation between plate and direct microscopic methods for most ecological circumstances (23). However, the validity of the microscopic count has been questioned by means of an ingenious approach, and it has been proposed that the higher population estimates result from accumulated dead cells (28). It is indeed surprising that 90 to 99 per cent of the soil bacteria have a nutritional pattern appreciably more complex than that known for other organisms, especially in view of modern knowledge of bacterial nutrition. Undoubtedly, the viable count is somewhat low because of the inadequacy of culture media; without question, direct counts are excessively high because many non-viable individuals are included in the estimates. Whether the true population is more accurately approximated by one or the other procedure must await future research. The unquestioned viability and biochemical potential of organisms detected as colonies on agar makes this, for the present at least, the more useful ecological yardstick.

In a highly fertile soil containing approximately 10^8 bacteria per cubic centimeter of space, assuming each cell has a volume of one cubic micron, then the bacteria occupy

$$\frac{10^8 \text{ bacteria} \times 1.0 \ \mu^3}{1 \text{ cc}} = \frac{10^8 \ \mu^3}{10^{12} \ \mu^3}$$

0.01 per cent of the total soil volume. Using a microscopic count of 10^9 per cubic centimeter, 0.1 per cent of the total volume would be bacterial protoplasm. On a weight basis, where the viable and microscopic counts are taken as 10^8 and 10^9 per gram respectively and the average bacterial cell is considered to have 1.5×10^{-12} g of moist, viable tissue, some 300 to 3000 lb live weight of bacteria are present in each acre furrow slice of land, i.e., 0.015 to 0.15 per cent of the total mass.

Bacteria are rarely free in the liquid phase of the soil as most cells adhere to clay particles and humus. A large part of the microflora is probably segregated into definite colonies developing in favorable microecological sites or into distinct masses associated with slimy bacterial secretions. Bacteria and the inanimate colloidal particles or even pure clays are attracted to each other; this effect is in part an electrostatic attraction of the soil for the bacteria. The adsorption results in a diminution in the number of bacteria passing through soil in moving water and causes a greater retention by the soil. Where adsorption is prominent, biochemical activities are affected.

The numbers and types of bacteria are governed to a large extent by soil type and cultivation practices. The population in most grasslands, for example, is greater than in comparable arable land, a result of the greater root density and the larger supply of utilizable organic matter coming from root decomposition and from plant debris. The population also becomes larger in going from cooler to warmer climatic areas. Bacterial density is influenced to a large extent by the organic matter content of the habitat (7, 11). Bacterial numbers are likewise higher in cultivated than in virgin land, but exceptions to this rule are not difficult to find; cultivation usually makes conditions more favorable for bacterial proliferation by means not as yet fully understood.

It is interesting to observe ecological extremes, noting the similarities and differences in biological composition and activity of various environments. In temperate zones, bacteria overwinter in frozen soil and, although there may be some dying off and partial selection for strains able to withstand low temperature, the effect is minor because the population following the thaw is similar in size and make-up to that of the previous autumn. The circumstances are somewhat different, however, in areas of the arctic which are frozen 9 to 10 months of the year. Here, in localities which never reach a temperature of more than 10°C, counts in excess of a million per gram are observed even when the soil temperature remains below the freezing point for a period of several months. Such bacteria are undoubtedly in a state of dormancy awaiting the spring thaw for activity to recur.

Desert soils present another extreme. Even in those soils which exist almost in an oven-dry state, bacteria are present. Spore-forming bacilli are dominant, a likely result of the unfavorable conditions for vegetative development.

Environmental Influences

Environmental conditions affect the density and composition of the bacterial flora, and non-biological factors can frequently alter to a great degree the nature of the population and its biochemical potential. The primary environmental variables influencing soil bacteria include moisture, aeration, temperature, organic matter, acidity, and inorganic nutrient supply. Many lesser variables such as cultivation, season, and depth have been described and are of undoubted significance, but their influence arises from combinations of the primary determinants.

Moisture governs microbial activity in two ways. Since water is the major component of protoplasm, an adequate supply must be available for vegetative development. But, where moisture becomes excessive, microbial proliferation is suppressed not by the overabundance of water, which is not deleterious per se, but rather because the oversupply limits gaseous exchange and lowers the available O_2 supply, creating thereby an anaerobic environment. The maximum bacterial density is found in regions of fairly high moisture content, and the optimum level for the activities of aerobic bacteria often is at 50 to 75 per cent of the soil's moisture-holding capacity. Further, the bacterial population of various soils is closely correlated with their moisture contents. Even the periodic variations in population of a single soil occurring with time are directly associated with fluctuations in moisture (11), emphasizing thereby the key biological role of water supply.

Waterlogging brings about a decrease in the abundance of bacteria developing in air—sometimes following an initial but brief rise in the number of aerobes—and a parallel stimulation of the strict anaerobes. This change from an aerobic to a largely anaerobic flora is effected by the disappearance from the system of free O_2 as a result of its utilization by O_2-requiring microorganisms so that only bacteria tolerant of low O_2 levels or complete anaerobiasis are capable of proliferation.

Temperature governs all biological processes, and it is thus a prime factor of concern to the bacteria. An association between population size and temperature has been shown (11), but such quantitative effects are in addition to distinctive qualitative changes. Each microorganism has an optimum temperature for growth and a range outside of which development ceases. The temperature range and the optimum for proliferation serve as a means of delineating three microbial groups. Most microorganisms are *mesophiles* with optima in the vicinity of 25 to 35°C and a capacity to grow from about 15 to 45°C. Mesophilic types constitute the bulk of the soil bacteria. Certain species develop best at temperatures below 20°C, and these are termed *psychrophiles*. There is no evidence for the presence of true psychrophilic bacteria in soil; the bacteria even in winter are cold-tolerant mesophiles rather than psychrophiles. *Thermophiles*, on the other hand, are ubiquitous. These are organisms which grow readily at temperatures of 45 to 65°C, and some, the obligate thermophiles, are incapable of multiplying below 40°C. Beyond its microbiological effects, temperature governs the rates of biochemical processes carried out by the bacterial flora, an increase stimulating the rate of reaction up to the point of optimum temperature for the transformation. For the temperatures found in most climatic regions, a warming trend favors the biochemical changes brought about by the microbial inhabitants.

Population size in mineral soils is directly related to organic matter content so that humus-rich localities have the largest bacterial numbers. The addition of carbonaceous materials also has a profound influence upon bacterial numbers and activities, and the plowing down of green manures or crop residues initiates a ready microbiological response. This stimulation is most pronounced during the first several months of decomposition and largely disappears after the first year.

Highly acid or alkaline conditions tend to inhibit many common bacteria as the optimum for most species is near neutrality. The greater the hydrogen ion concentration, the smaller generally is the size of the bacterial population. It follows, therefore, that the liming of acid environments would greatly increase bacterial abundance. Nevertheless, soils of pH 3.0 contain many bacteria.

Although organic carbon is the major constituent of the food supply, inorganic nutrients are required, and it is not surprising that the flora is sometimes affected by the application of mineral fertilizers (5). These substances serve a dual function since they supply both the plant and the microorganism with the needed minerals. Often fertilizers exert no beneficial effects, and in such instances the explanation is probably the same for macro- and microorganisms; that is, the supply in the soil exceeds the biological demand. A not uncommon observation, on the other hand, is the suppression of bacteria by ammonium-containing fertilizers. This is not because of the added nitrogen but rather is the result of the acidity generated through the microbial oxidation of ammonium to nitric acid.

Cultivation practices also exert numerous direct and indirect biological effects. Plowing and tillage operations are drastic environmental treatments that usually cause marked bacteriological alterations. Such changes vary with the nature of the operation, the soil depth, and especially the type of crop residues that may have been turned under. The effects noted seem to arise from improving the soil's structure and porosity, favoring the movement of air, altering the moisture status, and exposing inaccessible organic nutrients to bacterial action.

Season of year is a secondary ecological variable, secondary in the sense that it is composed of several well-defined primary variables. The net influence created by season, moreover, is not simple, compounded as it is by temperature, rainfall, crop remains, and the direct and indirect effects of plant roots. In temperate regions, a population burst occurs in the spring as the soil becomes warm and the organic materials from the previous fall and winter become accessible for decay. Usually, the viable population is greatest during the spring and the autumn, and a decline occurs during the hot, dry summer months. In autumn, there is an increase in numbers after the low point in summer because of the more favorable moisture status and the availability of residues of root or above-ground tissues. The population commonly diminishes in winter and remains in a state of biochemical inactivity; the bacteria are not eliminated during prolonged periods of freezing so that the microflora is ready for reactivation in the spring (13). Meteorological conditions during any single year may alter the usual seasonal sequence, e.g., a hot, rainy summer or a cool, dry autumn. The seasonal changes in numbers of bacteria are closely related to fluctuations in moisture and temperature (11). Alterations in moisture and temperature during the year may influence the bacteria directly; alternatively, the climatic factors may in part operate indirectly through the surface vegetation which is the source of the carbonaceous nutrients reaching the microflora as root excretions, sloughed-off subterranean tissues, or as crop debris.

Depth is another secondary ecological variable that affects the bacteria. In temperate zones, these organisms are almost all in the top meter, largely in the upper few centimeters. At the very surface of cropped land, the population is sparse as a result of the inadequate moisture and the possible bactericidal action of sunlight. Examination of a typical profile from the surface to the C horizon reveals an increase as one goes from the very surface down a few centimeters, but the numbers decline with greater depth. Some typical values for mineral soils are presented in table 1. In contrast with field soils, in which the greatest number of bacteria are found several centimeters below the upper crust, the highest population in shaded land of forest, orchard, or meadow is frequently in the top 1 to 2 cm. In organic soils, the population of bacteria often fails to decline appreciably with depth, sometimes being greater at 160 cm than at the surface

TABLE 1

Distribution of Microorganisms in Various Horizons of the Soil Profile (24)

Horizon	Depth	Organisms/g of Soil $\times 10^3$				
		Aerobic Bacteria	Anaerobic Bacteria	Actinomy-cetes	Fungi	Algae
	cm					
A_1	3–8	7800	1950	2080	119	25
A_2	20–25	1800	379	245	50	5
A_2–B_1	35–40	472	98	49	14	0.5
B_1	65–75	10	1	5	6	0.1
B_2	135–145	1	0.4	–	3	–

(1). Most of the changes associated with position in the profile are explained in terms of microbiological alterations produced by variation in the quantities of available organic carbon and O_2. Moisture, pH, and inorganic nutrients are probably of lesser consequence, but CO_2 concentration may be of some significance.

Morphological and Generic Groups

Bacteria can be subdivided into a number of morphological groupings, such divisions providing convenient means for describing the organisms indigenous to a given locality or responding to external influences. Soil contains a vast number and variety of bacteria and, because of this diversity, it has not been possible to describe all types or to determine the generic placement of all strains. Difficulty is even encountered in the characterization of soil bacteria on the basis of their morphology since many of the dominant strains exhibit several shapes in culture depending upon the age of cells and the medium used; for example, a common bacterium is a gram negative rod when young but becomes coccoidal and gram positive as the culture ages.

As a result of an intensive microscopic investigation of the microflora, Conn (4) proposed that the bacteria be considered in six morphological groups: large coccoidal forms, small coccoidal forms, short rods, rods of medium length, long rods, and spore-forming bacilli. Dominating the autochthonous population are the short, non-spore-forming rods and the coccoidal cells, the former often being the more frequently encountered. Most indigenous bacteria fall into these two categories while the large and medium-size rods and the spore-forming bacilli are relatively infrequent. A morphological scheme of classification is illustrated by the data in table 2. The short rods that change to cocci with age are largely representatives of *Arthrobacter*, a genus often comprising up to about one-eighth of the population. The spore-forming rods classified in the genus *Bacillus* are less common than the non-spore-forming rods, but they can be demonstrated without difficulty.

The bacteria are also frequently differentiated on the basis of the changes they bring about. Biochemically active strains may be investigated or isolated by the *elective culture* method in which a small quantity of soil is inoculated into a culture solution designed to favor one physiological group over another, e.g., a medium with cellulose as sole carbon source or with protein as nitrogen source.

TABLE 2

Morphology of the Predominant Bacterial Population in Several Canadian Soils (15)

	% of Bacteria in Each Class		
Classification	Tobacco Soil	Corn Soil	Flax Soil
Short rods, gram positive	23.3	23.1	7.7
Short rods, gram negative	13.3	26.9	15.4
Short rods, gram variable	11.7	5.8	7.7
Short rods changing to cocci	13.3	7.7	1.9
Coccoid rods, gram positive	18.3	21.2	53.8
Cocci	1.7	0.0	7.7
Long, non-spore-forming rods	6.7	5.8	0.0
Spore-forming rods	10.0	9.6	5.8

To obtain pure cultures, several serial transfers are made in the elective medium followed by plating on agar. Such techniques delineate biochemical classes which, though not necessarily abundant, are very important for fertility and crop production. Included are the nitrifying, ammonifying, urea-hydrolyzing, cellulolytic, and protein-decomposing bacteria.

Taxonomically, the true bacteria and related microorganisms belong to the class Schizomycetes. Ten orders are included in the class, but only three—Pseudomonadales, Eubacteriales, and Actinomycetales—contain species prominent in soil. The genera most commonly encountered are the following:

I. Order Pseudomonadales.
   A. Family Pseudomonadaceae. *Pseudomonas*
      Short, gram negative, non-spore-forming rods. Aerobic. Frequently produce blue or green fluorescent pigments.
II. Order Eubacteriales.
   A. Family Rhizobiaceae.
      1. *Rhizobium*. Gram negative, aerobic, non-spore-forming rods that form nodules on legumes. Numerically not abundant.
      2. *Agrobacterium*. Short, gram negative, non-spore-forming rods. Facultative anaerobes. Non-chromogenic.
      3. *Chromobacterium*. Short, gram negative, non-spore-forming rods. Facultative anaerobes. Produce violet pigments.

B. Family Achromobacteriaceae.
   1. *Achromobacter*. Gram negative, non-spore-forming, non-chromo-genic rods.
   2. *Flavobacterium*. Short, gram negative rods. Produce yellow or orange pigments.
C. Family Micrococcaceae.
   1. *Micrococcus*. Spherical cells, gram positive or sometimes gram negative. Cells in irregular groups.
   2. *Sarcina*. Spherical cells in packets. Usually gram positive. White, yellow, orange or red pigmentation.
D. Family Corynebacteriaceae.
   1. *Corynebacterium*. Rods straight or slightly bent, usually aerobic. Cells contain irregularly stained segments or granules. Gram positive. Soil forms often more aptly considered as arthrobacters.
   2. *Arthrobacter*. Usually rods when young becoming coccoidal. Gram variable when young, positive when old.
E. Family Bacillaceae.
   1. *Bacillus*. Aerobic or facultatively anaerobic rods that form endospores.
   2. *Clostridium*. Anaerobic rods that form endospores.
III. Order Actinomycetales.
A. Family Mycobacteriaceae. *Mycobacterium*
Gram positive, aerobic, non-motile rods. Acid-fast. (Many isolates originally placed in this genus are now considered to be actinomycetes of the genus *Nocardia*.)

Even a cursory examination reveals that the bacterial population consists of but a few predominant genera. Recent investigations indicate that strains of *Pseudomonas, Arthrobacter, Clostridium, Achromobacter, Bacillus, Micrococcus,* and *Flavobacterium* and fewer of *Chromobacterium, Sarcina,* and *Mycobacterium* are the most common (1, 9, 24, 27). Use of a medium containing 12 per cent gelatin has proved helpful in the study of certain of the bacteria since the large colonies appearing upon this medium are *Pseudomonas* and *Bacillus* species, both abundant types, while the many punctiform colonies consist of *Arthrobacter* and *Agrobacterium* cells. These four genera together with the actinomycetes comprise more than 90 per cent of the colonies developing upon gelatin.

The prevalence of pseudomonads has been demonstrated in both cropped and uncropped land (figure 2), and values in excess of a million per gram are not uncommon. The physiology and metabolism of this microbial group has been the subject of considerable inquiry.

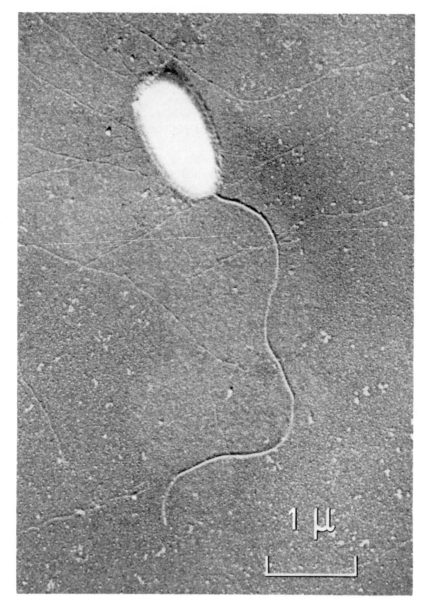

Figure 2A. Electron photomicrograph of a soil *Pseudomonas* sp.

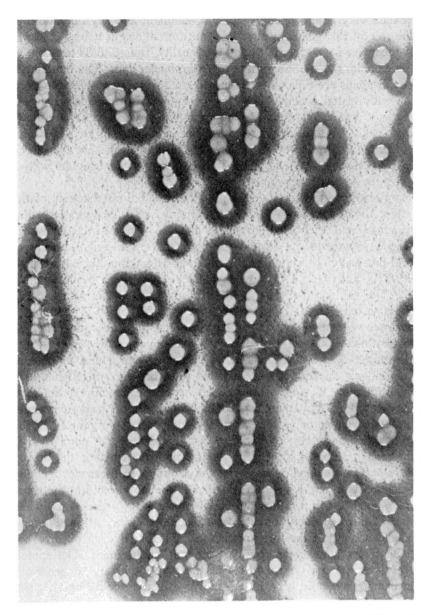

Figure 2B. Colonies of a soil *Pseudomonas* sp. (Courtesy of H. Veldkamp.)

On the other hand, soils contain many arthrobacters, which because of their very abundance must play a dominant and key function, but the role of this genus in chemical transformations in nature is as yet unrecognized. Depending upon the locality, from 5 to 35 per cent of the colonies are representatives of *Arthrobacter* spp. The boundaries of this genus are difficult to delineate, and there is considerable overlap with related genera. The most important of the neighboring genera is *Corynebacterium,* and saprophytic corynebacteria are quite common. The term coryneform has been proposed to include strains of *Corynebacterium* and *Arthrobacter;* the coryneforms are considered to be non-spore-forming, gram positive, non-motile bacteria with a tendency toward irregular shapes.

Related to the coryneforms are the true acid-fast bacteria of the genus *Mycobacterium.* These microorganisms are comparatively less common, and their significance is likewise not known. Frey and Hagan (6) devised a selective technique for the demonstration of acid-fast bacteria by the use of paraffin enrichment cultures incubated at 45°C, and their data show mycobacteria in every locale studied.

The enumeration and isolation of *Bacillus* spp. is an easy task since pasteurization of soil suspensions at 80°C for 10 to 20 minutes destroys vegetative cells but not endospores, and subsequent aerobic incubation eliminates the only other common spore formers, the clostridia. The well-characterized nature of the genus, aerobic to facultatively anaerobic, spore-forming rods, has encouraged intensive investigation. The numbers of *Bacillus* are commonly quite high, varying from 10^6 in cooler regions to 10^7 or more per gram in warmer latitudes. Commonly, some 5 to 20 per cent of the organisms of the A horizon are strains of *Bacillus,* but the size of the population is misleading since viable counts do not indicate whether the colony developed from a spore or a vegetative unit. In areas not recently amended with organic matter, *Bacillus* is probably found in the spore state, persisting in this dormant condition for many years. Only when specific nutrient conditions are provided do they become active, and it is as a result of the rare population burst that the soil becomes inhabited for many years by the dormant endospores. The spores, therefore, are the typical forms of the genus that are so numerous in unamended soils, and the vegetative cells are not biologically significant unless exogenous carbon sources are provided. *Bacillus megaterium,* *B. cereus,* and *B. subtilis* usually are the more frequently encountered species, but cultivation alters the preponderance of one or another of the species (18).

Certain of the enterobacteria serve as excellent diagnostic indicators of fecal contamination of water supplies, and they are thus important to the public health microbiologist. The presence of these enterobacteria in arable land may result from fecal droppings of animals or birds, but the ease of isolation from sites where chances of animal contamination are remote suggests that at least some of these bacteria are definite but minor soil inhabitants. *Aerobacter* is frequently encountered although *Escherichia coli* can be found as well. Of 617 strains obtained from soil by Griffin and Stuart (8), 15.2 per cent were classified as *E. coli*, 74.9 per cent were *Aerobacter*, 5.8 per cent were intermediates, and 4.1 per cent were irregular. Further study has revealed that *Escherichia* constitutes a smaller proportion of the group as fecal additions become more remote; the abundance of *Aerobacter* remains essentially constant regardless of animal droppings. This indicates that the latter are normal inhabitants whereas *Escherichia* is mainly derived from fecal sources.

Strictly anaerobic bacteria classified in the genus *Clostridium* occur in the most fertile areas in spite of the apparent availability of O_2. Complete aerobiasis, however, is not an actuality in natural conditions since, where microbial activity is high, the aerobes and facultative anaerobes consume O_2 and replace it with CO_2, lowering thereby the partial pressure of O_2 and permitting the proliferation of obligate anaerobes. This is especially true at microecological sites in the profile. To separate and obtain in pure culture the spore-forming *Clostridium*, advantage is taken of two physiological characteristics, the formation of heat resistant endospores and the capacity for anaerobic growth. The soil suspension is heated at 80°C for 10 minutes to kill the vegetative cells, and the remaining bacteria are plated directly on agar or further enriched by anaerobic incubation.

Common to both soil and animal droppings is a group of microorganisms known as myxobacteria. The vegetative forms of these organisms are flexible rods which move by gliding. Most possess a resting stage during the life cycle in which the resting cells typically are borne in specialized fruiting bodies. The life cycle is completed when the rods emerge from the fruiting bodies and resume their active metabolism (figure 3). For many years, the myxobacteria were considered as dung inhabitants rather than indigenous to soil, but the demonstration (21) of their frequency in land not manured for more than 100 years has established them firmly as true inhabitants. Most frequently found are *Myxococcus, Chondrococcus, Archangium,* and

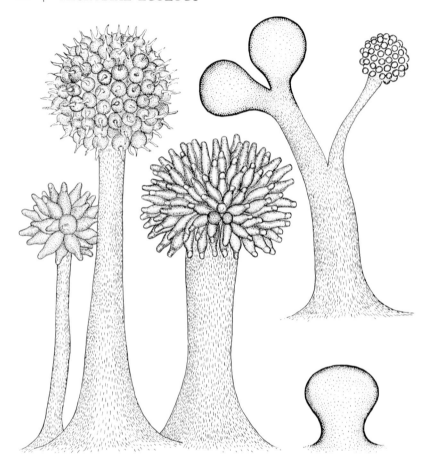

Figure 3. Drawing of a common myxobacterium (26).

Polyangium, but *Cytophaga* and *Sporocytophaga* may become numerous during the decomposition of cellulose.

Myxobacteria can be isolated by adding a small quantity of soil to the center of an agar plate previously seeded with a bacterial suspension. Following incubation, the fruiting bodies become apparent to the naked eye. This technique relies upon the ability of myxobacteria to lyse the cells of true bacteria and to use them as a food source. The mechanism of the lysis involves the excretion of extracellular, bacteriolytic enzymes which dissolve the bacteria. The killing, lysing, and feeding upon the simpler bacteria by the myxobacteria is possibly a significant factor in governing the composition of the flora. For the development of *Myxococcus fulvus, Myxococcus virescens,* and *Chondrococcus exiguus,* Singh (21) has shown a preference for gram negative bacteria and a greater susceptibility of non-pigmented cultures than bacteria forming pigments. Myxobacteria have been found in all arable soils and most grassland samples examined with counts ranging from about 2000 to 76,000 per gram (22). A greater population is encountered in moist environments as these organisms do not seem to be tolerant of arid conditions.

Bacterial Ecology

Division of the microflora into autochthonous and zymogenous categories provides a convenient ecological distinction, but the boundaries of the two classes are not always clear. Winogradsky (30) at the time of proposing the two categories felt that the micrococci were the dominant type in the autochthonous population, but subsequent investigation has not supported this view. Presumably, the autochthonous species are involved in the formation and decomposition of the dark-colored humus materials, but such hypothetical concepts require more precise substantiation in the light of modern biochemistry.

The indigenous flora is relatively stable in its composition and is not markedly influenced by treatment with organic amendments. Especially common in environments receiving no plant or animal remains are bacteria of the genus *Arthrobacter* and primitive actinomycetes classified as *Nocardia* spp. Hence, both may be considered as important autochthonous inhabitants. Species of *Agrobacterium* as well as *Bacillus* spores are also ubiquitous and are probably indigenous although the latter are in an inactive state, and as such they make no contribution to the chemical transformations carried out by the autochthonous flora. When the vegetative state is resumed, *Bacillus* may be considered as zymogenous in function.

The zymogenous flora includes microorganisms active in the transformations of added organic matter as well as species whose population responds markedly following the addition of inorganic nutrients. Limited as it is to added foods, the zymogenous microflora declines and enters a quiescent period as soon as the nutrient has been depleted. Conn has proposed that the following five microbial groups be considered zymogenous: organisms characterized on the basis of their physiological activities and including the cellulose decomposers, the bacteria utilizing N_2, and those converting ammonium to nitrate; the fungi that become active following application of organic matter; actinomycetes in the vegetative stage; *Pseudomonas;* and the vegetative state of *Bacillus* species which develop only in the presence of suitable carbonaceous nutrients. The aerobic spore-forming rods are noted most commonly when proteinaceous or other amino acid-rich materials are supplied or, alternatively, during the late stages of decomposition when the many proteins and growth factors synthesized by the primary flora become available to the secondary population. The report that *Pseudomonas* and *Bacillus* are stimulated in soils treated with crop residues is further evidence for the zymogenous nature of these genera (19).

Nutrition of the Dominant Flora

It has been pointed out that bacteria may be subdivided into taxonomic, morphological, and physiological categories. Since physiological differentiation provides a functional approach, it has the greatest pedological significance, but the individual physiological groups are not mutually exclusive, for a single culture may be able to utilize N_2, decompose pectin, and hydrolyze cellulose. A scheme based upon mutually exclusive types has been proposed using nutritional complexity as the determinative characteristic (16, 25). The nutritional approach has the further advantage of demonstrating for various treatments and environmental changes the specific growth requirements of the dominant bacteria.

To classify microorganisms by their nutritional habits, some 100 to 200 colonies are picked in a non-selective manner from dilution plates prepared upon soil extract agar. The growth of each of the isolates is then tested in seven media varying in complexity. On the basis of their development in these several media, the bacteria are divided into groups which require for maximum growth (I) no preformed growth factors, (II) one or several amino acids, (III) B vitamins, (IV) both amino acids and B vitamins, (V) unidentified factors in yeast extract, (VI) soil extract, and (VII) substances in both yeast and soil extracts. From the percentage of the isolates fitting into each category, it is possible to assess the relative incidence of the seven nutritional types in the sample under study.

From an examination of typical data (table 3), it is clear that only about one-tenth of the bacteria are able to grow readily in mini-

TABLE 3

Nutritional Requirements of the Predominant Bacteria (16)

Morphological Type	% of Each Nutritional Group Falling into Morphological Types						
	I	II	III	IV	V	VI	VII
Cocci, gram positive	5.3	3.0	4.8	9.8	15.1	11.8	11.6
Cocci, gram negative	5.3	0.0	14.3	4.9	3.8	0.0	0.0
Spore-forming rods	5.3	17.6	0.0	7.3	3.8	0.0	1.0
Non-spore-forming rods							
gram positive	10.5	11.8	19.0	29.3	13.2	11.8	8.7
gram negative	50.0	52.9	40.5	17.1	41.5	23.5	29.1
Pleomorphic bacteria							
gram positive	23.7	11.8	21.4	31.7	17.0	41.2	46.6
gram negative	0.0	3.0	0.0	0.0	5.9	11.8	2.0
Total bacteria, % in each nutritional class	7.9–14.6	8.4–12.1	10.3–14.9	7.3–17.0	9.4–22.4	3.0–7.0	29.1–32.3

mal media, the remaining nine-tenths requiring some growth substance for maximum development. About 10 per cent need amino acids, a like number require B vitamins, and about 30 per cent need a mixture of yeast and soil extracts for optimum development in culture solution. Strains with simple needs, those of groups I, II, and III, are mainly gram negative, non-spore-forming rods. Strains in groups VI and VII, isolates with complex demands, are commonly the pleomorphic coryneforms related to *Arthrobacter* and associated genera. Noteworthy are the nutritional requirements, especially for amino acids, of spore-forming *Bacillus* spp. These and similar results demonstrate that the nutrition of the soil bacteria varies considerably from the simple to the highly complex.

Several criticisms may be voiced against this approach. It relies, for example, upon the use of soil extract as a non-selective medium, but the absence of selectivity of soil extract media is open to debate. Further, the carbohydrate used, glucose, is known to be unavailable to at least part of the microflora. And, as with all viable counting techniques, the nutritional classification scheme is limited by the unsuitability of any one medium for growth of all members of the subterranean population. Nevertheless, important attributes of the bacteria have been established, and the demonstration of microorganisms dependent upon factors in soil extract not equated with known chemicals is indicative in itself of a nutritional uniqueness of the population adapted to the soil environment.

The ubiquity of amino acid and vitamin-requiring strains poses a problem as to the source of these substances; they must undoubtedly be produced continually in order to support such organisms. Often as many as one-fourth of the bacteria require one or more of the water-soluble vitamins. The answer seems to be in the ability of a large percentage of the bacteria developing in the absence of growth factors to synthesize such compounds and to excrete them into the surroundings (14, 20). Because of this degree of biological interdependence, the utilization by one bacterium of substances synthesized by its more versatile neighbor, it is not unlikely that amino acids, B vitamins, and possibly the more complex substances are important in governing the microbiological equilibrium, serving to explain in part why there is an indigenous microflora of soil distinctive from that found in other habitats.

Chemoautotrophic Bacteria

Chemoautotrophy is one of the unique habits of nutrition in the microscopic world. Microorganisms are divided into two broad classes with respect to their energy and carbon sources: *heterotrophic* forms, which require preformed organic nutrients to serve as sources of energy and carbon, and *autotrophic* microorganisms, which obtain their energy from sunlight or by the oxidation of inorganic compounds and their carbon by the assimilation of CO_2. Fungi, actinomycetes, protozoa, all animals, and most bacteria are heterotrophs. It should be mentioned that many and possibly all heterotrophs assimilate small quantities of CO_2, but the autotrophs alone use CO_2 as the sole carbon source. Autotrophs are of two general types: *photoautotrophs*, whose energy is derived from sunlight, and *chemoautotrophs*, which obtain the energy needed for growth and biosynthetic reactions from the oxidation of inorganic materials. Algae, the higher plants, and a few bacterial genera have a photoautotrophic nutrition. Chemo-autotrophy, on the other hand, is limited to relatively few bacterial species, yet it is of vast agronomic and economic importance.

The unique character of chemoautotrophs rests upon two attributes, their ability to utilize the energy obtained by the transformation of inorganic materials and their capacity to make use of CO_2 to satisfy the entire carbon needs. Some species are limited exclusively to inorganic oxidations and are considered to be obligate or strict chemoautotrophs; others, the facultative autotrophs, may obtain energy from the oxidation of either inorganic materials or organic carbon.

The obligate chemoautotrophs are specific for their energy sources and utilize only one or a small group of related compounds; e.g., nitrite for *Nitrobacter,* ammonium for *Nitrosomonas,* and certain inorganic sulfur compounds for species of *Thiobacillus.* Heterotrophs, on the other hand, have a more diversified nutrition.

The term autotrophy itself signifies the self-feeding habit of these bacteria. Nutritionally, they are the most primitive microorganisms since they have all the attributes of life yet they fulfill their needs from a completely inorganic environment. Physiologically, chemoauto-trophic bacteria are very complex because they have within the confines of the cell wall all the enzymes, vitamins, coenzymes, carbohydrates, and other protoplasmic constituents typical of the heterotroph, and these they create from the most primitive conditions. Consequently, their synthetic powers must be truly great.

The chemoautotrophic bacteria may be subdivided on the basis of the element whose oxidation provides the energy for growth and cell synthesis.

I. Nitrogen compounds oxidized.
   A. Ammonium oxidized to nitrite. *Nitrosomonas*
   B. Nitrite oxidized to nitrate. *Nitrobacter*
II. Inorganic sulfur compounds converted to sulfate. *Thiobacillus*
III. Ferrous iron converted to the ferric state. *Ferrobacillus, Gallionella*
IV. H_2 oxidized. *Hydrogenomonas, Desulfovibrio, Methanobacillus*
V. CO oxidized to CO_2. *Carboxydomonas*

The true autotrophic nature of some of these is in doubt, however. Many other bacteria also have been considered as chemoautotrophs, but the work is either too limited, lacks confirmation, or is open to question. Strict chemoautotrophy has been demonstrated unequivocally only in *Nitrosomonas, Nitrobacter, Ferrobacillus*, and certain *Thiobacillus* species. The hydrogen bacteria are characterized by a facultatively autotrophic nutrition as they use the oxidation of either organic molecules or H_2 for energy. Most chemoautotrophs are strict aerobes while those capable of proliferating in the absence of O_2 require the presence of an oxygen-rich substance, nitrate for *Thiobacillus denitrificans*, sulfate for *Desulfovibrio*, and CO_2 for *Methanobacillus*. The oxidized substances are converted to reduced products in process, N_2, H_2S, and CH_4, respectively.

The energy-yielding reactions in the metabolism of these organisms include the following:

$$NH_4^+ + 1\tfrac{1}{2}O_2 \rightarrow NO_2^- + 2H^+ + H_2O \quad Nitrosomonas \quad (I)$$

$$NO_2^- + \tfrac{1}{2}O_2 \rightarrow NO_3^- \quad\quad\quad Nitrobacter \quad (II)$$

$$S + 1\tfrac{1}{2}O_2 + H_2O \rightarrow H_2SO_4 \quad\quad Thiobacillus \quad (III)$$

$$2H_2 + O_2 \rightarrow 2H_2O \quad\quad\quad Hydrogenomonas \quad (IV)$$

$$4H_2 + SO_4^= \rightarrow S^= + 4H_2O \quad\quad Desulfovibrio \quad (V)$$

$$4H_2 + CO_2 \rightarrow CH_4 + 2H_2O \quad\quad Methanobacillus \quad (VI)$$

The mechanism of chemoautotrophy still remains a vexing problem that has attracted the attention of both microbiologists and biochemists. Essentially, the problem is to explain the unique position of the chemoautotroph in the microbial realm. The dilemma may be considered from the viewpoint of how the organisms obtain energy from inorganic oxidations or the way in which CO_2 rather than organic carbon is used as the carbon source for growth. Also in the realm of speculation is the reason that strict chemoautotrophs cannot obtain energy by decomposing organic materials.

Chemoautotrophic bacteria are important in nature because of the energy-yielding reactions they catalyze, and several of the processes for which they are responsible are essential for crop production. The formation of nitrate and sulfate provides the plant with two of its critical inorganic nutrients in assimilable form. Elemental sulfur has been used to control potato scab and to bring alkali soils into production, both actions a consequence of equation III. The reduction of sulfate to sulfide has an influence upon plant growth and is also involved in the corrosion of iron and steel pipes in the soil. Other autotrophic transformations are known which have broad geochemical or biological implications.

REFERENCES

Reviews

Burges, A. 1958. *Micro-organisms in the soil.* Hutchinson Univ. Library, London.

Conn, H. J. 1948. The most abundant groups of bacteria in soil. *Bacteriol. Rev.,* 12:257–273.

Lochhead, A. G. 1958. Soil bacteria and growth-promoting substances. *Bacteriol. Rev.,* 22:145–153.

Mishustin, E. N. 1956. The law of zonality and the study of the microbial associations of the soil. *Soils and Fert.,* 19:385–392.

Thornton, H. G. 1956. The ecology of micro-organisms in soil. *Proc. Royal Soc.,* B, 145:364–374.

Waksman, S. A. 1932. *Principles of soil microbiology.* The Williams and Wilkins Co., Baltimore.

Literature cited

1. Beck, T., and H. Poschenrieder. 1958. *Zent. Bakteriol.,* II, 111:672–683.
2. Boyd, W. L. 1958. *Ecology,* 39:332–336.
3. Cochran, W. G. 1950. *Biometrics,* 6:105–116.
4. Conn, H. J. 1928. *Soil Sci.,* 25:263–272.
5. Eno, C. F., P. J. Westgate, and W. C. Blue. 1956. *Proc. Soil Crop Sci. Soc. Fla.,* 16:165–175.
6. Frey, C. A., and W. A. Hagan. 1931. *J. Inf. Diseases,* 49:497–506.
7. Gray, P. H. H., and R. H. Wallace. 1957. *Canad. J. Microbiol.,* 3:711–714.
8. Griffin, A. M., and C. A. Stuart. 1940. *J. Bacteriol.,* 40:83–100.
9. Hopf, M. 1950. *Arch. Mikrobiol.,* 14:661–677.
10. James, N., and M. L. Sutherland. 1939. *Canad. J. Research,* C, 17:97–108.
11. Jensen, H. L. 1934. *Proc. Linnean Soc. N. S. W.,* 59:101–117.
12. Jones, P. C. T., J. E. Mollison, and M. H. Quenouille. 1948. *J. Gen. Microbiol.,* 2:54–69.
13. Katznelson, R. S., and V. V. Ershov. 1957. *Mikrobiologiya,* 26:468–476.
14. Lochhead, A. G. 1957. *Soil Sci.,* 84:395–403.
15. Lochhead, A. G. 1940. *Canad. J. Research,* C, 18:42–53.
16. Lochhead, A. G., and F. E. Chase. 1943. *Soil Sci.,* 55:185–195.
17. Maloy, O. C., and M. Alexander. 1958. *Phytopathol.,* 48:126–128.
18. Mekhtiev, S. J. 1957. *Mikrobiologiya,* 26:75–77.
19. Mitchell, R. B., J. E. Adams, and C. Thom. 1941. *J. Agric. Research,* 63: 527–534.
20. Payne, T. M. B., J. W. Rouatt, and A. G. Lochhead. 1957. *Canad. J. Microbiol.,* 3:73–80.
21. Singh, B. N. 1948. *J. Gen. Microbiol.,* 2:XVII–XVIII.
22. Singh, B. N. 1947. *Proc. 4th Intl. Cong. Microbiol.,* Copenhagen, pp. 465–466.
23. Skinner, F. A., P. C. T. Jones, and J. E. Mollison. 1952. *J. Gen. Microbiol.,* 6:261–271.

24. Starc, A. 1942. *Arch. Mikrobiol.*, 12:329–352.
25. Stevenson, I. L., and J. W. Rouatt. 1953. *Canad. J. Botany*, 31:438–447.
26. Thaxter, R. 1897. *Botan. Gaz.*, 23:395–411.
27. Timofeeva, A. G. 1954. *Mikrobiologiya*, 23:662–668.
28. Topping, L. E. 1938. *Zent. Bakteriol.*, II, 98:193–201.
29. Winogradsky, S. 1925. *Ann. Inst. Pasteur*, 39:299–354.
30. Winogradsky, S. 1924. *Compt. Rend. Acad. Sci.*, 178:1236–1239.

3

Actinomycetes

The true bacteria are distinctly different from the filamentous fungi, and many morphological characteristics separate the two broad types. There is, however, a transitional group between the simple bacteria and the fungi, a group with boundaries overlapping its more primitive and its more developed neighbors. These are the actinomycetes, which in soil are numerically second only to the bacteria.

The term actinomycete has no taxonomic validity since these organisms are classified as bacteria in a strict sense, all being Schizomycetes of the order Actinomycetales, but not all genera of the Actinomycetales are considered to be actinomycetes in common parlance. The actinomycetes are unicellular microorganisms that produce a slender, branched *mycelium* which may undergo fragmentation or may subdivide to form asexual spores. The mycelium is, in some genera at least, aerial and typically exhibits a distinct branching habit. The individual *hyphae* or filaments appear morphologically similar to the fungal filaments but are much less broad, usually 0.5 to 1.2 μ in diameter, a dimension analogous to that of the bacterial cell (figure 1). In addition to proliferation by vegetative means, certain actinomycetes produce asexual spores known as *conidia,* but there is no known sexual spore stage.

Despite their placement together with the bacteria, the relation of the actinomycetes to the fungi, particularly the Fungi Imperfecti, is apparent in four properties: (a) the mycelium of the higher actinomycetes has the extensive branching characteristic of the molds; (b) like the fungi, many actinomycetes form an aerial mycelium as well as conidia; (c) the growth of actinomycetes in liquid culture rarely results in the turbidity associated with unicellular bacteria,

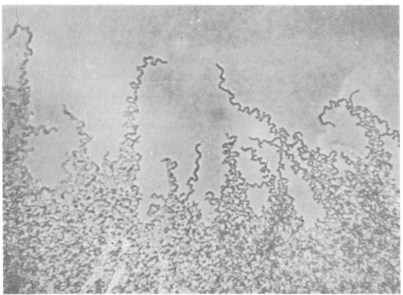

Figure 1. Mycelium of typical actinomycetes. Top, aerial mycelium of *Streptomyces;* bottom, edge of *Nocardia* colony. (Courtesy of H. Lechevalier.)

rather it occurs as distinct clumps or pellets; and (d) the growth rate in unrestricted conditions of at least some strains is not exponential as is the case with bacteria but cubic, a characteristic in common with many of the fungi (8). On the other hand, the morphology and size of hyphae, conidia, and of the individual fragments of species whose mycelium undergoes segmentation are similar to structures found among the bacteria. In addition, some actinomycete genera produce no aerial mycelium, and they closely resemble *Mycobacterium* and the coryneform bacteria in general morphology, staining reactions, and physiology. Another unique point for the taxonomic placement with the bacteria is the attack by viruses on both actinomycetes and true

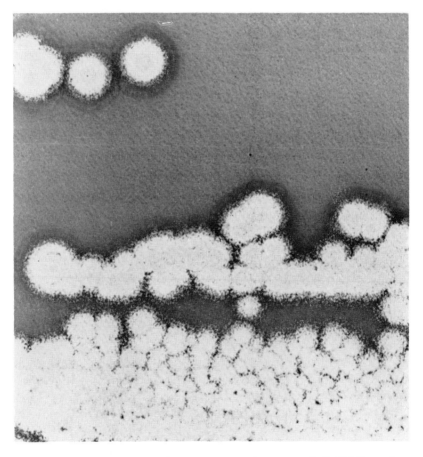

Figure 2. *Streptomyces* colonies on agar. (Courtesy of H. Veldkamp.)

bacteria while viruses are not reported to parasitize the filamentous fungi.

Recognition of colonies upon agar media is relatively simple providing the incubation period is sufficiently long. Whereas the bacterial colony consists of a large population of individuals derived from a single cell by binary fission, that of the actinomycete (figure 2) prior to sporulation consists of but one organism, a mycelium derived from a single propagative unit. The colonies of some genera developing upon the agar surface may have a firm consistency and adhere tenaciously to the solidified substratum; in certain of these genera, the surface appears powdery and often becomes pigmented when the aerial spores are produced. In the organisms having a simple mycelium, the colony has a more mealy consistency and often crumbles when touched.

Distribution and Abundance

Actinomycetes were known to early microbiologists, but they were largely overlooked because their slow growth on agar plates led to the tacit assumption that these microorganisms were of little importance in soil transformations. Only in recent years with the interest in the chemotherapeutic use of the antibiotics produced by the actinomycetes has the group been brought under close scrutiny.

Actinomycetes are numerous and widely distributed not only in soil but in a variety of other habitats including composts, river muds, and lake bottoms. They are present in surface soil and also in the lower horizons to considerable depths. In abundance, they are second only to the bacteria, and the viable counts of the two are frequently almost equal. Particularly in environments of high pH, a large proportion of the total population consists of the actinomycetes. Saprophytic existence is the rule among the free-living forms, but a few species can cause diseases of plants, domestic animals, and even humans.

A variety of microscopic or plating methods have been used in ecological investigations, but only the latter techniques are truly quantitative for these microorganisms. Despite the frequent use of plating, it is remarkable that the counts do not seem to be greatly affected by the composition of the medium, an indication that the organisms can utilize a variety of organic nutrients. Counts may be made upon the same plates that are used for bacterial enumeration, but special media are often preferable. In either instance, the period of incubation must be somewhat longer than for the bacteria because of the slow growth characteristics of the actinomycetes.

In their normal habitats, the actinomycetes may occur as conidia or as the vegetative hyphae, and both forms can give rise to colonies on agar media. Thus, a determination of colony numbers on agar media will not differentiate between propagative units derived from a single conidium, an unbroken cluster of conidia, or a hyphal fragment, and the onset of sporulation in soil will result in high counts despite the lack of appreciable change in total protoplasmic mass. Consequently, data suggesting large populations may be merely indicative of species producing numerous conidia, and the results of plating must then be considered as far from unequivocal in giving a true representation of the active mass of biological material, reflecting only the number of fragments that multiply when placed in proper circumstances.

The size of the population depends upon the soil type, particularly upon certain of the physical characteristics, organic matter content, and pH of the environment. Plating estimates give values ranging from 10^5 to 10^8 per gram in temperate zones, but lower figures have been found in acid peats, the tundra, and in waterlogged soils, and counts in excess of 100 million have been encountered occasionally. By and large, actinomycetes make up from 10 to 50 per cent of the total population determined by plating in both virgin and cultivated land. In alkaline areas, especially when dry, the relative abundance is spectacularly high. Johnstone (7), for example, reports that actinomycetes accounted for 95 per cent of the organisms in certain localities on the Bikini Atoll in the Pacific Ocean, a result probably due at least in part to the alkalinity.

Certain generalizations can be made with regard to the role of specific environmental characteristics in determining population size. By comparison with the true bacteria, actinomycetes are less common in wet than in dry areas. The population is likewise greater in grassland and pasture soils than in cultivated land, and the abundance in cultivated fields often exceeds that in adjacent virgin sites. Unfavorable, however, are peats, waterlogged areas, and environments whose pH is less than about 5.0. Soils in warm climatic regions are more conducive to an extensive actinomycete flora than those in cooler areas, and the size of the population in temperate latitudes tends to increase as one comes closer to the tropics. Consequently, the total number and percentage incidence of actinomycetes in the northern hemisphere

TABLE 1

Abundance of Actinomycetes in Various Soils (10)

Zone	Soils	Condition	No./g × 10^3 Total	Actino-mycetes	% Actino-mycetes
Tundra, taiga	Tundra-gley,	Virgin	2140	30	1.4
	gley-podzolic	Cultivated	4847	84	1.6
Forest-meadow	Podzol,	Virgin	1086	90	8.1
	gley-podzolic	Cultivated	2620	790	28.2
Meadow-steppe,	Chernozem	Virgin	3630	1300	35.4
steppe		Cultivated	4533	1570	35.1
Dry steppe	Chestnut	Virgin	3482	1200	34.7
		Cultivated	6660	2100	32.0
Desert steppe,	Brown soil,	Virgin	4490	1550	36.1
steppe	cerozem	Cultivated	7378	2380	33.6

increases moving from north to south (table 1). The population density will, of course, vary markedly in similar soils of any one locality, and it will be further influenced by season of year and by cultural practices.

Measurement of mycelial density on microscope slides buried in the soil demonstrates that the hyphae appear infrequently, suggesting thereby that the high values observed in the enumeration of viable units are the result of colonies derived from conidia. Further, as their filaments are always slender, actinomycetes contribute little protoplasmic mass despite the high viable counts (5). Nevertheless, hyphae can be found by use of the buried slide technique, and their abundance is affected by the season, rare in winter, more common in the summer (13). Such observations, however, may be upon the occasional actinomycete unit which develops into a vegetative filament.

In the plate method as applied to bacteria, each colony generally arises from a single cell in the environment sampled. As pointed out previously, a single actinomycete colony may originate from either a biochemically active hyphal fragment or a relatively inactive conidium so that the results of the usual plating techniques aid little in assessing the role of actinomycetes in nature. The observations of Skinner (11) have forced a breakthrough in the dilemma of enumeration. He observed that shaking of the *Streptomyces albidoflavus* mycelium with sand increased the apparent viable count because of hyphal fragmentation whereas shaking of the spores led to no such increase. As shaking had no effect on the spore count but it increased the number of viable units when the mycelium was present, a method was devised to determine whether *Streptomyces* was initially in the hyphal or conidial form. In the several soils examined in this way, shaking caused little variation in streptomycete count, demonstrating that the organisms exist largely as conidia (11). Because of the importance of these limited observations, more extensive study of other localities is warranted.

The dominance of conidia points to the resistance of these structures to deleterious environmental conditions. Many strains possess spores resistant to desiccation, these conidia persisting for many years in air-dry soil. The resistance of conidia to destruction allows the organisms to persist when the habitat becomes unfavorable for vegetative activity. The conidia of both *Streptomyces* and *Micromonospora* also exhibit a greater tolerance to heat than the hyphae, resisting temperatures which totally destroy the reproductive capacity of the mycelium. This thermo-tolerance of the actinomycete conidium is not as marked as the resistance to heat of bacterial endospores, and only a few degrees higher than the lethal temperature for hyphae results in inactivation of the conidia.

Environmental Influences

In qualitative and quantitative terms, the actinomycete flora is governed by the surrounding habitat. The stage of the life cycle which predominates, the size of the population, its biochemical transformations, and the genera and species found are determined by the forces acting within the environmental complex. Any one biological system is in the last analysis a reflection of the other biological systems functioning in association or in opposition and of the physical and chemical characteristics of the environment. For the actinomycetes, the primary ecological influences include the organic matter status, pH, moisture, and the temperature. Season of year and depth in the profile are also of no little consequence, but the role of these two variables seems to be largely an outcome of interactions among the primary determinants.

Actinomycetes are affected directly by the presence of available carbon, and their number is especially great in land rich in organic matter. This is true whether examination is by plate counting or by one of several microscopic techniques. In general, sites high in carbonaceous materials and humus have larger populations than habitats poor in organic matter. Amendment with organic nutrients such as protein derivatives, crop residues, legume tissue, bloodmeal, and barnyard manure increases the abundance of actinomycetes. The population may sometimes reach 10^8 per gram with crop residue turn-under, especially in environments reaching high temperatures. It is not uncommon for manured soil to have more actinomycetes than adjacent unmanured sites, and the relative abundance of these microorganisms is sometimes increased as well as the actual numbers. Upon organic matter additions, the bacterial and fungus flora usually respond initially, particularly if nitrogen is plentiful, and the response of the actinomycetes frequently does not become pronounced until the later stages of decay. This suggests that the greater growth rates and biochemical versatility of the bacteria and molds make them the initial agents of destruction whereas the actinomycetes only appear when the less readily available compounds have been metabolized and competitive stress has diminished.

As a group, these microorganisms are not tolerant of low pH, and the population size is inversely related to the hydrogen ion concentration. Most strains of *Streptomyces* and related forms fail to proliferate or have negligible activity below pH 5.0, and the actinomycetes in highly acid environments frequently make up less than 1 per cent of the total viable count. Acid-tolerant strains can be demonstrated with ease, but their scarcity suggests a minor biochemical significance. The fact that the limiting pH for most strains is in the vicinity of pH 5.0 has practical application in the control of certain plant diseases produced by *Streptomyces;* i.e., acidification of the soil is used to suppress the pathogen (figure 3). Even continuous applications of ammonium fertilizers without lime suppress the actinomycetes since the ammonium is oxidized to nitric acid by microbial action, and the resultant fall in pH leads to unfavorable growth conditions (1). Liming generally has a beneficial effect since vegetative development is favored by neutral or alkaline conditions, the population being most abundant in soils of about pH 6.5 to 8.0.

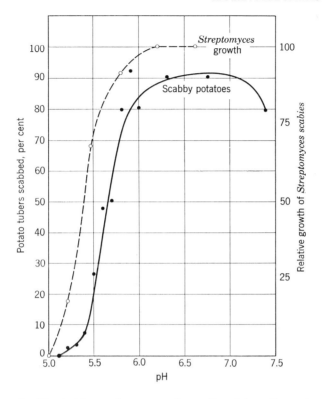

Figure 3. The incidence of potato scab as affected by soil reaction (4).

Moisture content is another critical environmental determinant. Under conditions of waterlogging or where moisture is above the microbiological optimum, for example at 85 to 100 per cent of the water-holding capacity, these microorganisms appear only rarely. This is a consequence of the aerobic metabolism of all common soil actinomycetes and the consequent inability to develop and spread when free O_2 is lacking. On the other hand, actinomycetes are not as greatly influenced by semi-dry conditions as are the bacteria, and the filamentous group tends to be favored by low moisture levels both in vegetative development and in conidia formation (5). Consequently, the numbers of actinomycetes remain high as soils dry out while the relative incidence of bacteria diminishes because of their lack of tolerance to arid conditions. Meiklejohn (9) has recorded the case of a severe drought in Kenya during which time the actinomycetes, initially representing less than 30 per cent of the colonies on dilution plates, made up more than 90 per cent of the viable organisms. Even in certain true deserts, these microorganisms often dominate the microscopic life, but moisture effects of this type are associated with the persistence of conidia because the vegetative hyphae undoubtedly require appreciable moisture for biochemical activity. Such data suggest that actinomycete spores possess a high degree of resistance to desiccation and persist for longer periods than other taxonomic groups.

Examination of hyphal density on glass slides incorporated in the soil shows that there is little growth of mesophilic actinomycetes at 5°C and essentially none at 39°C. Increasing the temperature from 5 to 27°C leads to greater development, and the optimum range is generally from 28 to 37°C (5).

Moisture, temperature, and the availability of organic matter from roots and plant residues to a large extent determine the microbiological influence of season. Counts are highest in spring and in autumn, the increase in the latter time of year usually being attributed to the return of plant residues to the soil. The scarcity in the winter presumably results from frost killing. During the hot, dry months of the summer, a decline likewise occurs but, because of their great tolerance to desiccation, the relative proportion of actinomycetes often is highest in the dry months.

These filamentous microorganisms are present in the A horizon as well as at considerable depths below the surface, but the cell density estimated by plating techniques progressively declines with depth in the profile. In many but not all soils, the percentage of actinomycetes in the total microflora becomes greater with depth so that they make up a larger segment of the subsurface population. No explanation for this anomalous behavior is yet available although it may be associated with the downward movement of conidia with water or a differential effect of O_2 or CO_2 on bacteria and actinomycetes. Even in the C horizon, counts may range from 10^3 to 10^5 per gram.

Taxonomy

Actinomycetes are classified within the order Actinomycetales, a category of bacteria that includes thread-like microorganisms forming elongated cells with a tendency towards branching. Differing from the fungal filaments, the hyphae are always slender and have a diameter rarely in excess of about one micron. Another difference from the fungi is the absence from the actinomycete cell wall of the chitin and cellulose commonly found among the molds. The order contains four families and nine genera, only the last seven of which are included by the non-taxonomic term, actinomycete.

  I. Mycobacteriaceae.
     Mycelium rudimentary or absent. Spores not produced.
     A. *Mycobacterium.* Gram positive, aerobic, mesophilic rods, commonly acid-fast. Non-motile and usually non-branching. Genus includes soil saprophytes.
     B. *Mycococcus.* Gram positive, aerobic, mesophilic cocci. Not acid-fast. Found singly, in clumps, or in short chains.
 II. Actinomycetaceae.
     True mycelium formed. Spores produced by hyphal fragmentation. Spores not in sporangia. In early growth, the mycelium is continuous, but subsequently it fragments into bacillary or coccoidal segments.
     A. *Actinomyces.* Anaerobic or microaerophilic. Conidia not formed. Typically parasitic, causing human and animal diseases.
     B. *Nocardia.* Obligate aerobes. Cells occur as slender filaments. Aerial mycelium rarely formed and conidia not produced. Colonies similar to those of true bacteria. Common soil organisms.
III. Streptomycetaceae.
     True mycelium formed. Vegetative mycelium does not fragment into small segments. Spores produced but not in sporangia.
     A. *Streptomyces.* Conidia formed in chains on aerial hyphae. Aerobic. Abundant in soil.
     B. *Micromonospora.* Conidia formed singly at the terminal end of short conidiophores, never in chains of spores. Aerobic with one exception. No growth at 50 to 65°C.
     C. *Thermoactinomyces.* Similar to the micromonosporas except for growth at 50 to 65°C.
 IV. Actinoplanaceae.
     True mycelium formed. Spores produced in sporangia.
     A. *Actinoplanes.* Sporangiospores motile. Aerial mycelium rare.
     B. *Streptosporangium.* Sporangiospores not motile. Aerial mycelium common.

Actinomyces, Actinoplanes, and *Streptosporangium* have been isolated from soil, but they are quite rare. *Mycobacterium* and *Mycococcus,* in common usage at least, are considered as bacteria. *Micromonospora* and *Thermoactinomyces* spp. can be demonstrated without difficulty, but their abundance is far exceeded by *Streptomyces* and *Nocardia.* Thus, the last two genera dominate the actinomycete flora (table 2) although *Nocardia* strains are frequently overlooked because their colonies are difficult to distinguish from those of bacteria.

TABLE 2

Abundance of Actinomycete Genera in Dry-Steppe Soils (12)

Genus	Dark Chestnut Soil		Chernozem		Solonetz	
	No. of Strains	% of Total	No. of Strains	% of Total	No. of Strains	% of Total
Streptomyces	59	72.0	73	79.3	49	98
Nocardia	22	26.8	19	20.7	1	2.0
Micromonospora	1	1.2	0	0.0	0	0.0
Total no. isolates	82		92		50	

Classification of the actinomycetes into separate and distinct species is difficult because of the frequent overlapping between strains, and sharp lines of demarcation between individual species are largely unknown. This has led to many controversies on the taxonomy of species within the several genera, particularly within *Streptomyces* and *Nocardia*. Likewise, the primitive actinomycetes are morphologically very similar to the true bacteria, and it is no simple task to demarcate the boundary between *Nocardia* and the genera *Mycobacterium* and *Corynebacterium*.

Streptomyces differs from *Nocardia* in that the former possesses a mycelium which does not divide into segments but which can give rise to conidia. The streptomycetes form a well-developed, non-septate mycelium and aerial hyphae which bear numerous conidia in distinct chain-like arrangements. These spores are formed by division of the sporogenous hyphae, the divisions progressing from the tip to the proximal end of the filament. When fully formed, the conidia have an oval to rod shape and resemble the cells of true bacteria in size and morphology. In the hyphae, growth is largely confined to the apical portion while the rest of the filament remains largely dormant. Turbidity is not formed in stationary liquid culture; rather the cells appear at the surface in a distinctive, flaky manner. In aerated liquid media, streptomycete growth is also not homogeneous and diffuse as with most bacteria, but typical mycelial pellets or clumps develop. Colonies on agar media tend to be tough and have a leathery consistency, and they resist destruction by mechanical force. The colony is frequently pigmented, but not uncommon is the production of water-soluble pigments which diffuse into the medium. An unforgettable attribute of the streptomycetes is the musty odor they elaborate, an odor reminiscent of freshly turned soil, and it is not unlikely that the rich, earthy smell in newly ploughed land is the consequence of the presence of these microorganisms.

The colonies of *Nocardia* and true bacteria bear a marked resemblance to one another in general features and in consistency. Because of this similarity, most population estimates of bacteria inadvertently include the nocardias so that the so-called "actinomycete" numbers represent in reality only the streptomycetes. Species of *Nocardia* have early in their life cycles a rudimentary mycelium which soon fragments into short, rod-like cells. Most strains produce no true aerial mycelium although some may exhibit a limited aerial development. Acid-fast staining is found among a few species. Many of the higher soil bacteria, especially *Mycobacterium, Corynebacterium,* and *Arthrobacter,* are related to species of *Nocardia* in morphology, and final placement of an isolate into one or another genus frequently is difficult. Brown (3) has reported that Skinner's method for the differentiation of spores and vegetative forms of *Streptomyces* also can be used to distinguish between the mycelial and rod stages of *Nocardia cellulans,* and her data indicate that this organism, when established in partially sterilized soil, exists mainly in the rod rather than the hyphal form. This is in agreement with the hypothesis that most actinomycete colonies appearing on dilution plates are derived from spores or resistant bodies in the soil.

Mesophilic actinomycetes which have a single conidium at the tip of specialized hyphal branches are placed in the genus *Micromonospora.* Compared to the streptomycetes and nocardias, the micromonosporas are relatively uncommon in soil although their presence is easily demonstrated. Their morphology is unique, each hypha being non-septate, 0.3 to 0.8 μ in diameter, while the spores are oval to round, 1.0 to 1.2 by 1.2 to 1.5 μ, and are produced singly at the terminus of the specialized conidiophores. Both conidia and mycelium are gram positive and non-acid-fast. In addition to its occurrence in soil, the micromonospora type has a peculiar ecological distribution. It or its thermophilic counterpart, *Thermoactinomyces,* is common in two other natural habitats, heating compost heaps and lake bottom muds. For example, as many as 10 to 20 per cent and occasionally up to 50 per cent of the total microbial flora of the lake bottom deposits in northern Wisconsin consist of *Micromono-spora* (14).

Of the three ubiquitous genera, *Streptomyces* is consistently the most numerous in arable land, *Nocardia* is abundant but is not as frequently encountered, while *Micromonospora* is generally scarce. Typically, some 70 to 90 per cent of the actinomycetes in virgin and cultivated fields are *Streptomyces,* less than a third are *Nocardia* strains, and *Micromonospora* rarely contributes more than about 5 per cent (6, 12). Although the other genera may be found occasionally, their scarcity suggests that theirs is an insignificant role.

Activity and Function

The slow growth habits and the late appearance of actinomycetes on dilution plates have been to a large extent the cause of the dearth of information on the physiology of these organisms. In recent years, however, the commercial value of their fermentation products has encouraged more intensive investigations, and the state of knowledge has been progressively improving. But, since the interest has come largely from the fields of fermentation biochemistry and pharmacology, the function of these organisms in nature still remains somewhat obscure.

The actinomycetes develop far more leisurely than most fungi and bacteria, a characteristic suggestive of their inability to be effective competitors and of their lack of prominence when the nutrient level is high and the pressure of competition great. The feeble competitive powers may explain their relative scarcity during the initial stages of plant residue decomposition. When nutrients become limiting and the pressure of the more effective competitors diminishes, the actinomycetes become more prominent.

Actinomycetes are heterotrophic feeders, and their presence is therefore conditioned by the availability of organic substrates. Utilizable carbon sources include simple and highly complex molecules from the organic acids and sugars to the polysaccharides, lipids, proteins, and aliphatic hydrocarbons. Cellulose is decomposed by many species in pure culture, but the rate of decomposition is invariably slow. Various strains can also degrade starch, inulin, and chitin; chitin hydrolysis is especially characteristic of the actinomycetes. The metabolism of unusual organic molecules such as paraffins, phenols, steroids, and pyrimidines is well documented for *Nocardia* spp. whereas *Micro-*

monospora strains decompose chitin, cellulose, glucosides, pentosans, and possibly lignin. Certain isolates develop well in media deficient in carbon, these being termed *oligocarbophilic* microorganisms.

Ammonium, nitrate, amino acids, peptones, and a number of proteins are utilized as nitrogen sources. The complex molecules are presumably degraded to ammonia, which then serves as the key compound in nitrogen assimilation. The ability to assimilate N_2 or to carry out denitrification is absent.

The order Actinomycetales has received special attention because many strains have the capacity to synthesize toxic metabolites (table 3). As many as three-fourths of the streptomycete isolates may produce the antimicrobial agents known as *antibiotics*. Among the major antibiotic substances produced by actinomycetes are streptomycin, chloramphenicol, chlortetracycline, oxytetracycline, and cycloheximide. Despite the great industrial and therapeutic value of these chemicals, there is still no clear picture of the function of the antibiotics in the

TABLE 3

Occurrence of Antibiotic Production among Actinomycetes (7)

Antibiotic Activity	Inhibition Zone	Test Bacterium		
		Bacillus subtilis	*Escherichia coli*	*Mycobacterium phlei*
	mm			
Nutrient Agar				
None	0	30	78	26
Weak	1–9	3	13	16
Medium	10–19	46	3	35
Strong	20–35	21	6	23
Glucose Asparagine Agar				
None	0	22	80	14
Weak	1–9	35	14	10
Medium	10–19	28	6	70
Strong	20–35	15	0	6

Data represent the percentage of actinomycetes tested which produced no, weak, medium, or strong antagonism against three test bacteria.

metabolism of the organism or of the significance of such compounds in natural processes. In addition to the production of antimicrobial metabolites, certain species of *Streptomyces* liberate extracellular proteases which lyse bacteria (2). The possession of enzymes of this type may be important in the microbiological equilibrium in soil.

Most actinomycetes are mesophiles with an optimum temperature in the range of about 25 to 30°C; thermophilic cultures, however, are not uncommon. These are generally facultative thermophiles, growing at 55 to 65°C as well as at 30°C, but the former range is often the more favorable. By contrast, obligate thermophiles fail to proliferate at the lower temperature. Thermophilic actinomycetes are common in soil, manure, heating hay, and compost heaps, and their presence has been established even in soils which never become warm. Isolation requires the inoculation of a suitable source material into nutrient solutions maintained at elevated temperatures followed by plating of the enrichments upon agar media incubated at these temperature extremes. Thermophiles are present in soil throughout the year, but only a few per cent of the thermophiles in winter are actinomycetes whereas the relative abundance rises in the summer (16). In heating manure piles, the population of thermophilic actinomycetes becomes enormous, e.g., up to 10 billion of these microorganisms are present per gram at 50 to 65°C. The more numerous strains in thermophilic processes are of the micromonospora type, classified generally as *Thermoactinomyces,* but species of *Streptomyces* often may dominate.

The activities of the actinomycetes in soil transformations are not clearly defined despite the great interest of recent years. Because microscopic examination reveals few actinomycetes in the mycelial stage and since present evidence indicates that the high plate counts are largely the result of conidial persistence, it would seem that the actinomycetes have a lesser biochemical importance than the bacteria and fungi. Nevertheless, there is evidence for these microorganisms participating in the following processes:

a. Decomposition of certain of the resistant components of plant and animal tissue. Actinomycetes do not respond immediately to the addition of natural carbonaceous materials but rather several weeks thereafter, suggesting that they fare poorly in competition with bacteria and fungi during the period when simple carbohydrates are present. They are effective competitors only when resistant compounds remain.

b. Formation of humus through the conversion of raw organic matter into the types of compounds native to the soil organic fraction. Many strains can produce in culture media the aromatic molecules that are assumed to be important in the humus fraction of mineral soils.

  c. Transformations at high temperature particularly in the rotting and heating of green manures, hay, compost piles, and animal manures (figure 4). In these conditions, the thermophilic actinomycetes may be the dominant group, sometimes to the extent that the surface of the compost pile takes on the white or gray color typical of this group. Here, *Thermoactinomyces*, certain streptomycetes, and species of spore-forming bacteria have the competitive advantage.

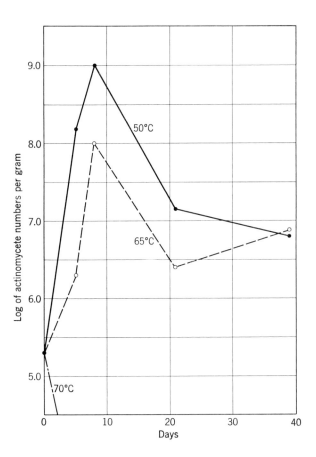

Figure 4. Effect of temperature on the development of actinomycetes in a manure compost (15).

d. Cause of certain soil-borne diseases of plants, e.g., potato scab and sweet potato pox.

e. Possible importance in microbial antagonism through the liberation of antibiotics.

REFERENCES

Reviews

Gottlieb, D. 1953. The physiology of the actinomycetes. *Symp., Actinomycetales, 6th Intl. Cong. Microbiol.,* Rome, pp. 122–136.

Waksman, S. A. 1953. The biology of the actinomycetes and their economic importance. *Symp., Actinomycetales, 6th Intl. Cong. Microbiol.,* Rome, pp. 3–12.

Waksman, S. A. 1959. *The actinomycetes. Vol. 1. Nature, occurrence, and activities.* The Williams and Wilkins Co., Baltimore.

Literature cited

1. Beliaev, G. N. 1958. *Mikrobiologiya,* 27:472–477.
2. Born, G. V. R. 1952. *J. Gen. Microbiol.,* 6:344–351.
3. Brown, M. E. 1958. *J. Gen. Microbiol.,* 18:239–247.
4. Dippenaar, B. J. 1933. *Sci. Bull. 136,* Dept. Agric., Union of South Africa.
5. Jensen, H. L. 1943. *Proc. Linnean Soc. N. S. W.,* 68:67–71.
6. Jensen, H. L. 1932. *Proc. Linnean Soc. N. S. W.,* 57:173–180.
7. Johnstone, D. B. 1947. *Soil Sci.,* 64:453–458.
8. Marshall, K. C., and M. Alexander. 1960. *J. Bacteriol.,* 80:412–416.
9. Meiklejohn, J. 1957. *J. Soil Sci.,* 8:240–247.
10. Mishustin, E. N. 1956. *Soils and Fert.,* 19:385–392.
11. Skinner, F. A. 1951. *J. Gen. Microbiol.,* 5:159–166.
12. Teplyakova, Z. F., and T. G. Maksimova. 1957. *Mikrobiologiya,* 26:323–329.
13. Thornton, R. H. 1953. *Research,* 6:38S–39S.
14. Umbreit, W. W., and E. McCoy. 1941. *A symposium on hydrobiology.* Univ. of Wisconsin Press, Madison, pp. 106–114.
15. Waksman, S. A., T. C. Cordon, and N. Hulpoi. 1939. *Soil Sci.,* 47:83–113.
16. Waksman, S. A., W. W. Umbreit, and T. C. Cordon. 1939. *Soil Sci.,* 47:37–61.

4

Fungi

The most abundant group of microorganisms in soil are the bacteria, and plate or microscopic counts invariably indicate their numerical preponderance. The bacterial cell, however, is quite small in size, and its length rarely exceeds 5 μ. In most well-aerated, cultivated soils, the fungi account for the largest part of the total microbial protoplasm. This dominance in mass is the result of the large diameter and the extensive network of fungus filaments. Especially in the organic layers of woodland and forest soils does the fungus network dominate the microbial protoplasm contained within the decomposing litter, but acid environments in general have the fungi as the major agents of decay.

Fungus filaments are commonly not visible to the naked eye, but they may be seen by direct examination of soil with specially designed microscopes or by the Rossi-Cholodny buried slide technique. Results of such ecological investigations demonstrate that fertile land may contain as much as 10 to 100 m of active fungus filaments per gram of soil. Assuming the mold filament has an average diameter of 5 μ and a specific gravity of 1.2, and taking the conservative estimate of 10 m, it would appear that the live weight of fungi is approximately 500 lb per acre.

Characteristically, the fungi possess a filamentous mycelium network of individual hyphal strands. The mycelium may be subdivided into individual cells by cross walls or *septa*, but many fungal species are non-septate. The hyphae of the non-septate fungi are continuous and multinucleate, the filaments bearing no cross walls. The hypha itself is rather broad and has a diameter appreciably greater than that found in the actinomycete filaments previously described. Individual hyphae may be vegetative or fertile, the fertile filaments producing either sexual or asexual spores. In nature, the conidia or asexual spores are abundant and widespread, the sexual spores relatively uncommon. In culture medium, the mycelium is usually colorless while the asexual spores frequently are strikingly colored. Size, shape, structure, and cultural characteristics are important in taxonomy since, in contrast with the bacteria, the fungi can be effectively differentiated into genera and species on the basis of morphology.

Distribution and Abundance

Several techniques have been developed for the study of the fungal flora, each with its own advantages. No single procedure, however, adequately describes the entire generic composition of the flora nor does any one method depict accurately the mass of vegetative hyphae in soil or the biochemical capacities of the population. The approach most frequently used for fungus enumeration is the plate count, in which dilutions of a soil specimen in sterile water are plated upon a suitable agar medium. Because bacteria and actinomycetes are usually more numerous than fungi, conventional laboratory media cannot be used as the development of fungal colonies on the petri dishes will be suppressed. Early microbiologists overcame the problem of suppression on solid media by acidifying the agar to pH 4.0, a reaction at which few bacteria and actinomycetes but most fungi develop. On the other hand, acidification is not necessary provided that appropriate bacteriostatic agents are included in the counting medium. Penicillin, novobiocin, and oxgall have been used to good advantage, but agar containing both rose bengal and streptomycin (14) is the usual choice.

Population estimates of fungi based upon plate counting are open to serious criticism. Since the colonies appearing upon the agar may be derived from a spore or a fragment of vegetative mycelium, the active or dormant nature of the viable unit in the original sample is unknown. Further, the readily sporulating genera appear in large numbers on the agar plates because each individual spore may give rise to a colony. It is not surprising that fungi sporulating profusely, e.g., *Penicillium* and *Aspergillus* spp., are isolated frequently. The mere act of shaking often introduces an error into the population estimate, for the agitation tends to rupture the mycelium and sporulating body into an indeterminate number of fragments each of which may produce a single colony. For these and other reasons, the results of plate counts must be interpreted with considerable care, bearing in mind the numerous shortcomings of the technique. Caution must be exercised, especially when high values are obtained for profusely sporulating species and low values for species which sporulate sparsely or in which the hyphae resist fragmentation during the agitation of the soil suspension. Within the framework of limitations, there is nevertheless a distinct place for plating techniques since they not only show relative numbers of viable units under different soil management practices but also serve as one of several qualitative means of demonstrating the types of fungi characteristic of a given habitat.

Fungi may be investigated in a number of ways not involving soil dilutions. Each additional technique serves to help in the ecological characterization of the composition of the flora. Procedures for direct microscopic observation of the upper soil crust *in situ* have been used occasionally, but the special apparatus required and the sparse data obtained have limited the widespread adoption of these methods. Examination of stained soil crumbs by microscopic means has also been attempted, but this approach too has provided little ecological information. The buried slide procedure, on the other hand, is a convenient means for the observation of microorganisms in situations not too different from the natural state. Introduced independently by Rossi (23) and Cholodny (7), the technique entails the burial of glass slides in soil for varying periods, following which time the slides are carefully removed, the excess soil dislodged by a gentle stream of water, and the preparation fixed with heat and examined microscopically after staining with rose bengal or erythrosin. In these preparations, visualization of the hyphal strands and the spatial arrangement of microorganisms in the habitat is possible (figure 1).

The soil plate method of Warcup (28) is of considerable value in qualitative and ecological studies. In this procedure, about 5 to 15 mg of soil are placed at the bottom of a sterile petri dish, and melted agar is poured over and mixed with the underlying soil. As the fungi develop, they migrate into the agar layer, where they may be observed. The operations in preparing soil plates are not as drastic as the agitation needed for conventional dilution plates so that spore clusters tend to remain more intact, a distinct benefit in investigations of the dominant population groups.

The immersion tube technique is another useful tool for the study of fungus ecology. The immersion tube is a glass or plastic cylinder

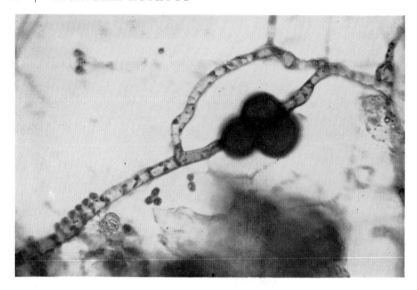

Figure 1. Fungus filaments and chlamydospores developing in soil treated with starch. (Courtesy of S. Ishizawa.)

with small openings in its side. After the tube is filled with a suitable solid medium and the apparatus sterilized, it is taken to the field and inserted tightly into a small hole bored in the soil. After an incubation interval of about 1 week, the cylinder is returned to the laboratory and isolations made from the hyphae developing through the agar (6, 18). The procedure does not unduly emphasize the sporulating genera as is the case with dilution counts and to some extent with the soil plate. As a consequence, it has been possible to demonstrate the abundance of many genera having no extensive capacity for sporulation but which are probably of considerable significance as agents of biochemical change. Because of the diversity of methods, it is not surprising that the results obtained by the various approaches frequently do not agree.

For the purposes of enumeration, conventional plate counts have been most widely used since, although the results are far from unequivocal, this procedure permits the greatest degree of quantification. Such estimates of microbial density reveal the presence in soil of populations typically ranging from as few as 20,000 to as many as 1,000,000 fungal units per gram, the unit being considered as any spore, hypha, or hyphal fragment which is capable of giving rise to a colony. At best, plate count values of fungi rarely amount to more than a few per cent of the bacterial count though, as pointed out above, these estimates are misleading.

Environmental Influences

The abundance and physiological activity of the fungus flora of different habitats vary considerably, and the population and its bio-chemical activities undergo appreciable fluctuation with time at any single site. Both the generic composition and the size of the flora vary with the type of soil and with its physical and chemical characteristics. Whether a given microorganism will be able to survive, adapt itself, and become established in a specific habitat will be determined by the surrounding environment. The major external influences imposed upon the fungus flora include the organic matter status, hydrogen ion concentration, organic and inorganic fertilizers, the moisture regime, aeration, temperature, position in the profile, season of year, and the composition of the vegetation.

Fungi are heterotrophic in nutrition, and neither sunlight nor the oxidation of inorganic substances provides these microorganisms with the energy needed for growth; fungal distribution is consequently determined by the availability of oxidizable carbonaceous substrates. In a general sense, the numbers of filamentous fungi in soil vary directly with the content of utilizable organic matter, but this microbial group is still present and of importance in areas low in organic matter. Jensen, for example, found a direct correlation between fungal density estimated by plating and the humus content of Australian soils, his data suggesting that the quantity of organic matter is a major determinant of fungal numbers (12). Improving the nutrient status by the incorporation of crop residues, green manures, or other energy-rich carbonaceous materials into soil has the anticipated effect of increasing the size of the population. At the same time, application of organic substrates alters the composition of the flora, and the relative dominance of genera such as *Penicillium, Trichoderma, Aspergillus, Fusarium,* and *Mucor* is markedly affected. The stimulation of mold action by supplemental organic matter is greatest during the first few months of decomposition, and the carbonaceous debris becomes completely permeated with a hyphal network. Certain species become abundant immediately upon addition of the carbon sources, but their numbers rapidly decline following the initial increase. By the nature of their response, these species are considered to be zymogenous. Other species, however, maintain high population levels for relatively long periods after the incorporation of plant residues (15). The response varies with the chemical composition of the substrate and with certain environmental characteristics, the fungi usually dominating the microflora following carbonaceous amendments to acid environments supplied with adequate nitrogen.

The hydrogen ion concentration is another of the major ecological variables governing the activity and composition of the flora. Many mold species can develop over a wide pH range, from the highly acid to the alkaline extremes. In culture, the capacity to grow readily at pH values as low as 2.0 to 3.0 is not uncommon, and numerous strains still are active at pH 9.0 or above. Because the bacteria and actinomycetes are uncommon in acid habitats, the population in areas of low pH is dominated by the fungi. This is not the result of the fungi finding their optimum in acidic conditions but rather it is a consequence of the lack of microbiological competition for the food reserve. Thus, the insensitivity of many of the molds to high hydrogen ion concentrations and the narrow pH range of most bacteria and actinomycetes lead to the ecological maxim that the fungi make up a larger percentage of the population and are responsible for a considerable portion of the biochemical transformations in acid habitats. It is not difficult, therefore, to understand why in certain grasslands 0.21 to 0.25 per cent of the count at pH 6.4 to 6.8, 0.31 to 0.34 per cent at pH 6.1 to 6.4, and 0.61 per cent in soils at pH 5.8 to 6.1 consist of fungal units (8). For similar reasons, liming reduces and treatment with acid-forming fertilizers increases fungal abundance.

Individual species, however, may show a lesser tolerance to high hydrogen ion concentrations than the general fungus community. A pH sensitivity can be of profound importance to soil-borne plant pathogens which, as a consequence of the pH range for vigor and growth, are more destructive at acid, neutral, or alkaline reaction. Pathogens such as *Plasmodiophora brassicae* fare best in acid habitats, and the disease produced by it is uncommon or mild in land of pH greater than 7.5. Other plant pathogens grow optimally in soils near neutrality whereas certain species are prolific in alkaline localities, and acidification may therefore become a practical control measure. Liming or acidification practices are to no avail for those disease-producing organisms which are not markedly influenced by pH.

The application of inorganic fertilizers may modify the abundance of filamentous fungi, but such alterations are frequently more the result of acidification than of nutrient addition. Treatment with fertilizers containing ammonium salts increases mold numbers because microbial oxidation of the nitrogen leads to the formation of nitric acid. Increasing fertilizer application rates magnify the stimulation, and the repeated annual addition of ammonium fertilizers favors the fungal and diminishes the bacterial and actinomycete counts.

All living things demand adequate moisture, and it is not surprising, therefore, that soil water has a direct effect upon the abundance and functions of fungi. Their capacity for catalyzing chemical changes is poor or lacking entirely when the water supply is low. Improvement in the moisture status of the environment favors fungal numbers so that, at suboptimal water levels, the count is positively correlated with moisture (table 1). If periodic measurements are made upon the fungi at a given site, the population density is found to be related directly to soil water content (12). Nevertheless, these organisms may persist in relatively semi-arid conditions. At the opposite extreme, when moisture is excessive, diffusion of the O_2 necessary for aerobic metabolism is inadequate to meet the microbiological demand, and the fungi are among the first to suffer. Many genera are affected detrimentally as the water level increases, but certain of the Mucorales become more numerous (20).

The filamentous fungi as a group are strict aerobes although exceptions are known. Even among the obligate aerobes, however, part of the mycelium may penetrate into locales where O_2 is absent, but

TABLE 1

Changes in Population of Fungi in Grassland at Various Moisture Levels (8)

Avg % Soil Moisture	Fungi/g $\times 10^3$			Spores as % of Total
	Total	Hyphal Units	Spores	
8.9	99	60	39	39
11.2	89	57	32	36
18.5	142	113	29	20
24.2	149	133	16	10
27.1	173	153	20	12

much of the hyphal mass must have ready access to air. This dependence upon O_2 probably explains to a great extent the concentration of fungi in the surface few inches. The requirement for O_2 is also a major cause of the virtual absence of fungi from the lower levels of undrained peats and from swamps and bogs. In waterlogged mineral soils, numbers are likewise reduced to such an extent that the biochemical activities of these filamentous microorganisms in excessively wet environments are negligible. Some organisms will still persist for long periods in these unfavorable circumstances, a fact possibly associated with the production of resistant spores. Once the flooded soils are drained, the molds recover and return rapidly to a position of importance (25).

Most fungi are mesophilic in their temperature relationships, and thermophilic growth is uncommon. A few thermophilic strains can be demonstrated in normal soil, but such variants become abundant only during the heating of rotting composts. The thermophiles will multiply at 50° but not at 65°C, and they are absent from composts that reach high temperatures. The incubation of soil dilution plates at 37°C shows the adaptation of *Aspergillus* and *Trichoderma* spp. to warm temperatures. Organisms actively growing at about 37°C seem to be localized in the surface horizons, where heating is appreciable during the summer months of the year. Agar plates incubated at 6°C, on the other hand, contain mainly *Cylindrocarpon, Mucor, Penicillium,* and *Cladosporium,* and the abundance of these genera relative to total fungi becomes greater with depth in the horizon (3). These ecological observations suggest a selection within the profile according to the optimal temperature range of individual genera of the microflora.

In cultivated soil, fungi are most numerous in the surface layers, but high counts are often observed in the B horizon of grass sod (table 2). The population frequently remains large in the subsoil, and it may be appreciable to a depth of 4 ft. A greater number of individual species occurs near the surface than deeper in the profile. At the same time, the dominant species change. The causes of the depth effect are not as yet fully established, but the organism concentration in the upper layers of the profile is to a large extent the result of the greater abundance there of readily available organic matter. The explanation of the qualitative changes within the fungus population of different horizons, on the other hand, may be associated with a strain adaptation to development at the low partial pressures of O_2 or the high concentrations of CO_2 in the deeper sites. An im-

TABLE 2

Distribution of Fungi in the Profiles of Two Canadian Soils (19)

Depth	Horizon	Fungi/g $\times$ 10^3				
		May 30	June 30	July 20	Aug. 30	Sept. 30
in.						
			Cultivated Field			
0–3	A_1	35	6	10	15	22
3–6	A_1	30	6	6	4	5
6–12	A_1	3	2	3	3	6
14–22	A_2	2	2	1	5	5
22–29	B_1	1	6	0	3	5
29–36	B_2	0	0	1	2	5
			Grass Sod			
0–3	A_1	19	15	38	44	7
3–6	A_1	12	7	13	10	4
6–12	A_1	13	4	5	5	4
14–22	A_2	6	19	7	19	21
22–29	B_1	4	18	17	12	25
29–36	B_2	9	18	37	21	14

portant selective effect of CO_2 becomes evident when the flora is divided into categories on the basis of vertical distribution: (a) fungi common throughout the profile; (b) those most numerous in upper layers or in surface litter but uncommon below 5 cm; and (c) strains rare in the upper regions but relatively common in lower depths. The surface fungi, group b, are inhibited by CO_2 while the microorganisms characteristic of the subsurface sites have a greater tolerance to the gas. Types a and c are thus apparently dominant below the surface because of their relative insensitivity to CO_2 rather than their capacity to proliferate at low partial pressures of O_2 (4). The influence of depth upon the abundance and species composition of the fungal flora therefore seems to be associated with the concentration of organic matter and the composition of the soil atmosphere.

Season of year exerts its influence in many ways. The warmth of spring usually is beneficial, but periods of summer drought or winter cold take their toll. The availability of organic matter is markedly influenced by season, and carbonaceous nutrients are abundant in the fall in the form of dying roots and plowed-under crop residues. As a result, counts tend to be high in the autumn and spring and decline during the summer and winter (table 2). Some localities may occasionally have active populations in the summer, but fungal action is always at a low ebb in regions having cold winters. With the return of the warm weather in spring, the mold life of the soil once more becomes rejuvenated.

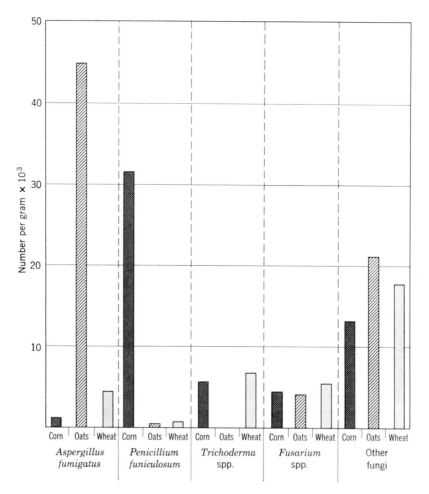

Figure 2. Frequency of fungi in soil under corn, oats, and wheat (11).

The effect of cropping is exerted not only through the contribution of organic substrates but also through differential influences of the plants themselves. The dominance of one or another fungus group is related to the type of vegetative cover. Certain of the microorganisms are associated with definite plant communities while others seem to be unaffected by the nature of the vegetation. In quantitative terms, for example, fields cropped continuously to oats contain more fungi than land cropped continuously to corn or wheat, suggesting a selective action by the oat plant. Qualitatively, the predominant fungus under oats is *Aspergillus fumigatus* while *Penicillium funiculosum* is the most numerous under corn (11, 13). This is shown in figure 2. Such data demonstrate the key role played by the vegetation in the make-up of the microflora in terms of both fungal density and species composition. The selective action of the plant may be the result of a microbiological response either to specific root excretions or to chemical constituents of the sloughed-off tissues undergoing decomposition.

Taxonomy

Considerable effort has been directed towards the establishment of the composition of the fungus flora of the soil. Mycologists in many countries have performed extensive studies of the genera and species that dominate in one or another ecological circumstance, and the results of their efforts have borne fruit. Although the entire dominant flora is not always well defined, a clear picture of the fungus inhabitants is now beginning to emerge.

Most isolates are placed in one of three classes, Fungi Imperfecti, Phycomycetes, or Ascomycetes. The most frequently encountered group developing upon agar media are strains belonging to the Fungi Imperfecti, molds which produce spores only asexually. In species of this class, the mycelium is septate, and the conidial type of asexual spore is borne on specialized structures known as conidiophores. Differing from the imperfect fungi, Phycomycetes and Ascomycetes produce spores by both sexual and asexual means. The filaments of the former are usually non-septate and unicellular, and the asexual spores are borne characteristically in sporangia. The filaments of the Ascomycetes, on the other hand, are septate, and these fungi form a definite number of ascospores in a sac-like body or ascus.

The following list is based upon Gilman's authoritative monograph upon the soil fungi. The genera tabulated are those most frequently encountered by conventional isolation procedures and, as such, they are undoubtedly of considerable importance in the biochemical transformations that take place.

I. Fungi Imperfecti.
   A. Moniliaceae. Conidiophores scattered in loose, irregular masses. Conidia and conidiophores either clear or bright in color. *Acrostalagmus, Aspergillus, Botrytis, Cephalosporium, Gliocladium, Monilia, Penicillium, Scopulariopsis, Spicaria, Trichoderma, Trichothecium, Verticillium.*
   B. Dematiaceae. Conidiophores scattered in loose, irregular masses. Conidia and/or conidiophores dark in color. *Alternaria, Cladosporium, Pullularia.*
   C. Tuberculariaceae. Conidiophores gathered into a sporodochium. *Cylindrocarpon, Fusarium.*
II. Phycomycetes.
   A. Mucorales. Sporangia containing asexual spores are globose to cylindrical. Zygospores formed. *Absidia, Cunninghamella, Mortierella, Mucor, Rhizopus, Zygorhynchus.*
   B. Peronosporales. Asexual spores motile, mycelium well developed, having single oospores. *Pythium.*
III. Ascomycetes.
   Filaments septate. Ascospores formed in asci. *Chaetomium.*
IV. Mycelia Sterilia.
   Filaments septate, conidia not formed. *Rhizoctonia.*

The class Fungi Imperfecti consistently contributes the greatest number of genera and species to the fungus community. Phycomycetes are not as numerous, but individuals of certain genera are quite abundant in cultivated fields while others are pathogenic to higher plants. Especially common among the soil Phycomycetes are members of the Mucorales, and a large proportion of the cultures of this order found in mycological collections are derived from soil. Ascomycetes are invariably found but, with the exception of the ubiquitous *Chaetomium*, the distribution of the many genera is sparse. *Rhizoctonia* is one of the more frequently isolated non-sporulating fungi, the Mycelia Sterilia, but special techniques such as the screened immersion plate method (26) are usually required to show its abundance. Several of the frequently encountered genera are shown in figure 3.

To account for the observed differences in the composition of the fungus flora, certain ecological generalizations have been advanced. For example, *Penicillium* spp. constitute an increasingly larger per-

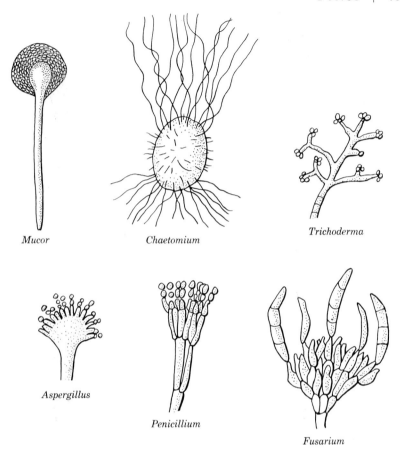

Mucor   Chaetomium

Trichoderma

Aspergillus

Penicillium

Fusarium

Figure 3. Common genera of soil fungi. (After J. C. Gilman.)

centage of the fungal population as the climate becomes cooler while samples taken in progressively warmer areas reveal greater numbers of *Aspergillus* spp. Thus, the former genus is particularly abundant in soils of the temperate regions, the latter in the tropics. The relative incidence of *Rhizopus* and *Fusarium* likewise seems to be greater with proximity to the equator (17). The aspergilli are also apparently favored in the dry prairies while representatives of the family Mucorales are of great frequency in wet locations (20). In woodland, *Mucor* and *Trichoderma* spp. are generally numerous whereas the percentage of penicillia increases in proceeding from pioneer to climax hardwood forests (27). Such generalizations must be taken as preliminary since the fungi isolated depend upon the individual habitat and the technique of isolation.

The media routinely used in microbiology laboratories are selective for specific nutritional types, and only certain fungi appear. A more complete nutrient substratum undoubtedly would show the presence of many other taxonomic groups. Conventional techniques, for example, fail to show the significance of the Basidiomycetes despite their regular occurrence in forest and prairie soils. This omission is a serious shortcoming in characterization of a microbiological habitat since the basidiomycete size is enormous by comparison with the microscopic dimensions of those fungi which are better adapted to the artificial circumstances of agar media. Distribution of the Basidiomycetes must, therefore, be assessed by direct examination of the environment, particularly with a view towards observing the fruiting stages of the organisms. Such studies reveal that the mushroom fungi are common in forests and grasslands, and that their presence and activity are governed to no small extent by the availability of carbonaceous materials, moisture, and temperature. Difficulties in isolation have delayed intensive physiological investigations of these higher fungi, but their role in the initial rotting of woody tissue, in lignin decomposition, and in mycorrhizal associations has been well documented.

Myxomycetes or slime molds are a unique fungal group found in soil. At one stage in their life cycle, the slime molds exist as individual *myxamoebae* that bear a remarkable resemblance to the true amoebae. The myxamoebae ultimately come together to form a fruiting body in which the organism produces its spores and, when conditions are suitable, the spores in turn give rise to the motile myxamoebae. To demonstrate the presence of slime molds, use is made of their habit of subsisting upon bacteria; i.e., the medium consists of a non-nutrient agar previously inoculated with an edible bacterium such as *Escherichia coli.* Results obtained by this method show that species of *Dictyostelium* were present in 33 of 38 arable sites and in 3 of 29 grassland soils examined in a typical investigation. At one time, Myxomycetes were considered to be inhabitants only of manure heaps, but their presence in permanent, unmanured plots suggests that they are indigenous to soil (24). By virtue of the selectivity in feeding of the myxamoebae, utilizing some but not all bacteria provided and preferring gram negative to gram positive bacteria (1), it would seem that such fungi are important not only in serving to help regulate the size of the bacterial population upon which they prey but also in effecting qualitative changes in the composition of the microflora.

Yeasts

Little attention has been given to the population of yeasts, but their presence may be demonstrated in most soils; hence, they are undoubtedly indigenous rather than invading organisms. Their numbers, however, are invariably small. The term *yeast* has no taxonomic validity, but the group is commonly taken to include those fungi that exist primarily as unicellular organisms and which reproduce by budding or fission. Two broad categories may be differentiated, the sporogenous group that produces ascospores and those that do not form ascospores. The ascospore-forming yeasts are placed in the class Ascomycetes and include such genera as *Saccharomyces, Pichia,* and *Hansenula.* The asporogenous or non-ascospore-forming yeasts of the Fungi Imperfecti include *Candida, Rhodotorula,* and *Cryptococcus.*

The genera of soil yeasts most frequently isolated are *Candida, Cryptococcus, Debaromyces, Hansenula, Lipomyces, Pichia, Pullularia, Rhodotorula, Saccharomyces, Schizoblastosporion, Torula, Torulaspora, Torulopsis, Trichosporon,* and *Zygosaccharomyces.* Certain sugar-tolerant strains capable of carrying out an active fermentation of carbohydrates may also be demonstrated, but their scarcity in most field soils indicates that these are alien rather than native organisms.

Since the yeasts grow readily at pH 4.0, no difficulty is encountered in the enumeration of yeasts—provided filamentous fungi are rare—as few bacteria or actinomycetes develop upon acidified agar. Enumeration of yeasts in the presence of the large numbers of filamentous fungi common to soil, on the other hand, is difficult because the latter proliferate more readily and tend to overgrow the former. However, a medium at pH 3.8 to 4.0 which contains 0.35 per cent sodium propionate suppresses both the bacteria and molds so that yeast counts can be made (9). The abundance of these organisms varies greatly with the locality under study, and counts from ca. 200 to 20,000 or more are not uncommon. Generally, populations of approximately 10^3 per gram are observed in temperate climates. Because of the scarcity of the yeasts, it is not yet possible to correlate population size with environmental factors. Further, their relative infrequency suggests that the role of yeasts in soil transformations is negligible, but future work should establish the precise significance of these organisms.

Function in Soil

The fungi contain no chlorophyll, and hence they must obtain carbon for cell synthesis from preformed organic molecules. In this regard, however, they are admirably suited since one or another strain can adapt itself to even the most complex of food materials. Among the carbon sources utilized are hexoses, pentoses, organic acids, disaccharides, starch, pectin, cellulose, fats, and the lignin molecule which is particularly resistant to bacterial degradation. Nitrogen frequently comes from ammonium or nitrate, but proteins, nucleic acids, or other organic nitrogenous complexes serve as well. Some species are nutritionally dependent, requiring B vitamins, amino acids, or other growth factors for active proliferation, but many develop fully in media containing only a sugar and inorganic salts. In the extreme condition of nutritional dependence are certain fungi which parasitize higher plants.

Difficulties have consistently been encountered in attempts to classify the fungi on the basis of the carbon sources supporting growth since the dominant soil genera can utilize a variety of carbonaceous substrates. Utilization of complex polysaccharides such as cellulose, pectins, and hemicelluloses is a characteristic associated with many of these filamentous microorganisms. A preliminary grouping scheme has been proposed which relies not upon energy sources but rather upon the growth factors necessary for maximum development (2), a classification similar to Lochhead's for bacteria. Studies relying upon this scheme have revealed that few soil fungi attain maximum growth in a medium containing no supplementary growth substances. The major nutritional types include those fungi stimulated by amino acids and by yeast extract, 30 to 40 per cent of the total isolates fitting into each of these two categories. Despite the fact that the growth of most cultures is increased by amino acids or yeast extract, 96 per cent are able to develop macroscopic colonies in unsupplemented glucose–inorganic salts media. This differs markedly from results obtained with bacteria.

Other proposals have been advanced to divide the soil fungi into functional groups. One scheme uses an ecological categorization based upon the microorganisms acting as initial colonizers of a particular substrate. Five main divisions are recognized: saprophytic sugar fungi, lignin decomposers, coprophilic fungi, predacious types, and root-inhabiting fungi (10). The first division is best exemplified by the Phycomycetes which rarely decompose lignin and cellulose and are limited to simple molecules; yet, these organisms do compete vigorously because of their physiological efficiency on the limited compounds available to them. Typical of the lignin decomposers are certain of the Basidiomycetes.

Predation is not rare among fungi. Amoebae and testaceous rhizopods are especially susceptible to the active species, which are largely certain phycomycetes and imperfect fungi. In the attack, the hypha penetrates the amoeba with a resulting decrease in motility of the animal and an eventual total cessation of movement. The fungus then slowly digests the cellular contents of the protozoan and assimilates the substances released. These predators seem to be obligate in their reliance upon the protozoa, and no spore germination occurs unless the prey is present (21). Nematodes are also entrapped and devoured, frequently by means of specialized appendages or hyphal extensions (figure 4). No definite functional niche has been established for the predacious species, but they may participate in the microbiological balance in soil, limiting the size and activity of the protozoan and nematode fauna.

Despite the limited value of quantitative estimates of numbers, considerable information is available on the function of the fungi. Present evidence indicates their role in arable soils to be largely as zymogenous organisms, but the spore forms must be considered autochthonous since they are largely inactive biochemically. In the mycelial condition, one of the major activities of the mold flora is in the degradation of complex molecules, and their response following the addition of mature plant residues, green tissues, or animal manures bears witness to this capacity (table 3). Upon the addition of organic matter, particularly to soils of low pH, the fungi become quite numerous. Representatives of all common classes can utilize and degrade the major plant constituents—cellulose, hemicelluloses, pectins, starch, and lignin. In woodland, the leaf debris becomes permeated with an extensive hyphal network that participates in the decomposition of the litter. The organic matter transformations brought about by filamentous fungi in well-aerated environments often may be more prominent than the reactions catalyzed by bacteria.

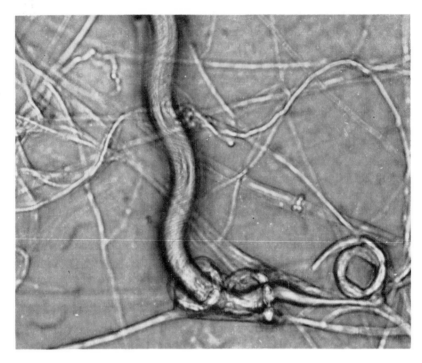

Figure 4. Nematode trapped by the fungus *Arthrobotrys conoides*. (Courtesy of D. Pramer.)

TABLE 3

Response of Fungi to Organic Matter Incorporation (16)

Soil Treatment	Fungi/g × 10³			
	7 Days	21 Days	35 Days	49 Days
None	7.90	7.55	4.06	4.74
Clover roots	70.0	68.0	64.4	43.2
Clover tops	—	—	48.0	43.0
Alfalfa roots	70.0	61.0	60.5	47.0
Alfalfa tops	—	—	72.5	36.8

The utilization of proteinaceous substances is another common characteristic, and as a consequence the fungi are active in the formation of ammonium and simple nitrogen compounds in soil. In the process of decomposition of the complex nitrogen-containing molecules, many genera and species participate. The microorganism benefits from the transformation since the proteinaceous material provides the organism with both nitrogen and carbon. Under certain conditions, however, the fungi will compete with higher plants for nitrate and ammonium and lead to a decrease of the soluble nitrogen content of the soil.

By the degradation of plant and animal remains, the fungi participate in the formation of humus from raw organic residues. Species of *Alternaria, Aspergillus, Cladosporium, Dematium, Gliocladium, Helminthosporium, Humicola,* and *Metarrhizum* synthesize lignin-like substances which resemble certain constituents of the native soil organic fraction (20). Some fungi can also produce substances similar in chemical structure to several of the carbohydrates extracted from soil organic matter. In addition, this group carries out a number of inorganic transformations and also influences the formation of stable aggregates by means of hyphal penetration and the mechanical binding of particles. Thus, the filamentous fungi are important biochemically by virtue of their ability to act upon and transform a wide variety of organic and inorganic compounds.

Pathogenicity is another characteristic associated with several soil-borne fungi. Certain normally saprophytic species may, at the opportune occasion, invade living tissue and function as agents of plant disease. At one extreme are the facultative parasites which normally develop upon inanimate materials but, for reasons not as yet fully understood, they do occasionally become concerned with the development of disease. At the opposite pole are the true parasites which are inactive in humus decomposition but which can persist for varying periods in an alien habitat when the host plant is no longer present. The former are indigenous to the environment, *soil inhabitants* capable of developing under the stress of intense microbiological competition; occasionally these may become unspecialized parasites. The latter are *soil invaders* or root inhabitants which may persist in soil, but they often find the environment inimical to their existence; these are the specific plant parasites whose growth requires the presence of a living host. Only a very small portion of the fungus flora is concerned with the development of disease.

A unique fungus association with higher plants is found in the structure known as the *mycorrhiza* or fungus root, a two-membered relationship consisting of root tissue and a specialized mycorrhizal fungus. The microorganism is highly habitat-limited, and it usually is found only in the immediate vicinity of or directly within the roots. The fungus is not a soil microorganism in a strict sense, and its ecological niche is properly within the root association. The adaptation to root tissues may be associated with the complex nutrient demand of the microorganisms, many requiring mixtures of vitamins and amino acids and some having never been cultivated in artificial media.

Mycorrhizae are divided into ectotrophic and endotrophic categories. In the ectotrophic association, the fungus forms a mantle around the exterior of the roots, a network composed of a mass of hyphae entering into the spaces between individual plant cells. Many trees, including some of economic importance, bear this type of subterranean structure. The fungus in the endotrophic mycorrhiza, on the other hand, penetrates the cells of the host. The latter association is quite common among the Ericaceae and Orchidaceae as well as in fruit trees, citrus, coffee, and various legumes. Species of Basidiomycetes and Ascomycetes, fungi rarely found in soil by dilution plating, are capable of forming ectotrophic mycorrhizae. *Boletus, Lactarius,* and *Amanita* among the Hymenomycetes and *Elaphomyces* of the Ascomycetes are typical genera active upon trees. Endotrophic mycorrhizal fungi include *Rhizoctonia, Phoma,* and *Armillaria.*

The formation of mycorrhizae is particularly pronounced in land low in phosphorus and nitrogen, and high nutrient levels are correlated with poor mycorrhizal development. Further, the production of these structures is most vigorous when the roots have a large reserve of available carbohydrates, especially following intensive photosynthesis. This may be an indication of the host supplying the invader with the carbohydrates necessary for its heterotrophic metabolism, but amino acids, B vitamins, or other growth factors cannot be excluded as factors provided by the root component. For many plants, the mycorrhiza exerts a beneficial influence; frequently no function can be attributed to the association, and occasionally detrimental effects ensue. Trees that bear ectotrophic mycorrhizae develop well in the absence of the invader, but the existence of the fungal relationship may sometimes be advantageous or even essential. Mycorrhizae are thus important in forestry, involved as they are in problems of reforestation and in afforestation of new land. In the absence of the fungus, moreover,

poor stands of seedlings are encountered, and inoculation may sometimes be practiced (29).

REFERENCES

Reviews

Chesters, C. G. C. 1949. Concerning fungi inhabiting soil. *Trans. Brit. Mycol Soc.*, 32:197–216.

Gilman, J. C. 1957. *A manual of soil fungi.* Iowa State Coll. Press, Ames.

Harley, J. L. 1960. *The biology of mycorrhiza.* Interscience Publishers, New York.

Kelley, A. P. 1950. *Mycotrophy in plants.* Chronica Botanica, Waltham, Mass.

Parkinson, D., and J. S. Waid, eds. 1960. *The ecology of soil fungi.* Liverpool Univ. Press, Liverpool.

Warcup, J. H. 1951. The ecology of soil fungi. *Trans. Brit. Mycol. Soc.*, 34: 376–399.

Literature cited

1. Anscombe, F. J., and B. N. Singh. 1948. *Nature*, 161:140–141.
2. Atkinson, R. G., and J. B. Robinson. 1955. *Canad. J. Botany*, 33:281–288.
3. Bisby, G. R., M. I. Timonin, and N. James. 1935. *Canad. J. Research*, C, 13:47–65.
4. Burges, A., and E. Fenton. 1953. *Trans. Brit. Mycol. Soc.*, 36:104–108.
5. Capstick, C. K., D. C. Twinn, and J. S. Waid. 1957. *Nematologica*, 2:193–201.
6. Chesters, C. G. C. 1948. *Trans. Brit. Mycol. Soc.*, 30:100–117.
7. Cholodny, N. 1930. *Arch. Mikrobiol.*, 1:620–652.
8. Eggleton, W. G. E. 1934. *J. Agric. Sci.*, 24:416–434.
9. Etchells, J. L., R. N. Costilow, T. A. Bell, and A. L. Demain. 1954. *Applied Microbiol.*, 2:296–300.
10. Garrett, S. D. 1951. *New Phytol.*, 50:149–166.
11. Herr, L. J. 1957. *Ohio J. Sci.*, 57:203–211.
12. Jensen, H. L. 1934. *Proc. Linnean Soc. N. S. W.*, 59:101–117.
13. Kommedahl, T., and T. D. Brock. 1954. *Phytopathol.*, 44:57–61.
14. Martin, J. P. 1950. *Soil Sci.*, 69:215–232.
15. Martin, J. P., and D. G. Aldrich. 1954. *Soil Sci. Soc. Am., Proc.*, 18:160–164.
16. Martin, T. L. 1929. *Soil Sci.*, 27:399–405.
17. Mishustin, E. N. 1956. *Soils and Fert.*, 19:385–392.
18. Mueller, K. E., and L. W. Durrell. 1957. *Phytopathol.*, 47:243.
19. Newton, J. D., F. A. Wyatt, V. Ignatieff, and A. S. Ward. 1939. *Canad. J. Research*, C, 17:256–293.
20. Orpurt, P. A., and J. T. Curtis. 1957. *Ecology*, 38:628–637.
21. Peach, M. 1955. In D. K. M. Kevan, ed., *Soil zoology.* Butterworth's Scientific Publications, London, pp. 302–310.
22. Pinck, L. A., and F. E. Allison. 1944. *Soil Sci.*, 57:155–161.

23. Rossi, G., and S. Riccardo. 1927. *Proc. Comm. III, 1st Intl. Cong. Soil Sci.,* Washington, pp. 9–13.
24. Singh, B. N. 1947. *J. Gen. Microbiol.,* 1:11–21.
25. Stover, R. H., N. C. Thornton, and V. C. Dunlap. 1953. *Soil Sci.,* 76:225–238.
26. Thornton, R. H. 1958. *New Zeal. J. Agric. Research,* 1:922–938.
27. Tresner, H. D., M. P. Backus, and J. T. Curtis. 1954. *Mycologia,* 46:314–333.
28. Warcup, J. H. 1950. *Nature,* 166:117–118.
29. Wilde, S. A. 1954. *Soil Sci.,* 78:23–31.

5

Algae

In almost every soil, in samples obtained from each continent and from the most remote islands, one finds the presence of algae, yet their position as indigenous soil inhabitants has often been the subject of considerable controversy. Algae are never as numerous as bacteria, actinomycetes, or fungi, and the lack of sufficient appreciation of this group can be attributed in part to the small population. Further, since the algae are photosynthetic organisms that usually require access to sunlight, many early microbiologists felt that algal existence was too precarious for them to be of significance in soil. Recent work, however, has led to a more complete knowledge of the ecology and importance of the terrestrial algae.

The algae are abundant in habitats in which moisture is adequate and light accessible. Their development on the surface of cultivated or virgin land is frequently noted with the naked eye, but isolates can be obtained from lower depths as well. Their presence can be demonstrated readily by the addition of a small amount of soil to a medium containing nitrate, potassium phosphate, magnesium sulfate, calcium and iron salts, and traces of other inorganic nutrients. The resultant growth is visible macroscopically as a green color appearing in the crude enrichments incubated in the sunlight. The distinctive green pigmentation associated with these minute plants results from their possession of chlorophyll, but other pigments often mask the green color of the chlorophyll.

Morphologically, algae may be unicellular or they may occur in short filaments, but the soil strains as a group are characteristically smaller and structurally less complex than their aquatic counterparts. Several representative species are shown in figure 1. Taxonomically,

85

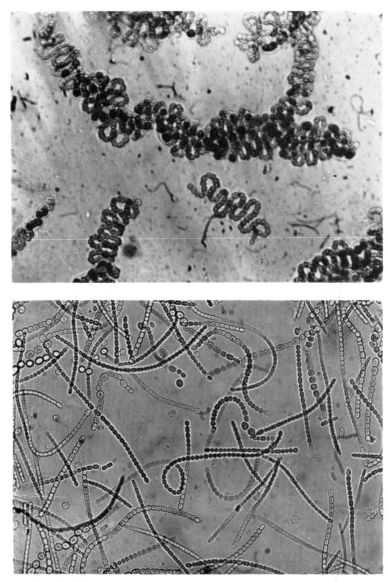

Figure 1A. Photomicrographs of some common algae. Top, *Anabaena spiroides;* bottom, *Anabaenopsis circularis* (18).

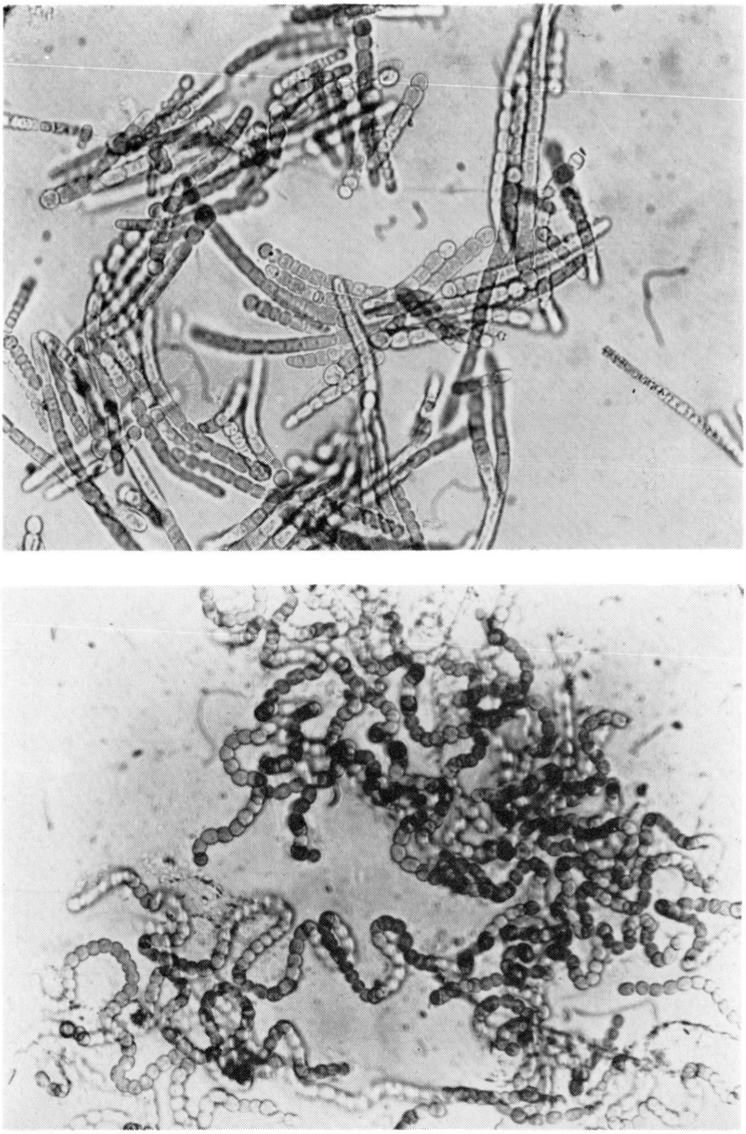

Figure 1B. Photomicrographs of some common algae. Top, *Tolypothrix tenuis;* bottom, *Nostoc* sp. (18).

all are placed together with the fungi in the phylum Thallophyta, both subphyla being separated from higher plants by their lack of differentiation into roots, leaves, and stems. The soil algae are divided into Chlorophyceae or green algae, Cyanophyceae or blue-greens, Bacillariophyceae or diatoms, and Xanthophyceae or yellow-greens. Other than the algae and certain alga-like protozoa, the only photosynthetic microorganisms are a few genera of bacteria whose habitat is usually aquatic rather than terrestrial.

Ecology

Algae are typified by the possession of a photoautotrophic nutrition which, through the agency of chlorophyll, endows them with the ability to use light as energy source and CO_2 for carbon. The photosynthetic mechanism makes them independent of the preformed organic matter which limits the development of heterotrophic organisms in nature. For autotrophic development, the algae must obtain water, nitrogen, potassium, phosphorus, magnesium, sulfur, iron, and other micronutrients in minute quantities from the soil. The atmosphere provides carbon as CO_2 and energy in the form of light, but some species may make use of nitrogen in the molecular state.

Algae found below the surface exist in complete darkness so that photoautotrophic life is impossible. Although many algae are obligate photoautotrophs and are, therefore, unable to grow in the absence of light, heterotrophy occurs in several species of Chlorophyceae, Cyanophyceae, and diatoms. These heterotrophic variants use the oxidation of organic carbon to replace the light in supplying energy for anabolic processes. Such species, properly classified as facultative photoautotrophs, metabolize a variety of carbohydrates including starch, inulin, sucrose, glucose, galactose, glycerol, and citric acid. Frequently, transfer of the organism to an inorganic medium and incubation in the light leads to an almost immediate resumption of photosynthesis, even following prolonged heterotrophic cultivation in the dark. That this type of heterotrophic nutrition is complex is evidenced by the fact that CO_2 is often required for heterotrophic growth in the dark (4). Nevertheless, even with those species adapted to heterotrophy, the growth rate in the dark is less than during photoautotrophic development.

The occurrence of these photosynthetic microorganisms has been recorded in soils throughout the world, but no definitive geographical localization of families, genera, or species has yet been presented. As a group, the algae are moderately adaptable to environmental change, persisting in unfavorable circumstances such as in alkaline and desert soils. The population tends to be concentrated immediately upon, directly below, and down to several inches under the surface layer. Those organisms in the upper zones probably function as photosynthetic plants, using the sunlight that does penetrate. This locale is the site of dominant algal activity. On the other hand, isolates have been obtained from subterranean zones where light fails to penetrate, often to depths of 50 to 100 cm. The existence of algae at considerable depth poses a problem as to their mode of life: do the subterranean forms have an active metabolism or do they exist passively? The latter alternative presupposes that the subsurface cells originate at the surface and are moved downward through water seepage, tillage practices, or by the movements of the fauna. The finding of these organisms at depths of up to 1 m in sites undisturbed by seepage and cultivation suggests that at least some strains may proliferate within the profile itself. These subterranean forms must live as heterotrophs because the light needed for photosynthesis is unavailable. Yet, though many algae multiply heterotrophically in the dark, it is doubtful whether they can compete effectively with the dominant heterotrophs for the limited supply of available organic matter. The evidence at present argues against active growth below the sunlight zone. At the surface, on the other hand, algae are favored since they are not restricted by the organic matter level and need not compete for organic carbon.

Many estimates of population size have been carried out. Abundance is typically assessed by preparing ten-fold dilutions of soil in sterile water, and inoculating aliquots into a liquid medium or into sterilized sand containing suitable inorganic nutrients. After incubation for 4 to 6 weeks in the light, the presence of algae is determined microscopically or by visual examination for the colored growth. Quantification is achieved by the most probable number procedure. Algae are also enumerated by fluorescence microscopy. Viable counting procedures give values ranging usually from about 100 to 50,000 per gram for samples taken from immediately below the surface of arable land, but results in excess of 10,000 per gram are uncommon. Under adverse conditions, the abundance of algae declines markedly. Surface samples frequently contain few organisms; alternatively, the population may be of the order of hundreds of thousands or even in the millions per gram where a distinct, visible bloom has developed.

The enumeration of algae in soil is of limited value because the significance of the observed numbers of algal units is difficult to interpret. Some species are filamentous and give low counts whereas others are unicellular, and each propagative unit represents an individual cell. At the same time, there are colonial forms in which the single colony yields many viable units.

Qualitative approaches to ecological research have yielded more fruitful dividends in defining the nature of the algal microflora (figure 2). Such studies have demonstrated that only the green algae, diatoms, and blue-green algae are numerous in soil. Much less frequently noted are the Xanthophyceae and certain of the chlorophyll-containing flagellates which are commonly classified as protozoa. The red and brown algae and the dinoflagellates are totally lacking. In temperate climates, the Chlorophyceae are usually the predominant group, followed closely by the diatoms, while the Cyanophyceae are the least numerous of the three major classes. Mitra (14) has demonstrated that the blue-greens are dominant to the Chlorophyceae in tropical soils while the diatoms are the least numerous.

Green algae, microorganisms of the class Chlorophyceae, are characterized by the possession of chromatophores that impart to the organisms a grass-green color. In addition to chlorophyll, the cells contain xanthophyll and carotene pigments. In soil, these organisms are usually unicellular, but filamentous types are not unknown. Members of the class are found ubiquitously, entirely dominating the algal flora in acid soils but still numerous in neutral and alkaline environments (11, 12). Species of *Ankistrodesmus, Chlamydomonas, Chlorella, Chlorococcum, Cladophora, Coccomyxa, Dactylococcus, Dictyosphaerium, Hormidium, Mesotaenium, Pleurococcus, Protococcus, Scenedesmus, Stichococcus, Trochiscia, Ulothrix,* and *Vaucheria* are widely encountered.

Diatoms, on the other hand, are unicellular or colonial algae surrounded by a highly silicified outer layer. The cell wall consists of two separate halves, one overlapping the other. In comparison with aquatic types, the terrestrial diatoms tend to be of smaller size, and the difference in dimensions applies not only to species but to strains within the same species. Apparently, the environmental conditions in terrestrial habitats favor development of the smaller individuals. The small size may be advantageous since it permits greater water and salt adsorption because of the greater surface:volume ratios of the cells. Several investigators (2, 13) have noted that diatoms are less frequent in acid soils, these algae faring best near neutrality or at

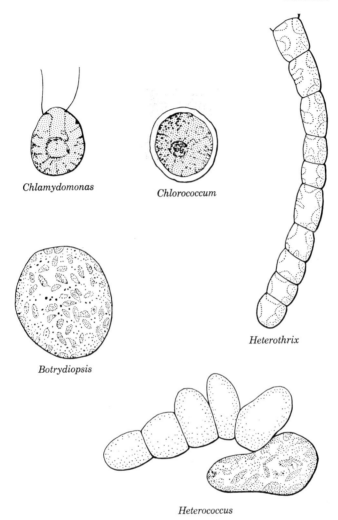

Chlamydomonas

Chlorococcum

Heterothrix

Botrydiopsis

Heterococcus

Figure 2. Several common algal genera of soil (10).

slightly alkaline reactions; even in culture a number of species are limited to pH values greater than 6.0. The prominent genera in soil include *Achnanthes, Cymbella, Fragilaria, Hantzschia, Navicula, Nitzschia, Pinnularia, Surirella,* and *Synedra.*

Distinct from the other classes are the blue-green algae. In contrast to the aforementioned microorganisms, the Cyanophyceae do not have their pigments localized in chromatophores but rather they are distributed throughout the cytoplasm. The nucleus, moreover, lacks the clear morphological organization associated with other green plants, a point of similarity to the bacteria. Another trait suggesting a phylogenetic relationship to the true bacteria is the ability of the blue-greens to divide by fission. Certain genera are unicellular and grow singly or in aggregates of individuals; *Anabaena* and others may be filamentous. The characteristic color of the group results from the presence, in addition to chlorophyll and the carotenoids, of a blue pigment known as phycocyanin. The blue-greens tolerate a wide range of temperatures, and thermophilic variants of *Phormidium* and *Oscillatoria* are often the major signs of life in hot springs. Studies in the field and in the laboratory indicate that the Cyanophyceae prefer neutral to alkaline environments. This sensitivity to the hydrogen ion concentration is clearly evident from the work of Lund (12), who reported their absence in soils of pH below 5.2 and their frequent appearance in neutral and calcareous land. Many soil genera have been recorded, but the ones most frequently described are *Anabaena*, *Chroococcus*, *Cylindrospermum*, *Lyngbya*, *Microcoleus*, *Nodularia*, *Nostoc*, *Oscillatoria*, *Phormidium*, *Plectonema*, *Scytonema*, and *Tolypothrix*.

The yellow-green algae of the class Xanthophyceae are relatively rare, but their isolation is not difficult. *Botrydiopsis, Bumilleria, Bumilleriopsis, Heterococcus,* and *Heterothrix* seem to be the most abundant

TABLE 1

Numbers of Common Algal Species in English Soils (3)

Species	Depth of Sample, in.			
	0–1	2	4	6
	No./g			
Chlorococcum humicola	2,070	1,300	2,070	400
Pleurococcus vulgaris	140	650	160	80
Chlorella sp.	11,000	5,330	4,200	1,030
Bumilleria exilis	200	40	410	50
Heterococcus viridis	1,030	820	5,330	1,640
Chlamydomonas muscicola	650	650	2,070	410
Stichococcus bacillaris	180	5	40	—

and widespread, but even these five are not prominent terrestrial organisms. Chlorophyll-bearing, unicellular flagellates of the genus *Euglena* and related genera are widely distributed but, though possessing a photosynthetic metabolism which relates them to the algae, these microorganisms also resemble the non-chlorophyll-containing protozoa. Frequently, the only significant cytological difference from the protozoa is the presence of the photosynthetic pigments.

The data of table 1 present a partial picture of the prominent algal species in a single English soil profile.

Distribution and Abundance

Catalogues of algal genera found in a single habitat are of unquestionable value, but a more complete biological picture is given by depiction of the broader community of organisms that dominates in a given environmental circumstance. Fenton (8) has investigated the algal vegetation of certain Scottish soils from this viewpoint. He noted that the Cyanophyceae represented the ecological or agricultural climax of the photosynthetic microflora whereas the Chlorophyceae preceded them in the development of the climax microbiological community. In these localities, the green algae were dominant in noncultivated fields, but the blue-greens made up the climax stage in permanent pasture, cultivated fields, and in manured land. This investigation applies to a single locale only, but similar floral associations may exist elsewhere as well.

In environments free of vegetation, the algae may play a critical pioneering role. Their early appearance in barren or denuded areas is especially noteworthy. For example, following volcanic eruptions which completely denude the surroundings of all higher forms of life, the algae are often primary colonizers, ultimately forming a gelatinous layer over the cinders. As the algae die and decay, the environment becomes more suitable for higher plants (17). Similar phenomena are not infrequently observed following burning. Booth (1) reported that large areas of eroded land in the United States bear algal crusts which initiate the plant succession cycle. In both volcanic and eroded areas, the Cyanophyceae seem to be the pioneering invaders. Thus, because of its capacity to utilize simple inorganic compounds, the photoautotrophic microflora seems to be among the earliest living forms in surroundings where life has been eliminated by natural or artificial agencies.

A definite algal population is present in many highly arid habitats. The organisms appear at the surface following a period of gentle rain and cause an increase in the tensile strength of the raincrust of the desert soils (9). Here too, the blue-greens are numerous, particularly species of *Microcoleus, Nostoc, Oscillatoria,* and *Nodularia.*

Another environment in which the algae have a great agronomic significance is in flooded paddy fields. The microbiological action is associated with the utilization of atmospheric nitrogen and the release of O_2. During the extended periods in which rice soils are waterlogged, an algal film forms at the liquid surface, eventually making up an appreciable biological mass. Providing the pH is above about 6.0 and the phosphorus level is high, the algal bloom consists largely of blue-greens. Of 56 paddy soil samples examined by Okuda and Yamaguchi (15), 53 showed evidence of Cyanophyceae which included species of *Nostoc, Tolypothrix,* and *Chroococcus.* The large acreage of land cropped to lowland rice makes a microbial contribution to the nitrogen and oxygen status of the paddy field a key factor in rice culture.

Environmental Influences

Because of the photosynthetic metabolism, one of the major environmental factors governing the activity of the heterotrophic microflora, the content of readily available organic carbon, has no appreciable bearing upon algal distribution. On the other hand, this same photosynthetic attribute imposes upon the algae the need for sunlight and CO_2. Obtaining an adequate supply of the latter rarely poses a problem as CO_2 and bicarbonates usually are produced in excess of the autotrophic demand whereas light accessibility is a dominant factor governing the distribution of photoautotrophic microorganisms. The need for sunlight is reflected particularly clearly in the vertical distribution of the algae. Thus, the population is most dense in the upper 5 to 10 cm and falls off dramatically with depth. Often the point of greatest concentration is in the surface centimeter, but sometimes a layer immediately below the topmost stratum has a larger population; generally, however, the trend is for a decline in numbers with depth. It cannot be doubted that algae are present far below the zone of light penetration, and counts up to 10^3 per gram have been recorded from the C horizon. However, as pointed out above, because of their feeble competitive powers in the heterotrophic state, a large proportion of these organisms undoubtedly is dislocated and carried down through mechanical cultivation, the burrowing habits of earthworms and other lower animals, and by the movement of water. Therefore, these cells probably exist in a dormant condition as aliens in a foreign environment.

Acidity determines to a large extent the qualitative composition of the photoautotrophic microflora. Each individual strain has an optimum pH and a range outside of which the organism fails to multiply. More than any other broad taxonomic group of microorganisms, the algae exist independently of other organisms. The reason for the relative independence lies in the fact that the chief nutritional limitation to heterotrophic development is the supply of organic matter, a restriction which has no bearing upon autotrophic proliferation. In contrast is the sparser fungal population in neutral than in acid soils, the result not of the inability of fungi to grow at neutral reaction but of the expropriation of much of the organic matter by rapidly growing bacteria; that is, the distribution of fungi is affected markedly by other members of the microflora. One may expect, therefore, that the optimum for algal development in nature would agree more closely to that defined in vitro than for any other broad microbial group with

TABLE 2

Abundance of Species of Various Algal Classes in English Soils (11)

| | | No. of Types Obtained | | | |
Soil	pH	Cyano-phyceae	Diatoms	Xantho-phyceae	Chloro-phyceae
Chalky grassland	8.2	5	4	2	8
Chalky grass heath	8.2	7	3	6	7
Mixed wood	7.6	3	9	2	7
Pine wood	7.2	0	0	1	9
Peat	6.6	1	4	2	9
Grass heath	6.2	2	1	5	14
Beech wood	5.2	0	2	1	14
Heath	4.6	0	1	1	18
Grass heath	3.7	0	0	1	12

the possible exception of the chemoautotrophs—which likewise are independent of carbonaceous materials. For example, members of the class Cyanophyceae generally develop best in pure culture from pH 7 to 10, and their occurrence in soil is likewise limited to neutral or alkaline conditions. None occur at pH values below 5 and few below 6 (table 2). Diatoms are similarly less frequently encountered in acid soils whereas they are numerous in calcareous areas. In marked contrast, species of Chlorophyceae are not appreciably limited by reaction, and they appear in regions with a diversity of hydrogen ion concentrations; as a consequence, the Chlorophyceae dominate the algal flora of acid habitats due to the absence of other forms (11).

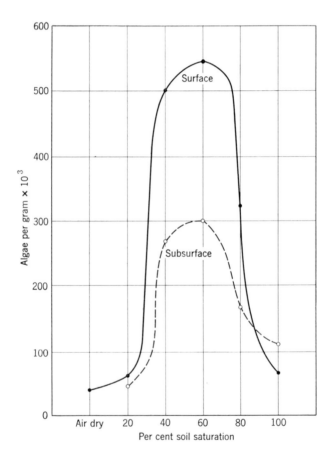

Figure 3. Effect of moisture on algae (16).

Moisture is apparently a common limitation to growth since algal development is usually enhanced by increasing the supply of available water (figure 3). In agricultural land, the quantity of water is often insufficient for algal development, and the extreme moisture variations in the surface layer play havoc with the metabolism of these microorganisms. Because of the dependence upon moist conditions, the population responds greatly following periods of precipitation or, in regions having a wet and dry season, to irrigation. In times of drought, when the soil becomes desiccated, the organism density falls drastically. Of the three dominant groups, the diatoms are most sensitive to drying while the Chlorophyceae and Cyanophyceae exhibit a greater persistence and may endure in a resting stage for several years even in sun-baked, tropical regions.

The requirement for moisture and adequate sunlight defines in part the seasonal influence. The water status is most favorable in spring and autumn, periods of the year when algae show maximum vigor. Freezing is highly detrimental as evidenced by the rapid population decline during the winter months. This stage is followed by a spurt in activity at the onset of the spring thaw. In the driest portion of the summer, the floral status is poor as the low water and intense sunlight take their toll. By and large, therefore, algal bloom is associated with wet, cool seasons during which the light intensity is not excessively high. Persistence under conditions of adversity is probably linked with the formation of dormant stages that provide the organism with a means of survival until the time that the environment becomes more favorable.

Significance

In a general sense, the algae cannot be considered as contributing appreciably to the many biochemical transformations necessary for soil fertility. Under the stress of competition from the bacteria, fungi, and actinomycetes, particularly below the surface, a group poorly adapted to heterotrophy could make only a small impression upon the many biological reactions. Yet, the photosynthetic microflora is capable of exerting a definite influence in certain environments in which it occupies a position far more important than the bacteria or fungi.

One of the major algal functions in terrestrial habitats is an outcome of their photoautotrophic nutrition. This function is in the generation of organic matter from inorganic substances. Those algae living at the soil surface convert CO_2 to carbonaceous materials; consequently, the photosynthetic microflora in some habitats is responsible for increases in the total quantity of organic carbon. The magnitude of these additions in agricultural land has not been accurately estimated, but the algal role in creating organic carbon *de novo* by colonizing denuded, barren, or eroded areas is beyond dispute. By this pioneering colonization, the biological cycle is reinitiated. The accumulation of organic matter in this manner has been demonstrated for desert soils of Arizona (9).

Coincidental with the colonization of barren surfaces is the ability of the algae to corrode and weather rocks. A thick layer of algal cells often is found covering the surfaces of rocks. Cells or colonies of bacteria and occasionally fungi may appear as secondary colonizers. The weathering of rocks through biological agencies of this type may be the result of carbonic acid formation from the respiratory CO_2 of the algae or it may be associated with the by-products of the bacterial and fungal utilization of the organic matter supplied by the algal protoplasm.

Algae also are conspicuous through their contribution to soil structure and erosion control. Booth (1) has reported that the surface bloom in sections of Oklahoma, Kansas, and Texas reduces erosion losses probably by means of the binding together of soil particles. In the rain crust of deserts, the algal population that develops following periods of precipitation tends to increase the tensile strength of the crust by an analogous mechanism; this too affects the physical structure of the surface soil (9).

The photosynthetic microflora of flooded paddy soils has a special sphere of influence. In algae as well as in higher plants, the photosynthetic process liberates molecular oxygen. Through the evolution of this gas, the algae can beneficially affect the growth of rice by providing part of the O_2 required by the submerged roots. The abundance of algae in flooded fields in the tropics is of such magnitude that the O_2 contribution cannot be ignored. Under controlled conditions, growth of tobacco is enhanced by the presence in unaerated culture solution of green algae (7) so that extension of the oxygenation phenomenon to the wet paddy field is not difficult.

Recent years have seen an upsurge of interest in one major agronomic contribution of certain of the algae, their capacity to utilize N_2 as nitrogen source for growth (table 3). The process ultimately leads to the enrichment of the environment with combined forms of

TABLE 3

Fixation of N_2 by Algae in Soil Culture (6)

Soil	Period of Incubation	N gain under different treatments		
		Control	+P	+P+Mo
	wk	mg	mg	mg
Chinsura clay, cropped	6	186	262	295
Chinsura clay, uncropped	6	147	232	284
Krishnagar sandy loam, cropped	6	143	160	167
Krishnagar sandy loam, uncropped	5	123	138	156
Kaity sandy loam, cropped	5	91	166	—
Sonarpur clay, cropped	5	58	70	—

nitrogen since the protoplasmic constituents formed from N_2 are released and decomposed upon decay of the cell. The capacity for N_2 assimilation is associated only with the class Cyanophyceae, but not all of the blue-greens can utilize molecular nitrogen. Neither the Chlorophyceae nor the diatoms have representatives capable of performing this function.

In vast areas of the Far East, rice has been produced each year for centuries with no known addition of nitrogen in the form of manure or chemical fertilizers. The nitrogen would thus seem to be derived from the air over the paddy field and, as rice itself cannot utilize N_2, the nitrogen gains were assumed to be associated with free-living microorganisms. The results of careful experimentation have revealed that an increase in bound nitrogen only occurs in waterlogged soils containing an abundant blue-green algal bloom. The nitrogen gains are negligible if the algal growth is poor (15). Investigations in the laboratory show that the increases amount to as much as 1.0 mg of nitrogen per gram of soil when the flooded samples are incubated in the light for 2 to 3 months (5). There can be no doubt, therefore, of the significance of the blue-greens in the nitrogen economy of paddy soils. *Anabaena, Calothrix, Chroococcus, Cylindrospermum, Nostoc, Plectonema, Schizothrix,* and *Tolypothrix* are the predominant genera concerned in nitrogen-enriching activities.

Because the blue-green algae, including species capable of making use of N_2, make up a large proportion of the population in arid land

and in areas denuded by volcanoes or other means, one must take into consideration the possibility of biological nitrogen accumulation here as well. Since these several genera obtain not only carbon but nitrogen from the atmosphere, a gain of organic forms of both elements may take place. Evidence in support of this contention has been provided from a number of sources. In biological if not frequently in agricultural terms, therefore, the algae are important members of the microflora of soil.

REFERENCES

1. Booth, W. E.   1941.   *Ecology*, 22:38–46.
2. Brendemuhl, I.   1949.   *Arch. Mikrobiol.*, 14:407–449.
3. Bristol-Roach, B. M.   1927.   *J. Agric. Sci.*, 17:563–588.
4. Casselton, P. J.   1959.   *Nature*, 183:1404.
5. De, P. K.   1936.   *Indian J. Agric. Sci.*, 6:1237–1245.
6. De, P. K., and L. N. Mandal.   1956.   *Soil Sci.*, 81:453–458.
7. Engle, H. B., and J. E. McMurtrey.   1940.   *J. Agric. Research*, 60:487–502.
8. Fenton, E. W.   1943.   *Trans. Botan. Soc. Edinburgh*, 33:407–415.
9. Fletcher, J. E., and W. P. Martin.   1948.   *Ecology*, 29:95–100.
10. Fritsch, F. E., and R. P. John.   1942.   *Ann. Botany*, 6:371–395.
11. John, R. P.   1942.   *Ann. Botany*, 6:323–349.
12. Lund, J. W. G.   1947.   *New Phytol.*, 46:35–60.
13. Lund, J. W. G.   1945.   *New Phytol.*, 44:196–219.
14. Mitra, A. K.   1951.   *Indian J. Agric. Sci.*, 21:357–373.
15. Okuda, A., and M. Yamaguchi.   1956.   *Soil and Plant Food*, 2:4–7.
16. Stokes, J. L.   1940.   *Soil Sci.*, 49:171–184.
17. Traub, M.   1888.   *Ann. Jard. Botan. Buitenzorg*, 7:221–223.
18. Watanabe, A.   1959.   *J. Gen. Applied Microbiol.*, 5:21–29.

6

Protozoa

The four microbiological groups discussed in previous chapters, the bacteria, actinomycetes, fungi, and algae, constitute the microflora of the soil. Numerically, the microscopic members of the plant kingdom dominate the population, but they are not the only biological forms of ecological and biochemical significance. Many representatives of the animal kingdom spend part or all of their life underground. The subterranean fauna contains protozoa, earthworms, nematodes, insects, and a variety of mammals. Invariably, however, the most abundant of the invertebrates found are the protozoa, the simplest forms of animal life.

The phylum Protozoa contains primitive, unicellular organisms ranging in size from several microns up to one or more centimeters. The terrestrial species are all microscopic, however, and they are characteristically smaller than their aquatic relatives. These animal cells are typically devoid of chlorophyll, but transitional genera resemble the algae and possess chloroplasts containing chlorophyll pigments.

The life cycle of many protozoa consists of an active phase wherein the animal feeds and multiplies and a resting or *cyst* stage where the cell secretes a thick coating about itself. In its encysted condition, the animal can withstand deleterious environmental influences and persist for many years. Reproduction of protozoa is usually asexual, taking place by fission of the mother into two daughter cells, a process which occurs by either longitudinal or transverse division. Only a few of the protozoa reproduce sexually. Here, two cells similar in appearance fuse, their nuclei unite with an exchange of genetic material, and two new individuals ultimately emerge.

101

The distribution of protozoa has been investigated intensively by microbiologists throughout the world. The presence of the unicellular animals has been noted in equatorial, subtropical, and temperate regions and in the arctic and antarctic as well. No arable soil examined to date has been entirely devoid of protozoa although some localities yield but a single species while others contain a great diversity of types. From the ecological and the agronomic viewpoints, however, geographical studies have not been of profound importance because the reasons for the dominance of individual species or genera in given localities have not been established.

Taxonomy

Protozoa are classified on the basis of their means of locomotion. Some move about by virtue of one or more long *flagella* or whips, others by means of short, hair-like *cilia,* and a third group by temporary organelles known as *pseudopodia.* Certain parasitic genera are devoid of specialized structures for movement. On the criterion of locomotion, the phylum Protozoa is divided into five classes: (*a*) Mastigophora or flagellates which are motile by means of flagella; (*b*) Sarcodina, sometimes termed rhizopods, which possess pseudopodia; (*c*) Ciliata or ciliates which bear cilia through the entire active stage of life; (*d*) Suctoria, differing from Ciliata in that the cilia of the former are present only when the organism is young; and (*e*) Sporozoa, parasitic protozoa with no specialized locomotory organelles. Only the first three will be considered here as the Suctoria and Sporozoa are not soil inhabitants.

Organisms of the class Mastigophora usually are endowed with one to four flagella, but occasional species possess more than four. The strains found in soil characteristically are small, 5 to 20 μ in length. Protozoologists often separate this group into Phytomastigophora and Zoomastigophora, the former containing chlorophyll and growing photosynthetically and the latter being devoid of the green pigment and thereby limited to a heterotrophic existence. There is little question that the flagellates dominate the microfauna of terrestrial habitats. Among the many genera described, special mention may be made of *Allantion, Bodo, Cercobodo, Cercomonas, Entosiphon, Heteromita, Monas, Oikomonas, Sainouran, Spiromonas, Spongomonas,* and *Tetramitus* (1, 5, 8). The alga-like flagellates are best repre-

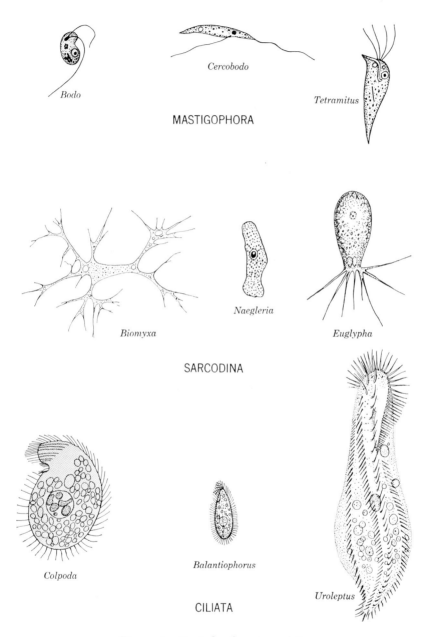

Bodo

Cercobodo

Tetramitus

MASTIGOPHORA

Biomyxa

Naegleria

Euglypha

SARCODINA

Colpoda

Balantiophorus

Uroleptus

CILIATA

Figure 1. Typical soil protozoa (8).

sented by *Euglena* and *Chlamydomonas*. Some typical genera are shown in figure 1.

Members of the class Sarcodina move by means of temporary protoplasmic extrusions from the cell body. Because there is no rigid external surface, the shape of the animal body changes frequently as the organism sends forth or withdraws its pseudopodia. In this way, the Sarcodina differ markedly from the flagellates and ciliates in which the organelles of locomotion are essentially permanent structures. The soil rhizopods or Sarcodina are of two types: some have a shell-like structure, others possess none. When the shell is present, the pseudopodia extend through distinct openings. The most frequently encountered representatives of the class are *Amoeba, Biomyxa, Difflugia, Euglypha, Hartmanella, Lecythium, Naegleria, Nuclearia*, and *Trinema* (figure 1).

Movement among the Ciliata results from the action of the vibrating hairs situated around the protozoan cell. The hairs are short and numerous, and several thousand may be found on a single individual. In size, the terrestrial ciliates are often as small as 10 μ yet they range up to 80 μ in length, but aquatic species are distinctly larger and some attain a size of 2 mm. The typical soil forms include *Balantiophorus, Colpidium, Colpoda, Enchelys, Gastrostyla, Halteria, Oxytricha, Pleurotricha, Uroleptus*, and *Vorticella* (1, 5, 8).

Nutrition

The energy for protozoan growth is obtained in several ways. At the extreme of nutritional independence are the photosynthetic protozoa, those alga-like flagellates that synthesize their protoplasm from CO_2 using energy derived from sunlight. Photoautotrophy, however, is rare in the animal kingdom, the chlorophyll-containing phytoflagellates being the sole animals to possess the capacity for photosynthesis.

The vast majority of protozoa are dependent upon preformed organic matter either as *saprozoic* feeders, obtaining their nutriment from soluble organic and inorganic substances, or by a *holozoic* nutrition characterized by a direct feeding upon microbial cells. The significance in soil of saprozoic feeding is unknown, and the dominant mode of nutrition is generally considered to be holozoic. Available to the predaceous protozoa are bacteria and occasionally other protozoan strains. In holozoic nutrition, the ingested particle of food, viable or inanimate, is surrounded by a vacuole wherein digestion takes place. Since such food particles contain proteins, polysaccharides, sugars, and lipids, the individual protozoan cell must be able to form all the enzymes necessary to mediate the decomposition. Ultimately, undigested portions are released back into the external environment.

The preying upon bacteria can be demonstrated by simultaneous inoculation of pure cultures of protozoa and bacteria into sterile soil and noting the change in abundance of the latter group. Initially, the bacterial population rises, reaching a maximum size by about the end of one week. The active protozoa are scarce up to this point, but their subsequent numerical increase is accompanied by a drastic fall in bacterial density as a result of the animals' activities. For any one holozoic protozoan, many bacterial cells must be ingested to generate enough protoplasm to permit a single cell division. It has been estimated that one species of Sarcodina requires approximately 40,000 bacteria per cell division. Consequently, bacteria must reproduce at a rapid rate merely to keep pace with their predators.

Such estimates suggest that the protozoa are important in limiting the size of the bacterial population, consuming the latter when they are present in excess. Since bacterial development is important to soil fertility, a hypothesis was advanced that the microfauna, through its predatory action, has a detrimental influence upon crop production (7). Although the hypothesis is certainly attractive, no strong evidence has been brought forth in its behalf, and most experimental results minimize the direct agricultural importance of this biological interaction. On the other hand, it is possible to argue that the unicellular animals do indeed serve as a check on the bacteria in the microbiological equilibrium that exists in the highly populated soil habitat. Any competitive, antagonistic, or preying influence should affect deleteriously one or another organism or process, but the biological equilibrium cannot be readily manipulated to suit the needs of man.

These micropredators are quite selective in their bacterial nutriment. In addition to feeding upon algae and other protozoa, holozoic protozoa are capable of ingesting bacteria of the genera *Aerobacter, Agrobacterium, Bacillus, Escherichia, Micrococcus,* and *Pseudomonas* among others, but only certain bacteria are susceptible to attack, and many are entirely unsuitable. Actinomycetes and yeasts tend to be poor nutrient sources (6, 9).

TABLE 1

Utilization of Bacteria by *Leptomyxa reticulata* (11)

Bacterial Trait	No. of Strains Tested	Percentage of Strains		
		Completely Utilized	Partially Utilized	Not Utilized
Pigmentation				
None, yellow	65	52	25	23
Orange, brown	13	46	31	23
Red, blue, violet, green	10	0	30	70
Gram reaction				
Gram positive	41	46	24	29
Gram negative	52	44	29	27

The bacterial prey may be divided into three types: readily digested bacteria, slowly eaten strains, and those which are attacked only on rare occasions or not at all. Any single species may be a food source for one protozoan but be entirely inedible by another. The preference goes beyond species boundaries since some strains of one species may be susceptible while others are resistant. Singh (2, 11) has investigated the feeding habits of soil amoebae and has shown that certain of them can digest as many as 49 to 55 of 87 bacterial isolates tested. There seems to be no relation between the gram staining reactions of the bacteria and their edibility, but cultures with red, green, or violet pigmentation, for reasons as yet unknown, are unsuitable (table 1); that is, the pigmented strains are less readily attacked than the unpigmented ones.

Attempts to ascertain the reasons that organisms are rejected as food sources have met with little success. By and large, inedible bacteria excrete no toxins inhibitory to protozoa, a fact supported by the observation that susceptible strains are eaten in the presence of resistant bacteria. *Serratia marcescens* is an exception because it will produce a toxin which protects both itself and other strains in its vicinity. The presence of toxic cell constituents likewise does not seem to account for the preferential feeding phenomenon (13). Regardless of the explanation for the selectivity of the holozoic microfauna, it would seem that the digestibility of bacteria is probably of greater importance than their numbers in determining the abundance of protozoa. Further, it is possible that the composition of the bacterial flora is influenced by the protozoa since strains of lesser edibility would have a greater persistence and would not be subject to the vagaries of the microfauna. Whether the latter relationship is of consequence in governing the composition of the indigenous bacterial population of soil must await future investigation.

When edible bacteria are no longer available or when the environment becomes in some way unfavorable, the active protozoan enters the cyst stage. Encystment allows the organism to persist for many years in conditions unsuitable for development of the biochemically active stage of the protozoan. The appearance of cysts is related to an inadequate nutrient supply, low O_2 tensions, or other types of unsuitable environments. These specialized bodies are more tolerant to harmful chemicals, acids, germicides, and high temperatures than are the vegetative cells, and they remain viable through long periods of drought. Consequently, the cysts usually serve a protective rather than a reproductive function. Encystment, however, is not a guarantee of rejuvenation as not all cysts return to active life. Once nutrients are again accessible or the harmful influences are dissipated, the microorganism will excyst and enter into its active

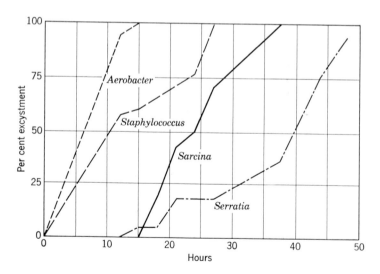

Figure 2. Excystment of amoebae in the presence of four bacterial species (6).

stage of life in which it feeds, reproduces, and moves from place to place. The results in figure 2 demonstrate that the return to the metabolically active form is related to the bacterial species in the vicinity of the cyst. Some bacteria allow for rapid excystment, others permit only a slow return, and certain bacterial groups favor quick but incomplete excystment (6).

Distribution and Abundance

Examination of cultivated and virgin soils of all continents and from a variety of land management practices has revealed the presence of a rich and heterogeneous protozoan fauna. Populations are sometimes as large as 100,000 to 300,000 cells per gram although values between 10,000 and 100,000 are more typical. Yet, only a small percentage of the individuals constituting the subterranean population are protozoa. Counts made of bacteria in comparable areas always are several-fold higher. On the other hand, the protozoan cell has a mass appreciably greater than that of the bacterium so that the gross weight of the microfauna often exceeds that of the bacteria.

For the development, enrichment, or enumeration of protozoa, the use of liquid or agar media containing soil extract is often recommended; these media are especially suitable for the rhizopods and ciliates. Hay or manure infusions have also proved to be of value. A nutrient medium for culture of soil protozoa should not permit overgrowth by the bacteria which are numerically in excess in soil dilutions. One technique based upon the principle of utilizing deficient media employs a non-nutrient agar to which is added an edible bacterial strain for the protozoa to feed upon. The nutrient source is commonly a short, gram negative, non-spore-forming bacterium. Inherent to this technique is the problem of choosing a bacterium which is digestible by the greatest proportion of the protozoan fauna. Singh (12) recommends the incorporation into the agar of cells of an *Aerobacter* sp. which is edible to a variety of flagellates, rhizopods, and ciliates. Either living or dead bacterial cells can be used. At best, the estimates of population size will not be absolute since the results will vary with the bacterium chosen as food source, i.e., its relative edibility. If the indigenous bacteria in the soil dilutions are required to play the role of prey on the agar plates, the results will be far more variable.

For the enumeration of protozoa, a common procedure is the standard dilution technique, in which serial ten-fold dilutions are made from the soil sample and aliquots inoculated into a medium containing the selected bacterium. Because protozoa do not form distinct colonies, it is necessary to rely upon the criterion of growth on the dilution plates. Thus, the absence or presence of protozoa can be ascertained by microscopic examination of each plate and the record of positives at each dilution used to estimate the most probable number of protozoa in the original sample. Measurements of population density can thereby be made with a reasonable degree of accuracy.

By the techniques described, it has been established that the flagellates usually are more abundant than the rhizopods (Sarcodina) whereas the ciliates are relatively uncommon. Occasionally, the rhizopods are the rare type and the ciliates numerous. With certain media, the rhizopods may seem as populous as the flagellates, but as a rule the flagellates tend to dominate in absolute numbers and in the variety of species while the ciliate population is sparse (table 2). Providing that the environment is not deleterious, there may be from 5000 to 200,000 flagellates, a similar range for the rhizopods, and usually less than 1000 ciliates per gram. Such values, although only the grossest of approximations, indicate that the flagellates and rhizo-

TABLE 2

Abundance of Protozoa in Two English Soils (3)

	Broadbalk Field			Harpenden Field		
Date	Flagel- lates	Ciliates	Amoebae	Flagel- lates	Ciliates	Amoebae
Feb. 1–Mar. 5	32,000	20	1,500	13,500	10	500
Mar. 8–Apr. 15	29,800	40	1,400	9,300	0	500
Apr. 17–June 6	23,300	130	1,600	7,100	20	500
June 13–Sept. 20	31,200	120	18,600	25,700	10	17,000
Oct. 10–Dec. 15	42,300	20	23,200	23,300	10	10,000
Dec. 21–Mar. 6	20,500	40	2,200	12,000	0	1,500
Mar. 13–June 5	19,700	20	5,100	13,500	0	450

Values are in numbers/g. Each figure represents the average of 10 counts taken during the indicated period.

pods are well adapted to the physical and chemical environment of the soil, possibly because of their small size, while the limited moisture supply and physical barriers make the ciliates poorly suited to the habitat.

An almost invariable feature of the population estimates is the marked degree of variability in samples taken at daily intervals. Fluctuations on a day to day basis are observed in total numbers, in abundance of the various species, and in percentage of active forms. In a one-day period, the numbers may rise from hundreds to hundreds of thousands. Some evidence has been obtained that the daily changes in protozoa are related inversely to the size of the bacterial flora, one increasing as the other decreases. The idea of a natural equilibrium between predator and prey is highly tempting, but the experimental results are still equivocal. It would seem that the populations of predator and prey should balance one another in a steady state condition, but other environmental factors may stimulate one of the two groups to a state of unbalance. In the field, such environmental changes would be expected continually through the influence of temperature, sunlight, and rainfall.

Counting procedures of the types outlined above estimate both the active and cystic population. The number of cysts, however, indicates the protozoan potential rather than the biochemically im-

TABLE 3

Effect of Manure on Number of Amoebae in Barnfield Soil (10)

| | No./g | | | |
| | Untreated | | Manured | |
Date	Active	Cystic	Active	Cystic
April 27	530	1,790	16,040	2,060
May 13	4,040	4,840	29,210	9,590
May 28	13,900	4,100	49,550	3,550
June 20	6,540	1,940	34,130	5,870
July 8	4,040	4,020	52,500	11,000
August 27	8,770	3,730	22,300	10,500

portant fauna. For the differentiation of cysts from active cells, soil is treated overnight with 2 per cent hydrochloric acid, a procedure which destroys vegetative but not resting forms. The difference in counts made prior to and following acid exposure represents the number of active animal cells. Data obtained by this method have established that the cyst stage predominates at low soil moisture levels while excessive water permits emergence of the active individual. This change of stage is demonstrated most dramatically in the population shift that takes place when a dry soil is moistened. But even in daily examinations, sometimes the cysts predominate, sometimes the active protozoa. On some days, no active individuals can be found, and the entire microfauna exists in the encysted condition, yet, within 24 hours, the metabolically active cells emerge and reach numbers in the vicinity of 10,000 per gram. The diurnal fluctuations are probably related to moisture, temperature, and food supply. Some typical data for active and encysted amoebae are presented in table 3.

Environmental Influences

The presence of an adequate food supply is critical to the well-being of the soil protozoa, and the size and activity of the microfauna are seemingly interrelated with the bacterial density. As pointed out above, this relationship is not firmly established, and only intensive research will establish the presence or lack of an association. Nevertheless, the general rule that environmental circumstances favoring bacteria tend to likewise affect protozoa still holds within certain limits.

Protozoa are found in greatest abundance near the surface of the soil, particularly in the upper 6 in. They are scarce in subsoils, but occasional isolates may be obtained from depths of a meter or more. The population is thus most dense where the bacteria are especially numerous in the profile. A similar explanation may account for the greater protozoan numbers in manured plots than in parallel plots receiving no barnyard manure (table 3); i.e., the applied organic matter permits the development of a larger microflora, which then serves as nutriment for the micropredators. Alternatively, the beneficial effect of manure may be partly the result of a direct microbiological stimulation by the extensive root system developed as a consequence of the improved fertility status. Should the saprozoic habit be of greater importance in soil than present concepts suggest, then the influence of depth may result from the availability of organic matter in the A horizon.

Moisture level is of significance both qualitatively and quantitatively. It has often been stated, with considerable justification, that the water content of the environment is a major limitation to protozoan proliferation. An adequate water supply is essential for physiological activity and lateral or vertical movement. The flagellates are tolerant of low moisture, and they can develop in drier conditions than the other microfaunal types. Indeed, the flagellates are dominant in regions of the Sahara desert (14). Ciliates, on the other hand, are abundant only when the moisture status is high. When the supply of water is too low for life processes, the protozoa encyst and remain in the cyst form until the environment becomes more conducive to their growth.

Unequivocal conclusions regarding the role of aeration, hydrogen ion concentration, and temperature are not possible because of inadequate study of the influence of these environmental factors upon protozoa. Aerobic metabolism is the rule for these microorganisms, but occasional species grow at low partial pressures of O_2 or under complete anaerobiasis. The survival of the obligate aerobes at low O_2 tensions is probably rather short and their functions sluggish at best. With regard to acidity, most protozoa exhibit no marked sensitivity to pH although an optimum can always be established. Certain species can, in pure culture, proliferate at pH 3.5 and others at values above 9.0, observations that are in accord with the abundance of protozoa in soils of the same range of acidities. On the other hand, many strains will not tolerate the extremes of reaction and fare poorly outside the range from pH 6 to 8. Certain of the Sarcodina are favored by the high acidity such as that found in acid peats, but they are infrequent in arable land of neutral to alkaline reaction (8). Temperature is another physico-chemical feature of importance, the most favorable environments being both cool and damp. Excessive warmth is detrimental. The influences of moisture, aeration, pH, and temperature are highly complex and cannot be explained entirely on the basis of the supply of bacterial cells.

Role in the Biological Equilibrium

Despite the ubiquity and abundance of protozoa in virgin and uncultivated land, little is known of their function in soil. Techniques for direct experimentation are still inadequate, and the attributes of the protozoa in the dynamic biological equilibrium of terrestrial habitats therefore must be inferred on the basis of their activities in culture solution. The lack of knowledge is especially disturbing because their great number and large cell size indicate that these organisms are important members of the microscopic population.

The lack of convincing and definitive ecological and biochemical data has not, however, hindered speculation on the role of these organisms in soil. The chief hypothesis advanced, based upon the feeding habits in enrichment cultures, is that the protozoa serve to regulate the size of the bacterial population. Some indirect and incomplete evidence can be found to support the thesis that the micro-

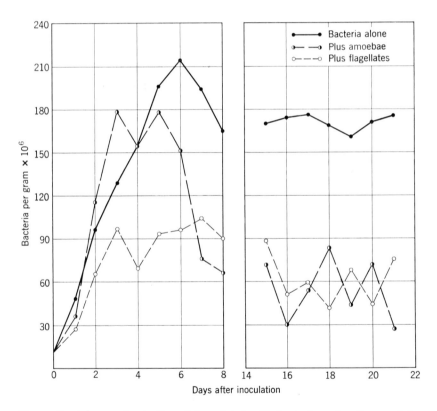

Figure 3. Changes in sterile soil inoculated with bacteria and cultures of the amoeba, *Dimastigamoeba gruberi*, and the flagellate, *Cercomonas crassicauda* (4).

fauna causes a decrease in bacteria through the animals' nutritive habits (figure 3). If protozoa do destroy the edible bacteria present, it would be expected that bacterial transformations would likewise be affected. The postulate of early microbiologists that the microfauna was detrimental to fertility because of its suppressive effect upon the beneficial bacterial transformations has lacked direct experimental proof, however. Since some protozoa do not necessarily develop at the expense of bacteria, it may be that the saprozoic types participate in the decomposition of plant remains. This would seem doubtful in view of the intense competition for organic compounds by fungi and bacteria. For the present, consequently, final conclusions with regard to the function of protozoa in soil environments must be withheld.

Non-protozoan Fauna

Many higher animals spend a large part of their entire life cycle in the soil. Various of these organisms are permanent inhabitants of the subterranean habitat; others are merely transients. Some consideration needs to be given to the non-protozoan fauna although the subject falls outside of the scope of microbiology. A full and detailed presentation is given in Kevan's book, *Soil zoology.* The animal population consists of nematodes, earthworms, flatworms, slugs, snails, centipedes, millipedes, wood lice, certain arachnids, and many insects. These organisms feed upon other animals, animal excreta, plants, or upon inanimate materials. As a rule, the development of the macrofauna requires well-aerated environments, adequate moisture, and warm temperatures. Manuring tends to be beneficial.

Each acre of soil contains up to several hundred pounds of animal tissue. The dominant groups are the earthworms, insects, nematodes, and millipedes. The earthworms are of considerable agronomic importance because of their burrowing and channeling habits, the result of this activity being reflected in the improvement of soil aeration, drainage, and structure. By the channeling, a considerable quantity of soil material is translocated. These segmented worms are sensitive to environmental change, and they are benefited by high organic matter levels, good drainage, and non-acid conditions.

Nematodes or eelworms have attained prominence because of their role in attacking higher plants, but free-living types are likewise found in soil. The latter use organic debris, microorganisms, or other nematodes as food sources. The presence of numerous species of insects has been demonstrated. Especially common are ants, termites, springtails and the larvae of flies and beetles. As with the nematodes, the insects may be free-living or, alternatively, they may feed upon plant roots. Snails and slugs spend part of their life cycle underground, but they are frequently seen beneath rocks, plant debris, and in shady areas. Spiders, mites, and ticks are among the other common invertebrates. In forests and prairies are seen a number of animals which actively burrow into the ground, and their channels may occasionally be quite prominent.

The agricultural importance of the macrofauna rests upon its contributions to fertility, soil structure, and plant disease. Nematodes are of especial concern to the pathologist, but physical injury to plant roots by other animals is not uncommon. By the burrowing of the various animals and by the contribution of earthworm casts to aggregate formation, the macrofauna exerts a beneficial action upon drainage, aeration, and soil structure. In addition, the fauna serves as an adjunct to the microflora by direct participation in organic matter decomposition and, indirectly, by the physical intermixing of crop debris and forest litter with the underlying soil so as to permit more rapid microbiological action.

REFERENCES

Reviews

Kevan, D. K. M., ed. 1955. *Soil zoology.* Butterworth's Scientific Publications, London.
Kitching, J. A. 1957. Some factors in the life of free-living protozoa. In R. E. O. Williams and C. C. Spicer, eds., *Microbial ecology.* Cambridge Univ. Press, Cambridge, pp. 259–286.

Literature cited

1. Allison, R. V. 1924. *Soil Sci.,* 18:339–352.
2. Anscombe, F. J., and B. N. Singh. 1948. *Nature,* 161:140–141.
3. Crump, L. M. 1920. *J. Agric. Sci.,* 10:182–198.
4. Cutler, D. W. 1923. *Ann. Applied Biol.,* 10:137–141.
5. Dixon, A. 1937. *Ann. Applied Biol.,* 24:442–456.
6. Kunicki-Goldfinger, W., W. Drozanski, D. Blaszczak, J. Mazur, and J. Skibinska. 1957. *Acta Microbiol. Polon.,* 6:331–344.
7. Russell, E. J., and H. B. Hutchinson. 1909. *J. Agric. Sci.,* 3:111–144.
8. Sandon, H. 1927. *The composition and distribution of the protozoan fauna of the soil.* Oliver and Boyd, London.

9. Severtzoff, L. B. 1924. *Cent. Bakteriol., Orig.*, I, 92:151–158.
10. Singh, B. N. 1949. *J. Gen. Microbiol.*, 3:204–210.
11. Singh, B. N. 1948. *J. Gen. Microbiol.*, 2:8–14.
12. Singh, B. N. 1946. *Ann. Applied Biol.*, 33:112–119.
13. Singh, B. N. 1941. *Ann. Applied Biol.*, 28:52–64.
14. Varga, L. 1936. *Ann. Inst. Pasteur*, 56:101–123.

7

Viruses

The individual cells or filaments of bacteria, actinomycetes, fungi, algae, and protozoa are consistently small, but all are visible by light microscopy. Beyond the resolution of the light microscope, however, is a group of unique organisms dependent for their development on a suitable host. These submicroscopic agents, the viruses, are of considerable economic and medical importance because of the diseases of plants, animals, and humans for which they are responsible. Yet, not until recent years has attention been focused upon the biology of these infective agents.

Each viral particle requires for its reproduction the presence of a viable, metabolizing organism, and for the virus to be in its active phase, it must be situated within the host cell. In the absence of the host, little activity and no reproduction or duplication are possible. Moreover, viruses are limited in their host ranges; i.e., they parasitize only specific plants, animals, or microorganisms. This specificity has led to a categorization on the basis of the type of host. There is thus a group of viruses pathogenic to plants, a second to animals, and another to microorganisms. The infective agents of the last category, the bacterial and actinomycete viruses, are commonly termed *bacteriophages* although some authors prefer an additional subdivision for the *actinophages*. Submicroscopic, biological agents will not, so far as is presently known, attack fungi or algae. Even among those genera and species of bacteria and actinomycetes which have representatives susceptible to bacteriophage attack, a remarkable degree of host specificity is apparent. It is not uncommon for a virus capable of infecting representatives of one genus to have no such action on a phylogenetically related genus. Likewise, a single bacteriophage type may

117

TABLE 1

Effect of Bacteriophages on Strains of Three Bacterial Genera (3)

		Lysis of Test Bacteria				
	A. radiobacter Strains			*Arthrobacter* Strains		*R. leguminosarum* Strains
Bacteriophage Isolated on	R	I	S	E	B	2	6
Agrobacterium radiobacter							
strain R	+	+	+	−	−	−	−
strain I	+	+	−	−	−	−	−
strain S	−	−	+	−	−	−	−
Arthrobacter							
strain E	−	−	−	+	−	−	−
strain B	−	−	−	−	+	−	−
Rhizobium leguminosarum							
strain 2	−	−	−	−	−	+	+
strain 6	−	−	−	−	−	+	+

+ lysis.
− no lysis.

find several but not all species of the genus suitable for invasion, and susceptibility to a specific bacteriophage is often associated with only certain of the strains of a single species (table 1).

Despite the fact that viruses cause diseases of many agronomic and horticultural crops, it is the rare plant-infecting virus which can persist or overwinter in soil. These uncommon forms are often considered to be soil-borne, but they are soil-borne only in the sense that they retain their infective capacity for some time after crop removal. Such viruses do not multiply in soil; rather they persist for varying periods in a condition resistant to inactivation. By this criterion, the viruses responsible for the mosaic diseases of wheat, oats, and tobacco and the pathogens inducing the big vein disease of lettuce and the corky ringspot of potatoes are soil-borne. Several of these may persist for periods of a year or more, but the land usually can be rendered non-infectious by treatment with chloropicrin, formaldehyde, carbon disulfide, or by steam sterilization. Certain animal and human viruses likewise will remain infective in soil for periods ranging up to several months. The persistence of the mouse encephalomyelitis virus, for example, is greatest in neutral environments, negligible in acid conditions, and of intermediate duration in alkaline soils (8).

Like their counterparts which affect higher plants and animals, the bacteriophages have a minute body that can pass without difficulty through ultra-fine filters designed to retain bacterial cells. Morphologically, the bacterial viruses usually possess head- and tail-like structures (figure 1). The diameter of the bacteriophage rarely exceeds 0.05 to 0.10 μ. The tail is somewhat larger, about 0.2 μ in length, but it is quite narrow.

Following the entry of the bacteriophage into the bacterium, the tail being the point of attachment, *lysis* of the host cells takes place. If the bacterium is growing on agar, the lytic area is seen as a zone of clearing known as a *plaque;* in like fashion, infection in liquid media is evidenced by a decrease in turbidity of the bacterial suspension as

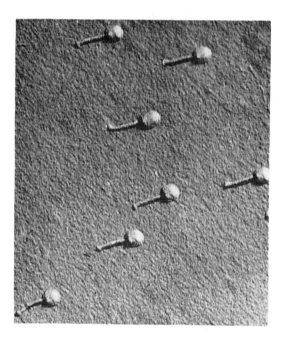

Figure 1. Bacteriophage particles viewed under the electron microscope.

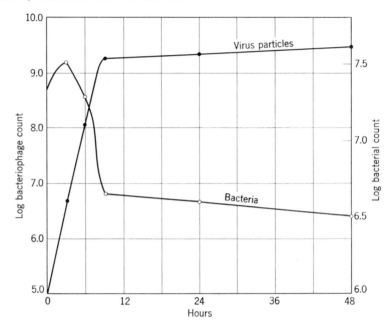

Figure 2. Changes in populations of bacteria and bacteriophages during infection (7).

lysis proceeds. The cellular dissolution is accompanied by a marked increase in the number of bacteriophage particles and a sharp decline in the number of viable bacteria in the medium (figure 2). Purification of the viruses can be accomplished by passing the suspension of lysed bacteria through a filter designed to retain residual, intact cells. Such enrichments are not difficult to achieve since the rupture of a single, infected cell often leads to the release of several hundred virus particles, each of which is potentially invasive. Thus, by use of high bacterial concentrations, counts in excess of 10^{10} bacteriophage particles per milliliter of culture medium can be attained.

Viruses are first recognized through the symptoms they induce in the host. With bacterial and actinomycete viruses, the initial abnormality is the appearance on solid media of plaques or, in liquid media, the clearing of turbid cell suspensions. The bacteriophage may then be propagated in cultures of a susceptible microorganism from which it can be ultimately separated and purified by filtration and high-speed centrifugation. When necessary, the enumeration of infective units is performed on agar in a fashion analogous to the conventional plate count. After dilutions are made, the bacteriophage suspension is pipetted onto a plate previously inoculated with a suitable microbial species and, following an appropriate incubation period, the clear plaques counted (figure 3). Under such conditions, each plaque originates from a single bacteriophage particle deposited upon the plate, there to multiply at the expense of the adjacent bacterial growth.

In order to demonstrate the presence in soil of a specific bacteriophage, a sample of soil is incubated with the host bacterium to allow for an increase in the population of the virus in question. A small quantity of the treated sample is then added to a nutrient medium previously inoculated with the host. After 24 to 48 hours, the lysed suspension is passed through a sterile bacteriological filter and the filtrate tested for its capacity to lyse a fresh, rapidly growing culture

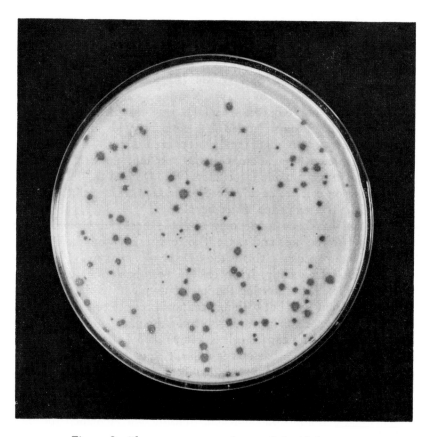

Figure 3. Plaques on an agar plate seeded with bacteria.

of the microorganism. By such methods, bacteriophages specific for *Aerobacter, Agrobacterium, Arthrobacter, Pseudomonas, Rhizobium,* and *Streptomyces* (2, 3) as well as *Azotobacter* and *Nocardia* have been demonstrated in a variety of soils. The absence of viruses which parasitize filamentous fungi is of considerable interest because streptomycetes, organisms related phylogenetically to the primitive fungi, are readily infected. Likewise, the autotrophic ammonium- and sulfur-oxidizing bacteria are apparently resistant to infection although further inquiry may reveal bacteriophages specific for these inadequately studied microorganisms.

One group of bacteriophages potentially important in agriculture is capable of bringing about the lysis of the bacteria which form nodules on the roots of legumes. These bacteria, members of the genus *Rhizobium,* function in symbiosis with legumes to convert atmospheric nitrogen to a form utilized by the plant. Should the bacteria within the nodule be parasitized by the virus, material economic losses could ensue. Bacteriophages specific for *Rhizobium* spp. can be isolated directly from soil or from roots of a number of leguminous species. For example, Katznelson and Wilson (6) found the bacteriophage for the alfalfa rhizobium in every alfalfa field examined, but in only occasional sites not cropped to alfalfa was the virus encountered (table 2). It has been suggested that the poor yields attendant upon continuous cropping of alfalfa and clovers are caused by a build-up of the bacteriophage population with the resultant destruction of the plant-*Rhizobium* symbiotic association (4). Despite the fact that no final conclusion can yet be advanced to rule out this possibility, there is little definitive evidence in its behalf.

Mention has been made only of those bacterial viruses which vigorously lyse the host and cause it to release large numbers of free bacteriophage particles. This is the *lytic* or *virulent* type of bacteriophage. Not infrequently, however, the host bacterium carries the virus within itself, transferring the infecting unit to its daughter cells without apparent lysis but with an occasional release of free viral particles. Such bacteriophages are *temperate,* the phenomenon is termed *lysogenicity,* and the carrier cell is known as a lysogenic bacterium. Detection of lysogenic bacteria is difficult since lysis is not immediately apparent. For purposes of identification, the lysogenic strain is mixed with an indicator or susceptible strain which will be attacked by the viruses borne by the former. Lysogenicity may have associated with it a unique phenomenon, *transduction,* in which the bacteriophage serves to transmit certain genetic characteristics from one

TABLE 2

Presence of Bacteriophage for *Rhizobium meliloti* in New York Soils (6)

Soil	pH	Age of Stand	Bacteriophage Incidence
		yr	
Forest soil	4.90		—
Forest soil	4.99		—
Pasture	5.27		—
Alfalfa field	5.27	6	+
Alfalfa field	5.85	3	+
Alfalfa field	6.10	8	+
Wheat field	6.11		+
Pasture	6.20		—
Alfalfa field	7.39	1	+

host to a newly infected bacterium. Transduction serves essentially as a unidirectional transfer of a portion of the nuclear apparatus of the microbial architecture. The characters thus transferred, traits which may alter the nutrition or physiology of the newly infected cell, usually are passed between strains of the same species, but the transmission of genetic material may occasionally take place between closely related genera.

Of potential significance to the possible role of bacteriophages in soil is the capacity of organic residues, humus, and clay to adsorb viruses. Substances known to remove bacteriophages from solution include non-susceptible bacterial cells, fungi, clay, and plant materials. Soils rich in clay generally adsorb more of the virus particles than sandy soils, but the organic matter likewise seems to be of consequence (1, 5). Factors such as clay and organic matter content of soil undoubtedly influence the action and spread of bacterial viruses, and they may at the same time be influential in the spread of plant diseases by soil-borne viruses.

The practical significance of bacteriophages and plant and animal viruses in soil is difficult to assess. The overwintering of disease-producing agents no doubt has a bearing upon crop production because the pathogen can initiate infection of susceptible crops the following season. Little is known of the agronomic importance of the bacteriophages, however, and the extensive investigations of the viruses lysing *Rhizobium* spp. have not yielded sufficiently strong evidence to warrant the conclusion that the infective agents have any relationship to legume yields. Despite the abundance of suitable bacteria of many genera in soil, the viruses attacking them are never numerous. This fact suggests that there is some check upon the spread of the submicroscopic particles. The presence of such a check can be demonstrated indirectly by showing the sensitivity in vitro of many soil bacteria to soil-derived bacteriophages; that is, the bacteria are vigorously lysed in culture solution, yet they exist and multiply in nature.

It is often assumed that the importance of the bacteriophage to the ecology of its host is solely a result of lytic influences, the phage presumably acting by the destruction of susceptible bacterial strains with which it comes in contact. Alternatively, it is possible that the virus may participate in the transmission of genetic material from one bacterium to another through transduction. This transfer could give to the receptor cell physiological properties which might be of competitive advantage, such as new nutritional or biochemical attributes. Experimental verification of transduction as an event in nature, however, is lacking. Nevertheless, this means of genetic exchange may prove to be of importance in the evolution and variation of microorganisms.

REFERENCES

Reviews

Anderson, E. S. 1957. The relations of bacteriophages to bacterial ecology. In R. E. O. Williams and C. C. Spicer, eds., *Microbial ecology*. Cambridge Univ. Press, Cambridge, pp. 189–217.

Luria, S. E. 1953. *General virology*. John Wiley and Sons, New York.

Literature cited

1. Bershova, O. 1938. *Mikrobiol. Zh.*, 5:161–180.
2. Carlucci, A. F., and R. L. Starkey. 1956. *Bacteriol. Proc.*, 1956:35.
3. Conn, H. J., E. J. Bottcher, and C. Randall. 1945. *J. Bacteriol.*, 49:359–373.
4. Demolon, A., and A. Dunez. 1935. *Trans. 3rd Intl. Cong. Soil Sci.*, Oxford, 1:156–157.
5. Katznelson, H. 1939. *Trans. 3rd Comm., Intl. Soc. Soil Sci.*, New Brunswick, A:43–48.
6. Katznelson, H., and J. K. Wilson. 1941. *Soil Sci.*, 51:59–63.
7. Kleczkowska, J. 1945. *J. Bacteriol.*, 50:81–94.
8. Murphy, W. H., O. R. Eylar, E. L. Schmidt, and J. T. Syverton. 1958. *Virology*, 6:612–622.

THE CARBON CYCLE

INTRODUCTION

The most important single element in the biological realm and the substance that serves as the cornerstone of cell structure is carbon. Plant and microbial tissues contain large quantities of carbon, approximately 40 to 50 per cent on a dry weight basis, yet the ultimate source is the CO_2 which exists in a perennially short supply, only some 0.03 per cent of the earth's atmosphere. Carbon dioxide is converted to organic carbon largely by the action of photoautotrophic organisms— the higher green plants on land, the algae in aquatic habitats. These photoautotrophs supply the organic nutrients needed for heterotrophic animals and the non-chlorophyll-containing microorganisms.

Carbon is continually being fixed into organic form by photosynthetic organisms under the influence of light and, once bound, the carbon becomes unavailable for use in the generation of new plant life. It is thus essential for the carbonaceous materials to be decomposed and returned to the atmosphere in order for higher organisms to continue to thrive. It has been estimated that the vegetation of the earth's surface consumes some 90 billion kg CO_2 per annum, about one twenty-fifth of the total supply of the atmosphere. With the conversion of so much of the plant-available carbon to organic form each year and the limited supply in the air, it is manifestly apparent that the major plant nutrient element could rapidly become exhausted in the absence of microbial transformations.

In its barest outlines, the carbon cycle revolves about CO_2 and its fixation and regeneration. Chlorophyll-containing plants utilize the gas as their sole carbon source, and the carbonaceous matter thus

125

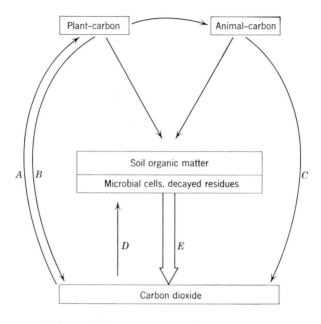

A. Photosynthesis   C. Respiration, animal
B. Respiration, plant   D. Autotrophic microorganisms
                E. Respiration, microbial

The carbon cycle.

synthesized serves to supply the animal world with preformed organic carbon. Upon the death of the plant or animal, microbial metabolism assumes the dominant role in the cyclic sequence. The dead tissues undergo decay and are transformed into microbial cells and a vast, heterogeneous body of carbonaceous compounds known collectively as humus or as the soil organic fraction. The cycle is completed and carbon made available with the final decomposition and production of CO_2 from humus and the rotting tissues.

8

Some Aspects
of Microbial Physiology

Prior to a consideration of the various transformations brought about by the microflora, it is necessary to review some of the details of microbial nutrition and physiology. The capacity to grow in a given habitat is determined by an organism's ability to utilize the nutrients in its surroundings. At the same time, the organism exists in an environmental complex, and its nutritional and physiological characteristics will determine to a great extent its ability to get along with its neighbors. Hence, not only the function but the very existence of a species in the soil habitat is conditioned by its nutritional and biochemical versatility.

Many of the points made in the following discussion are presented in considerable detail in textbooks on microbial physiology and biochemistry. However, a brief discussion will serve to set the stage for an understanding of the specific processes that are brought about by the microflora of natural environments.

Nutrition

Nutrients serve three separate functions: providing the materials required for protoplasmic synthesis; supplying the energy necessary for cell growth and biosynthetic reactions; and serving as acceptors for the electrons released in the reaction that yields energy to the organism (table 1). In aerobes, O_2 serves the last function. In strict or facultative anaerobes, either an organic by-product of metabolism

TABLE 1

Nutrients Required by Microorganisms

1. Energy source	Organic compounds Inorganic compounds Sunlight
2. Electron acceptor	O_2 Organic compounds NO_3^-, NO_2^-, N_2O, $SO_4^=$, CO_2, Fe^{+++}
3. Carbon source	CO_2, HCO_3^- Organic compounds
4. Minerals	N, P, K, Mg, S, Fe, Ca, Mn, Zn, Cu, Co, Mo
5. Growth factors *	
a. Amino acids	Alanine, aspartic acid, glutamic acid, etc.
b. Vitamins	Thiamine, biotin, pyridoxine, riboflavin, nicotinic acid, pantothenic acid, p-aminobenzoic acid, folic acid, thioctic acid, B_{12}, etc.
c. Others	Purine bases, pyrimidine bases, choline, inositol, peptides, etc.

* Where growth proceeds in absence of growth factors, the compounds are presumably synthesized by the organism.

or some inorganic substance replaces the O_2. Among the energy sources for the heterotrophic soil population are found cellulose, hemicelluloses, lignin, starch, pectic substances, inulin, chitin, hydrocarbons, sugars, proteins, amino acids, and organic acids. The conversion of these organic substances to more oxidized products releases energy, and a portion of the energy released is used in the synthesis of the protoplasmic constituents from the building blocks of biological tissues. However, in order to be made use of, the foodstuff must penetrate into the organism. Often, the energy source enters with no difficulty, but microbial cells are impermeable to many complex molecules; these compounds must be first solubilized and simplified prior to their serving within the cell's confines as energy sources.

The mineral composition of microorganisms is remarkably similar, and bacteria, fungi, actinomycetes, algae, and protozoa generally contain the same elements. Nitrogen, phosphorus, potassium, magnesium, sulfur, iron, and probably calcium, manganese, zinc, copper, cobalt, and molybdenum are integral parts of the protoplasmic structure. From these essential nutrients plus carbon, hydrogen, and oxygen is built the microbial cell. The differences in nutrition among members of the microflora is not linked with the essential mineral substances but rather with molecules containing carbon and nitrogen. The number of elements required for life is not large, but the metabolic role of the few needed is, with few exceptions, unclear. In several instances, however, it has been observed that a mineral is required for a specific reaction in decomposition or in cell synthesis. A number of these inorganic substances are assimilated in extremely small quantities, so small that the requirement is not always detected. For example, probably most microorganisms contain vitamin B_{12}, a cobalt-containing molecule, yet the need for cobalt is difficult to establish because the optimum cobalt concentration is appreciably less than one part per billion of medium. Ingredients of the culture solution usually contain quantities of cobalt in excess of the need.

Organic constituents make up a large fraction of the total protoplasmic material. Carbohydrates, proteins, amino acids, vitamins, nucleic acids, purines, pyrimidines, and other substances constitute the working apparatus of the biological machine. The complexity of the cell's interior is in marked contrast to the simplicity of its surroundings, and only a few of the materials from the habitat—or culture medium—are assimilated without further modification. Nevertheless, microorganisms differ greatly in their synthetic abilities. Frequently, an organism is unable of itself to synthesize one or more of its structural building blocks. Where this occurs, the organism must be provided with the necessary materials. These substances, the *growth factors*, are organic molecules required in trace quantities for growth. The need for one or several growth factors—amino acids, vitamins, or other structural units—has considerable ecological importance because a species needing them will only grow in habitats where the organic molecules are present. On the other hand, a growth factor need not be essential. Many species are stimulated by growth factors, but grow, slowly to be sure, in the absence of individual substances; in these instances, the chemical is stimulatory rather than essential. Metabolically, the position of a growth factor as stimulatory rather than essential may be taken to reflect a metabolic condition in which the organism produces the substance in question but at a rate insufficient to meet the demands for rapid proliferation.

At the simplest nutritional extreme are the chemoautotrophs, organisms which synthesize all protoplasmic constituents from inorganic salts, CO_2, O_2, and water. Somewhat more exacting are the heterotrophic bacteria, actinomycetes, and fungi that require some simple carbon source—often a sugar or organic acid suffices—and inorganic nutrients. In this group are found bacteria such as *Pseudomonas* and fungi like *Aspergillus*. A large proportion of the soil microflora develops at least to some extent in a medium containing a simple source of organic carbon, nitrogen in the form of ammonium or nitrate salts, and a number of inorganic substances. More exacting yet are the microorganisms which, because they are unable to form their own vitamins or amino acids, require one or more of these growth factors. Development of these more exacting species is dependent upon a supply of the appropriate factor or factors. *Bacillus* spp., for example, often lack the ability to synthesize one or several amino acids or vitamins. At the extreme of nutritional dependence are microorganisms requiring a host of essential substances, a nutritional complexity associated with the inability of the organism to synthesize many of the requisite building blocks of the cell's architecture (table 2). In soil,

TABLE 2

Composition of Culture Media for Several Aerobic Bacteria

	Nitrobacter agilis	*Pseudomonas* sp.	*Arthrobacter* sp.	*Bacillus subtilis*
Energy source	KNO_2	Glucose	Sucrose	Glucose
Carbon source	$KHCO_3$	Glucose	Sucrose	Glucose
Minerals	KNO_2	NH_4Cl	$(NH_4)_2SO_4$	NH_4Cl
	K_2HPO_4	K_2HPO_4	KH_2PO_4	K_2HPO_4
	$MgSO_4$	$MgSO_4$	$MgSO_4$	KH_2PO_4
	$FeSO_4$	$FeSO_4$	$FeSO_4$	$MgSO_4$
		$CaCl_2$	$CaCO_3$	Na_2SO_4
			$MnSO_4$	$FeSO_4$
			$ZnSO_4$	$MnSO_4$
			$CuSO_4$	$CaCl_2$
Growth factors	—	—	Biotin	Glutamic acid
			Thiamine	Cysteine
			B_{12}	

the existence of species with complex requirements is unsure since the growth factors must be obtained from the environment; this group contains organisms whose activity is closely regulated by other biological systems in the environment.

Carbon dioxide, a product of both aerobic and anaerobic metabolism, is important not only because it completes the carbon cycle but also because of its direct influence upon growth. Chemoautotrophic and photoautotrophic microorganisms must have CO_2 as it is their sole carbonaceous nutrient. However, the gas is stimulatory to and often required by many heterotrophs, and growth of some species will not proceed in its absence. A part of the CO_2 supplied, even to heterotrophs, is incorporated into the cell substance. The requirement for this gas rarely presents a problem in soil because of its continual evolution from decaying organic matter. On the other hand, CO_2 at certain concentrations is toxic to a number of fungi, and the inhibition may have a considerable biological influence since individual fungus species vary in their sensitivity to the gas. Hence, its release during decomposition may alter the composition of the subterranean population.

Oxygen, a requirement for all aerobes, may likewise serve as an ecological determinant. Thus, although most fungi are obligately aerobic, there is considerable variation among microorganisms in the capacity to grow at low partial pressures of O_2. Certain strains develop to some extent using O_2 dissolved in the culture medium when there is none in the gas phase; others exhibit no such capacity. Further, the rate and extent of growth and the ability to sporulate is affected by the aeration status of the environment.

At this point it is possible to pose the problem of the physiological basis of microbial ecology. Why is one microorganism suited to a given habitat while another is unable to find a foothold therein? *Mycoplana* and *Penicillium* are native soil genera; *Lactobacillus* and *Actinomyces* are aliens. No definite answers can yet be given to account for the occurrence or lack of occurrence of most organisms. The reader, however, may wish to speculate on the problem. Surely, the ability to use the carbon sources of the habitat, either animate or inanimate, is of prime importance. In soil, the possession by an organism of a simple nutrition would also be advantageous, but the presence of numerous bacteria requiring individual vitamins or amino acids is indicative of the synthesis of these molecules in soil. Additional physiological characteristics that must be considered in proposing a rational basis for microbial ecology are growth rate, the presence of spores or other mechanisms of survival in deleterious circumstances, cell size, motility, the ability to withstand the attack of predators or lytic species, etc. The various fields of microbiology—bacteriology, mycology, phycology, and protozoology—have an ever-increasing store of knowledge on the nutrition, physiology, and metabolism of microorganisms, but with few exceptions this knowledge has yet to be applied from the conditions of the test tube to the more dynamic state in nature.

Growth

In any discussion of the rate of microbiological processes, some attention must be given to the growth of the dominant microorganisms. Most investigations of the growth patterns have been concerned with the true bacteria for which the characteristics of proliferation are now well established.   Consider the development in optimal conditions of a bacterial population of size a.   As bacteria reproduce by binary fission, one mother cell dividing into two daughters in a period known as the *generation time*, the final population, b, is

after one generation	$2 \times a$
after two generations	$2 \times 2 \times a$
and after three generations	$2 \times 2 \times 2 \times a$

Therefore, the final population, b, after n generations is

$$b = a \times 2^n$$

Hence, bacterial growth is ideally exponential because the size of the population is related to an exponential function of the base 2.   As logarithms are likewise exponents of some base figure, bacterial growth is logarithmic in character, and a plot of the logarithm of the number of bacteria as a function of time yields a straight line, at least during the active period of growth.   This stage is therefore known as the *logarithmic phase* of growth.   Should each daughter have the same biochemical activity as its mother cell, then a plot against time of the logarithm of some change brought about by the culture would be linear.   This can be shown for a number of bacterial transformations: e.g., the assimilation of N_2 by *Azotobacter* spp. or the oxidation of ammonium by *Nitrosomonas* spp. (figure 1).

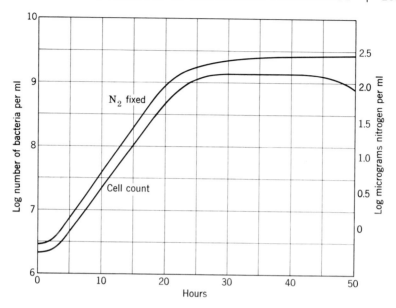

Figure 1. Growth and N_2 fixation by *Azotobacter* sp. in culture medium.

It is simple to calculate the generation time, g, from the relationship between the initial and final population in the logarithmic phase.

$$b = a \times 2^n$$

$$\log b = \log a + n \log 2$$

$$0.301n = \log b - \log a$$

$$n = \frac{\log b - \log a}{0.301}$$

However, the generation time is the number of generations in the selected time interval, t. Hence

$$g = \frac{t}{n}$$

$$g = \frac{0.301t}{\log b - \log a}$$

The generation time varies considerably, depending upon the organism, the temperature, and the medium. For example, the period required for one generation—equivalent to the time in which the population exactly doubles—is 20 minutes for *Bacillus cereus,* 35 minutes for *Pseudomonas fluorescens*, 2 hours for *Rhizobium leguminosarum*, and 11 hours for *Nitrosomonas europaea*. The generation time is likewise least at the optimum temperature and pH and increases as the environment becomes progressively more unfavorable.

Logarithmic growth occurs only during a portion of the culture cycle. As the supply of nutrients diminishes or as metabolic wastes accumulate, the rate of development declines. Frequently, the factor responsible for the decline is difficult to establish, but nutrient deficiencies or staling products are the usual causes. Ultimately, the culture reaches its peak population density, and the dying of the individual cells offsets the appearance of new bacteria; this is reflected by a diminution in the population size.

In nature, bacteria do not exist in pure culture, and the logarithmic phase is not frequently encountered in a highly mixed flora. However, the addition to soil of certain substances, ammonium or thiosulfate salts for example, may result in a logarithmic transformation rate; i.e., the logarithm of the quantity of ammonium or thiosulfate oxidized is linear. Under such circumstances, the demonstration of a logarithmic conversion serves to indicate that bacteria are the responsible agents.

The growth patterns of filamentous microorganisms have not received as much attention as those of the bacteria. Among the filamentous microorganisms, however, there is an active stage during which time the rate of increase of cell mass and cell activity is highest. In some fungi and actinomycetes, there is evidence that the increase is cubic so that a plot of the cube root of mycelium weight or activity against time yields a straight line. The period of optimal development is maintained until some factor in the environment becomes limiting. When the supply of O_2 or nutrients is insufficient to meet the demand, the increase in protoplasmic mass of many of the filamentous microorganisms appears to be linear. In the later stages, there is no further gain in mass; finally, autolysis or self-decomposition leads to the slow digestion of the protoplasm with a release of soluble substances into the medium.

Many factors affect microbial development. Two of the more important variables to which frequent references are made are temperature and pH. In soil, the influence of temperature and pH on organic matter decomposition, herbicide persistence, and on other processes has considerable agronomic importance. The effect of temperature and acidity is exerted in two ways, by altering the composition of the microflora and by directly influencing the individuals making up the population. It might be assumed that a specific microorganism would be most prominent in soils having a pH or maintained at a temperature near the organism's optimum. That this is not the case is a result of the interactions between individuals. A species that proliferates readily at the warmer or colder temperature extremes or at the extremes of acidity or alkalinity will predominate in these circumstances because of the lack of competition, despite the fact that the environment is not particularly favorable for the dominant species. The same can be stated for moisture.

Biochemical Considerations

Chemical reactions may take place with the liberation or utilization of energy. The energy released by one reaction may be used to do work or to drive a second reaction that will not proceed on its own. In an isolated system, the transfer of energy from one process to another is complete; that is, there is neither a net loss nor a net gain. In natural processes, however, a portion of the energy is dissipated to the surroundings in the form of heat.

Growth of microorganisms requires an energy input. This is accomplished by the biological oxidation of organic or inorganic compounds. In aerobic heterotrophs, the oxidation may be visualized as

$$C_6H_{12}O_6 + 6O_2 \rightarrow 6CO_2 + 6H_2O + \text{energy} \qquad (I)$$

For an aerobic autotroph, a typical reaction is

$$2NH_4Cl + 3O_2 \rightarrow 2HNO_2 + 2H_2O + 2HCl + \text{energy} \qquad (II)$$

The conversion of glucose to CO_2 or ammonium to nitrite releases considerable energy, but not all of that released is captured by the microorganism. The ratio of the amount captured by the biological system to the amount released in the oxidation is known as the *free energy efficiency*. Thus, when it is stated that the oxidation of ammonium to nitrite releases 66 kcal, the quantity actually used by *Nitrosomonas* is the product of the (energy yield) $\times$ (free energy efficiency).

In equations I and II, the oxidant appears to be O_2; that is, the energy is liberated when O_2 acts on the sugar or on ammonium. In reality, biological oxidations usually proceed not by the addition of O_2 but by the removal of hydrogen (dehydrogenation) or of electrons.

Thus, the following two equations entail oxidations although O_2 is not involved.

$$Cu \rightarrow Cu^{++} + 2e^-$$ (III)

$$RH_2 \rightarrow R + 2H$$ (IV)

The electrons or hydrogens must now be disposed of. This is usually accomplished by a reaction with O_2, the oxygen thereby acting as an *electron (or hydrogen) acceptor*. Consequently, O_2 is not the immediate cause of the oxidation but rather the acceptor in aerobic microorganisms of the electrons liberated. In the absence of this gas, a number of other substances may be electron acceptors, e.g., nitrate for strains of *Pseudomonas*, sulfate for *Desulfovibrio*, and CO_2 for *Methanobacterium*. Instead of water being produced through the reduction of O_2 by the electrons (or H), the products are N_2, H_2S, and CH_4 for nitrate, sulfate, and CO_2, respectively. These substances do not serve as sources of oxygen, an early but incorrect concept, but as receptors of electrons.

With anaerobic bacteria, the metabolic system is basically the same. *Clostridium, Lactobacillus,* and other anaerobes grow in the absence of O_2 yet no inorganic electron acceptors are used. In these bacteria, hydrogens removed from the organic compound are dissipated by reaction with one of the products of carbohydrate breakdown. Thus, in the lactic acid fermentation of glucose:

$$\underset{\text{glucose}}{C_6H_{12}O_6} \rightarrow \underset{\text{pyruvic acid}}{2C_3H_4O_3} + 4H$$ (V)

$$4H + 2C_3H_4O_3 \rightarrow \underset{\text{lactic acid}}{2C_3H_6O_3}$$ (VI)

Not all reactions produce or consume energy. Many complex compounds must be transformed to simpler forms prior to use by the organism. For example, in those microorganisms which utilize cellulose, the long-chain carbohydrate is converted to simple sugars.

$$\underset{\text{cellulose}}{(C_6H_{10}O_5)_n} + nH_2O \rightarrow \underset{\text{glucose}}{nC_6H_{12}O_6}$$ (VII)

This first stage provides no useful energy to the active species, and it is only the subsequent metabolism of glucose that provides energy for cell synthesis. Yet, the initial attack is necessary in order to convert the cellulose into the sugars that are assimilated. The same holds for hemicelluloses, chitin, pectin, and a number of other structurally complex carbohydrates.

The mere carrying out of an oxidation, either in the presence or in the absence of O_2, is not sufficient for the acquisition of biologically useful energy. In order for the energy to be applied effectively in growing organisms, its storage and release must be carefully regulated. This is effected by means of compounds such as adenosine diphosphate (ADP) and adenosine triphosphate (ATP). When the microorganism is releasing energy by oxidation, a portion of that liberated is used to convert adenosine diphosphate and inorganic phosphate into adenosine triphosphate.

$$\text{ADP} + \text{phosphate} + \text{energy} \rightarrow \text{ATP} \qquad (\text{VIII})$$

When there is a demand for energy in cell synthesis or for reductive reactions, adenosine triphosphate is converted back to adenosine diphosphate with the controlled release of the energy.

$$\text{ATP} \rightarrow \text{ADP} + \text{phosphate} + \text{energy} \qquad (\text{IX})$$

ATP and several closely related compounds thus serve as the energy storehouses in microbial metabolism.

Consider once again the case of the anaerobes. These microorganisms accumulate certain incompletely oxidized products during growth; i.e., not all of the potential energy in the carbon source is released. This incomplete oxidation and incomplete energy yield is reflected in the few molecules of ATP produced for each molecule of carbonaceous nutrient metabolized. In the anaerobic decomposition of glucose by yeast, to cite a single example, the net yield is only two ATP molecules for each glucose molecule degraded. In those aerobic organisms which convert simple sugars to CO_2 and water, getting the full value of the oxidation, a total of about thirty-eight ATP molecules are formed for each molecule of glucose transformed. Thus, aerobic processes liberate far more energy than anaerobic reactions. Further, since the oxidation of carbohydrates is used for the formation of protoplasm, the greater energy release in air is associated with a greater microbial cell synthesis per unit of organic nutrient.

The various reactions concerned in microbial metabolism require the presence of enzymes. An *enzyme* may be defined as a protein produced by a living cell which functions in catalyzing a chemical reaction. Being proteins, enzymes are denatured at high temperatures, and their activity is also affected by pH. The compound which is changed by enzymatic action, the *substrate*, serves as the basis of enzyme nomenclature. Thus, cellulase, chitinase, and xylanase are the catalysts concerned in the degradation of cellulose, chitin, and xylan, respectively. Some enzymes are named on the basis of both the substrate and the type of reaction; e.g., the enzyme removing hydrogen from succinic acid is succinic dehydrogenase while the catalyst concerned in reducing nitrate is designated as nitrate reductase.

Enzymes exhibit a marked specificity for individual substrates or individual processes; i.e., they function in catalyzing a single type of transformation of one or of a few closely related substrates. This implies that a multitude of enzymes is required in the metabolism of even a unicellular organism. In addition to specificity, another attribute to be borne in mind is the cellular site of enzyme action. Some catalysts, the *intracellular* enzymes, perform their function within the confines of the cell. Others, the *extracellular* enzymes, are concerned with reactions outside of the organism that synthesized the catalyst. The latter are very important in decomposition of polysaccharides such as cellulose and the hemicelluloses because the microbial cell is impermeable to the large polysaccharide molecule. Without the extracellular enzymes, polysaccharide decomposition could not take place. Another useful distinction in enzymology is made between those catalysts always produced by the cell, the *constitutive* enzymes, and those formed only in the presence of the specific substrate. The latter, the *adaptive* enzymes, are likewise of significance in the decomposition of polysaccharides since many of the extracellular catalysts implicated in polysaccharide decomposition are adaptive in nature.

REFERENCES

Cochrane, V. W. 1958. *Physiology of fungi.* John Wiley and Sons, New York.

Fogg, G. E. 1953. *The metabolism of algae.* Methuen and Co., London.

Fruton, J. S., and S. Simmonds. 1958. *General biochemistry.* John Wiley and Sons, New York.

Lamanna, C., and M. F. Mallette. 1959. *Basic bacteriology.* The Williams and Wilkins Co., Baltimore.

Oginsky, E. L., and W. W. Umbreit. 1959. *An introduction to bacterial physiology.* W. H. Freeman and Co., San Francisco.

Waksman, S. A. 1959. *The actinomycetes. Vol. 1. Nature, occurrence, and activities.* The Williams and Wilkins Co., Baltimore.

9

Organic Matter Decomposition

The organic matter subjected to microbial decay in soil comes from several sources. Vast quantities of plant remains and forest litter decompose above the surface. Subterranean portions of the plant and the above-ground tissues that are mechanically incorporated into the soil body become food for the microflora. Animal tissues and excretory products are also subjected to attack. In addition, the cells of the microorganisms serve as a source of carbon for succeeding generations of the microscopic population. The chemical nature of the organic matter is clearly very complex, and investigations of the transformations and the responsible organisms have therefore been extremely interesting but not without problems arising from the heterogeneity of the natural substrates.

The diversity of plant materials that enter the soil presents to the microflora a variety of substances which are both physically and chemically heterogeneous. The organic constituents of plants are commonly divided into six broad categories: (a) the most abundant chemical constituent, cellulose, varying in quantity from 15 to 60 per cent of the dry weight; (b) hemicelluloses, commonly making up 10 to 30 per cent of the weight; (c) lignin, which usually makes up 5 to 30 per cent of the plant; (d) the water-soluble fraction, in which is included simple sugars, amino acids, and aliphatic acids, these contributing 5 to 30 per cent of the tissue weight; (e) ether and alcohol-soluble constituents, a fraction containing fats, oils, waxes, resins, and a number of pigments; and (f) proteins which have in their structure much of the plant nitrogen and sulfur. The mineral constituents, usually estimated by ashing, vary from 1 to 13 per cent of the total tissue.

As the plant ages, the content of water-soluble constituents, proteins, and minerals decreases and the percentage abundance of cellulose, hemicelluloses, and lignin rises. On a weight basis, the bulk of the plant is accounted for by cellulose, the hemicelluloses, and lignin. In wood, there are particularly large amounts of cellulose, lignin, and also hemicelluloses while the water and solvent-soluble materials occur in small quantities. These substances constitute the mixed and highly diverse substrates utilized by the soil population in the decomposition and mineralization of carbon.

Carbon Assimilation

Organic matter decomposition serves two functions for the microflora, providing energy for growth and supplying carbon for the formation of new cell material. Carbon dioxide, methane, organic acids, and alcohol are merely waste products as far as microbial development is concerned, metabolic wastes released in the acquisition of energy. The essential feature for the soil inhabitants themselves is the acquisition of energy and carbon for cell synthesis.

The cells of most microorganisms commonly contain approximately 50 per cent carbon. The source of the element is the substrate being utilized. The process of converting substrate to protoplasmic carbon is known as *assimilation*. Under aerobic conditions, frequently from 20 to 40 per cent of the substrate-carbon is assimilated; the remainder is released as CO_2 or accumulates as waste products. The extent of assimilation can be estimated roughly by adding known quantities of various organic compounds to soil and determining the per cent of the added substrate-carbon that is retained (15). The chemical nature of the organic material has a bearing on the magnitude of assimilation, but ultimately the carbon incorporated into newly generated microbial tissues will in turn be decomposed.

The fungal flora generally releases less CO_2 for each unit of carbon transformed aerobically than the other microbial groups because the fungi are more efficient in their metabolism. Efficiency is here considered as the effectiveness in converting substrate-carbon into cell-carbon and is commonly calculated from the ratio of cell-carbon formed to carbon source consumed, expressed as a percentage.

The more efficient the organism, the smaller the quantity of organic products and CO_2 released. Inefficient cultures, by contrast, lose most of the carbon as wastes and form little cell substance. By and large, filamentous fungi and actinomycetes exhibit a greater efficiency than aerobic bacteria although individual species vary greatly. Anaerobic bacteria utilize carbohydrates very inefficiently, leaving considerable carbonaceous products. Much of the energy in the original substance is not released by the anaerobes, and the incompletely oxidized compounds that are excreted may still be utilized for growth when air re-enters the habitat. During decomposition by fungi, some 30 to 40 per cent of the carbon metabolized is used to form new mycelium. Populations of aerobic bacteria, less efficient organisms, assimilate 5 to 10 per cent while anaerobic bacteria incorporate only about 2 to 5 per cent of the substrate-carbon into new cells (31).

At the same time as carbon is assimilated for the generation of new protoplasm, there is a concomitant uptake of nitrogen, phosphorus, potassium, and sulfur. Assimilation of inorganic substances can be of great practical significance because, agronomically, nutrient assimilation is an important means of *immobilization,* that is, a mechanism by which microorganisms reduce the quantity of plant-available nutrients in soil. Because microbiological immobilization is determined by the utilization of nutrient elements for cell synthesis, the magnitude of immobilization is proportional to the net quantity of microbial tissue formed and is related to carbon assimilation by a factor governed by the C:N, C:P, C:K, or C:S ratio of the newly generated protoplasm. For example, if the average cell composition of the microflora is taken as 50 per cent carbon and 5 per cent nitrogen, the nitrogen immobilized would be equal to one-tenth of the carbon going into the production of microbial cell substance.

The efficiency of cell synthesis is governed by environmental conditions, and it may vary over a considerable range. Organisms under one set of circumstances may liberate an end-product not produced in another situation; for example, acid or alkaline reactions frequently alter the type of products. At the low level of available nutrients associated with soil, one might expect that a microorganism must be efficient if it is to compete well, particularly if it happens to be a slow grower. Among the rapidly growing species as typified by many bacteria, on the other hand, inefficiency may not be a serious handicap.

Decomposition and Carbon Dioxide Evolution

The most important function of the microbial flora is usually considered to be the breakdown of organic materials, a process by which
the limited supply of CO_2 available for photosynthesis is replenished.
The number and diversity of compounds suitable for microbiological
decay are enormous. A host of organic acids, polysaccharides, lignins,
aromatic and aliphatic hydrocarbons, innumerable sugars, alcohols,
amino acids, purines, pyrimidines, proteins, lipids, and nucleic acids
undergo attack by one or another microorganism. Any compound
that is synthesized biologically is subject to destruction by the soil
inhabitants; otherwise these compounds would have accumulated in
vast amounts on the earth's surface. In addition to biosynthetic products, many of the compounds synthesized by the organic chemist are
readily decomposed.

Since organic carbon degradation is a property of all heterotrophs,
it is commonly used to indicate the level of microbial activity. Several techniques have been developed to measure decomposition rates.
These include (a) measurement of CO_2 evolution or O_2 uptake,
(b) determination of the decrease in organic matter either chemically or by weight loss, and (c) observation of the disappearance of
a specific constituent such as cellulose or lignin. The evolution of
CO_2 is usually measured by passing CO_2-free air over the surface of
a soil sample maintained at constant temperature. The CO_2 liberated enters the flowing air stream and can be estimated by gravi-
metric or volumetric means following absorption. Manometric procedures have also been adapted to the assay of organic matter decomposition. In the manometric technique, gas exchange is measured
in two respirometer flasks in the presence and absence of alkali. The
first flask detects O_2 uptake, the second O_2 uptake plus CO_2 evolution;
the difference between the manometers attached to the two flasks
gives the carbon mineralization rate (figure 1). In both the manometric and the flowing-air procedures, decomposition can be measured at
regular time intervals without physically disturbing the soil.

Three separate, simultaneous processes can be distinguished during organic matter transformations. First, plant and animal tissue
constituents disappear under the influence of microbial enzymes. At
the same time, new biological tissue appears, a synthesis of new microbial cells which brings about an increase in soil of the proteins, poly-

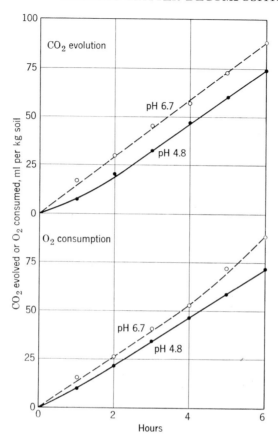

Figure 1. CO_2 production and O_2 consumption in unlimed and limed soil (23).

saccharides, and nucleic acids typical of bacterial and fungal proto-plasm. Third, certain end-products of the breakdown are excreted into the surroundings, there to accumulate or to be further metabolized.

The diversity of substrates and their chemical heterogeneity are staggering, but certain biochemical phenomena are universal in mi-crobial metabolism. An organism gets energy for growth only from reactions occurring within the confines of the cell so that, where the substrate is too large or complex to penetrate the cell surface, the compound first must be transformed into simpler molecules to allow the organism to derive energy from the oxidation. Insoluble polysac-charides are commonly hydrolyzed to soluble, simple compounds.

And, although the polysaccharides, proteins, aromatic substances, and other nutrients are quite dissimilar in their chemical and physical properties, following their initial degradation, the metabolic sequences concerned in the decomposition within the cell consist of the same general biochemical pathways. Regardless of the structural peculiarities of the starting material, the carbon in the substrate will ultimately be metabolized through the same steps and via the same intermediates. With molecules as different as cellulose, the hemicelluloses, proteins, pectin, starch, chitin, and aromatic hydrocarbons, the final steps in metabolism involve only a few simple sugars and organic acids. The initial stages alone differ, the steps transforming the original compounds into the common intermediates. This is the basis of the doctrine of comparative biochemistry, that there is a certain underlying unity in metabolic reactions.

Two decomposition processes are of significance to the present discussion: the decomposition of soil organic matter and the decay of added substrates. The decomposition of native organic matter (humus) reflects the biological availability of soil carbon while the release of CO_2 following the addition of relatively simple substrates is an estimation of the potential carbon-mineralizing capacity of the microflora. *Mineralization* is a convenient term used to designate the conversion of organic complexes of an element to the inorganic state. The two processes, the breakdown of humus and the decay of added carbonaceous materials, will be considered separately although the characteristics of the two are frequently similar.

Decomposition of Soil Organic Matter

The rate at which CO_2 is released during the mineralization of humus varies greatly with soil type. Under controlled conditions in the laboratory and at temperatures maintained in the mesophilic ranges, 20 to 30°C, the rate of CO_2 production is commonly from 5 to 50 mg CO_2 per kg soil per day, but figures of 300 mg or more are occasionally encountered. The range of 5 to 50 mg in the laboratory is equivalent to 10 to 100 lb per acre per day although values of 20 to 30 lb are more common in the field during the warm season of the year. These results are those observed under normal, undisturbed conditions. On the other hand, when a soil sample is air dried and then remoistened, there is a spurt in CO_2 evolution which lasts for several days followed by a decline to a lower rate of carbon mineralization (11). Using the figure of 20 lb CO_2 volatilized per acre per day as a mean value for the four warm months of the year, it can be calculated that about 2500 lb of CO_2 are lost to the atmosphere for each acre, an appreciable microbial activity and a significant portion of the total organic matter present. From field data, it is possible to demonstrate that about 2 to 5 per cent of the carbon present in humus can be mineralized per annum, but the figures vary appreciably in different localities.

The major factors governing humus decomposition are the organic matter level of the soil, cultivation, temperature, moisture, pH, depth, and aeration. It is evident that those environmental influences which affect microbial growth and metabolism will modify the rate at which either native organic matter or added compounds are transformed. The decomposition of soil organic matter can be differentiated from the decay of added substances by the addition of C^{14}-tagged materials to soil and measurement of the radioactivity of the CO_2 released. Carbon from added substrates is recovered as CO_2-C^{14}, that from humus as the unlabeled carbon.

The magnitude of carbon mineralization is directly related to the organic carbon content of the soil; that is, the release of CO_2 is proportional to the organic matter level. A similarly high correlation is noted between the percentage of humus and the O_2 uptake. The results of table 1 show that approximately the same percentage of the total organic carbon is mineralized at various depths except in the surface samples that had recently received vegetative remains.

The production of CO_2 is also influenced by the addition of organic materials. Applications of barnyard manure and plant residues typically stimulate CO_2 release, but until the introduction of radio-isotopes into agricultural research, it was not possible to ascertain whether the additional CO_2 arose largely from the decomposition of added carbonaceous materials or from humus. However, by adding substances labeled with C^{14} to distinguish between the two organic matter sources, it has been clearly demonstrated that the supplemental carbon speeds up humus mineralization (4). Presumably, the large population that builds up in response to the added substrate turns upon the humus components and brings about the greater rate of decay.

Cultivation enhances organic matter destruction. For example, after 25 or more years of cropping, the mean organic matter content of 28 soils of Georgia had decreased from 3.29 to 1.43 per cent, a loss of more than half. After a rapid decline of the organic carbon level

TABLE 1

The Effect of Depth on Carbon Mineralization in Marshall Silt Loam (20)

Depth of Sample	Soil Organic Carbon	CO_2 Formed	Soil Carbon Oxidized
in.	%	mg/14 days	%
0–2	3.72 *	564 *	4.3 *
2–5	2.41	121	1.4
5–8	1.94	73	1.1
8–12	1.42	66	1.4
12–16	1.00	46	1.3
16–20	0.70	37	1.5
24–30	0.42	19	1.3
36–43	0.27	14	1.5
50–58	0.28	13	1.4

* Contains recent grass residues.

in the first few years, the decrease becomes more gradual with further cultivation. In one sandy loam, for example, a virgin forest soil contained 2.30 per cent organic matter, but the concentration had fallen to 1.59 per cent after 3 years of cultivation (10).

Temperature, moisture, and reaction are also critical environmental variables. Humus decomposition can proceed at temperatures down to the freezing point, but it is accelerated by increasing temperatures. Moisture level likewise affects soil respiration, and the environment must contain sufficient water for maximum microbiological action. Other factors being equal, carbon mineralization is most rapid in neutral to slightly alkaline soils. As expected, therefore, liming acid soils enhances carbon volatilization (figure 1).

The greatest rate of CO_2 evolution occurs near the surface of the profile where the highest concentration of plant remains is found. At greater depths, the rate of CO_2 production diminishes, and little is volatilized at depths of 2 to 4 ft (table 1). This decrease in activity parallels the drop in the organic carbon level so that the proportion of the total carbon oxidized in a given time interval remains relatively constant.

One of the major microbiological changes in organic soils is the phenomenon of subsidence, wherein the soil itself shrinks through biological decomposition. The subsidence is of great practical importance since it leads to loss of agricultural productivity and to problems in road construction and maintenance. Subsidence may range from 0.1 to more than 3 in. per year. Although the major cause appears to be biological, wind erosion and physical shrinkage contribute to the effect. Because of the economic problems arising from the subsidence of organic soils, considerable attention has been given to the factors affecting the process (4, 27).

Some insight can be gained into the biochemistry of humus breakdown by a consideration of the products formed. Most intermediates in the decomposition of the soil organic fraction are probably metabolized as quickly as they are produced since the rate-limiting step in the breakdown is undoubtedly the attack on the complex molecules of humus. In well-drained soils, acids and alcohols are probably formed, but these are readily metabolized by aerobic bacteria, actinomycetes, and fungi. Schwartz, Varner, and Martin (24) examined the organic acids of several gray-brown podzolic soils of Ohio. They noted that acetic and formic acids were present in quantities far in excess of all other simple organic acids. Acetic acid was found to the extent of 0.73 to 1.08 meq per 100 g of soil whereas formic acid was detected in smaller amounts, 0.51 to 0.87 meq per 100 g. Traces of lactic and succinic acids in roughly equivalent amounts were also demonstrated (table 2). The addition of glucose neither altered the type

TABLE 2

Organic Acids Present in Various Soils (24)

Soil	Meq Acid/100 g of Soil			
	Group 1 *	Acetic	Formic	Group 2 †
Brookston silty clay loam	0.02	1.08	0.70	0.02
Crosby silt loam	0.03	0.97	0.64	0.02
Miami silt loam	0.04	0.73	0.51	0.02
Wooster silt loam	0.03	0.75	0.87	0.03

* Probably long-chain fatty acids.
† Lactic and succinic acids.

of organic acids found nor did it appreciably affect their concentrations. There is as yet no adequate explanation of why acetic and formic are the only two organic acids of consequence.

Simple substrates that are added to soil are readily metabolized but always with an apparent lag period prior to the maximal oxidation rate. The lag represents the time necessary for the population to increase to an extent sufficient to cause rapid organic matter turnover. Ethanol, however, is oxidized readily with no preliminary lag. This anomalous characteristic of ethanol decomposition has been reported in a number of soil types. A break in the rate of ethanol oxidation does occur when the amount of gas consumed is equivalent to 1 mole O_2 for each mole of ethanol, a ratio which suggests the accumulation of acetic acid.

$$CH_3CH_2OH + O_2 \rightarrow CH_3COOH + H_2O \qquad (I)$$

Acetate is also oxidized without a lag period, but the activity quickly declines (26). Since ethanol and acetate are metabolized immediately, it seems likely that the autochthonous population is adapted to these substrates through repeated and frequent encounters. Thus, the two compounds are probably continuously formed and metabolized. Should this indeed be true, ethanol and acetate would be natural intermediates in humus decomposition.

Breakdown of Added Carbonaceous Materials

A number of factors affect the mineralization of added organic materials. The rapidity with which a given substrate is oxidized will depend upon its chemical composition and the physical and chemical conditions in the surrounding environment. Temperature, O_2 supply, moisture, pH, available minerals, and the C:N ratio of the plant residue are the chief environmental influences. The age of the plant, its lignin content, and the degree of disintegration of the substrate presented to the microflora also govern the decomposition. As with humus breakdown, those factors which affect microbial growth and metabolism will alter the rate of decay of added plant or animal remains.

Temperature is one of the most important environmental conditions determining how rapidly natural materials are metabolized. A change in temperature will alter the species composition of the active flora and at the same time have a direct influence upon each organism within the population. Microbial metabolism and hence carbon mineralization is slower at low than at elevated temperatures, and warming is associated with greater CO_2 release. Appreciable organic matter breakdown occurs at 5°C and probably at cooler values, but plant tissue rotting is increased with progressively warmer conditions; the individual constituents of the plant also disappear more rapidly. Moreover, increasing the temperature shortens the time required before the maximum rate of CO_2 evolution is attained (3).

Each individual microbial species and the biochemical capacities of the population as a whole have temperature optima. Because the composition of the flora varies from locality to locality and is altered even in a single site treated with different plant residues, a single optimum for organic matter breakdown cannot be found. Thus, there are reports that the maximum rates of decay of carbonaceous nutrients take place at 30 to 35, at 37, and at 40°C. In the vicinity of the optimum, taken at about 30 to 40°C, temperature fluctuation has little effect on decomposition. In the range below the optimum, generally from 5 to 30°C, rising temperature accelerates plant residue destruction. Above about 40°C, the rapidity of decomposition declines except in those special circumstances where thermophilic decay is initiated.

Air supply likewise governs the extent and rate of dissimilation of added substrates. This effect is a consequence of the role of O_2 in microbial metabolism. Carbon dioxide is released from completely anaerobic systems through the activities of the obligate and facultative anaerobes, but aeration invariably stimulates carbon mineralization. For example, Acharya (1) demonstrated that the decomposition of rice straw is most rapid aerobically, slower in waterlogged conditions, and least pronounced under complete anaerobiasis. The decay of the major plant constituents is affected in the same way, i.e., the processes are depressed as the supply of O_2 diminishes.

Moisture too must be adequate for decomposition to proceed. Microorganisms grow readily in liquid culture media provided the O_2 supply is ample; in soil, on the other hand, high moisture levels reduce microbial activities not as a result of the water itself but rather indirectly, by hindering the movement of air and thus reducing the O_2 supply. Hence, when an increase in moisture is observed to stimulate CO_2 release, water is limiting; however, if additional water reduces the rate of transformation, then there is a deficiency of O_2. At low moisture, supplemental water has a profound influence on decay while similar additions at moisture levels near the optimum result in

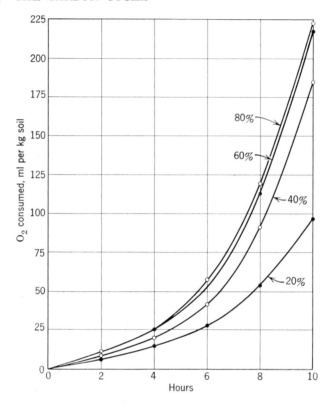

Figure 2. The influence of moisture on O_2 uptake by soil treated with a mixture of amino acids. Moisture expressed as percentage of water-holding capacity (14).

little change. Respiration of the soil microflora developing at the expense of simple or complex organic nutrients is commonly greatest at about 60 to 80 per cent of the water-holding capacity of the soil (figure 2).

Another major factor determining the rate of carbon turnover is the hydrogen ion concentration. Each bacterium, fungus, and actinomycete has an optimum pH for growth and a range outside of which no cell proliferation takes place. In addition, individual enzymes elaborated by a single microbial strain are affected by reaction. Not only does pH determine the growth rates and enzymatic potentialities of individuals making up the microflora, but it also governs the type of microorganisms concerned in the carbon cycle of any habitat. Decomposition typically proceeds more readily in neutral than in acid soils. Consequently, the treatment of acid soils with lime accelerates the decay of plant tissues, simple carbonaceous compounds or native soil organic matter.

Nitrogen is a key nutrient substance for microbial growth and hence for organic matter breakdown. Plant and animal tissues always contain some nitrogen, but its availability and amount vary greatly. If the nitrogen content of the substrate is high and the element is readily utilized, the microflora satisfies its needs from this source, and additional quantities are unnecessary. If the substrate is poor in the element, decomposition is slow, and carbon mineralization will be stimulated by supplemental nitrogen. In the latter circumstances, nitrogenous amendments cause an increase in CO_2 evolution and a greater loss of cellulose, hemicelluloses, and other plant polysaccharides. Nitrogen-rich materials such as legumes or blood meal are metabolized very rapidly, and the microflora responds little if at all to supplemental nitrogen while the addition of ammonium or nitrate to straw or other nitrogen-deficient substrates greatly enhances decomposition. Differing from mineral soils where the level of available nitrogen is usually too low to allow for maximum rates of carbohydrate breakdown, application of inorganic nitrogen salts to peats does not stimulate glucose decomposition, suggesting a large reserve in the organic soils (27).

Despite the greater carbon loss from the soil as a result of nitrogen treatment of protein-poor crop residues, humus formation is benefited. The explanation for this observation rests upon the fact that plant residues remain partly decomposed for long periods of time if nitrogen is lacking, and they do not become converted to humus (22). Yet, though applied nitrogen commonly stimulates the rate of residue breakdown, the total quantity of CO_2 ultimately liberated is the same with or without the supplement. The limited inorganic nutrient supply is merely recirculated through successive populations.

A number of investigators have reported that the rate of decomposition of plant materials depends upon the nitrogen content of the tissues, protein-rich substrates being metabolized most readily (18). This can be seen if plant residues are arranged in order of decreasing rates of mineralization: sweet clover (3.14 per cent nitrogen); alfalfa (3.07 per cent); a group containing red clover (2.20 per cent), soybeans (1.85 per cent), millet (1.17 per cent), and flax (1.73 per cent); another group decayed even less quickly containing hemp (0.88 per cent), corn stalks (1.20 per cent), cane sorghum (0.87 per cent), and sudan grass (1.06 per cent); and lastly wheat and oat straw with 0.50 and 0.61 per cent nitrogen. Such observations are not unexpected in view of the high nitrogen demands of the microbial population. Because crop plants generally contain about the same amount of carbon, usually about 40 per cent of the dry weight, their nitrogen contents can be compared by use of the C:N ratio. Thus, a low nitrogen content or a wide C:N ratio is associated with slow decay.

Generalizations of this sort must nevertheless be accepted with some reservation as it is not easy to determine the precise causal relationship of the enhanced decay. Other factors are operating in addition to nitrogen. For example, the report that tissues of young plants are metabolized faster than mature tissue apparently substantiates the nitrogen or C:N ratio hypothesis for velocity of decomposition because the immature plants have a higher nitrogen content. But a complete chemical investigation shows changes in other plant constituents as well; e.g., maturation is accompanied by lignification and related alterations. Thus, the slower release of CO_2 from rotting natal grass than from crotalaria is not a result solely of the lower nitrogen content of the former since additions of nitrogen never allow for natal grass to be decomposed as quickly. Crotalaria, however, contains a smaller quantity of hemicellulose, lignin, and cellulosic constituents than natal grass, and these constituents may affect the decay (9). Hence, the nitrogen content or C:N ratio of plant residues frequently is a convenient tool for predicting the rate of decomposition, yet it is not the sole determinant.

During the mineralization of materials containing little nitrogen, the C:N ratio tends to decrease with time (figure 3). This results from the gaseous loss of carbon while the nitrogen remains more tightly bound in organic combination for as long as the C:N ratio is wide. Therefore, the percentage of nitrogen in the residual substance continuously rises as decomposition progresses. The narrowing of the ratio in the decay of nitrogen-poor substrates is not linear, the curve approaching a ratio of approximately 10:1 asymptotically.

The C:N ratio of soil is one of its characteristic equilibrium values, the figure for humus being roughly 10:1 although values from 5:1 to 15:1 are not uncommon. This critical ratio is a reflection of the dynamic equilibrium that results from the dominating presence of a microbiological population, the ratio being similar to the average chemical composition of microbial cells. As a rule, microbial protoplasm contains 5 to 15 parts of carbon to 1 part of nitrogen, but 10:1 is a reasonable average for the predominant aerobic flora. A

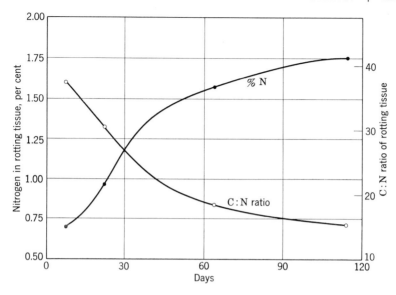

Figure 3. Changes in the nitrogen content of decomposing barley straw (13).

change in the population brought about by anaerobiasis or the accumulation of fractions resistant to further decay can modify the C:N equilibrium value of humus.

Consider the incorporation into soil of a residue having a wide C:N ratio. The microflora carrying out the decomposition will develop to the extent of the available mineral and nitrogen supply, and all the immediately available nitrogen will be assimilated and bound in organic complexes. Assuming that the aerobic population contains 50 per cent carbon and 5 per cent nitrogen and assimilates one-third of the substrate-carbon, then 1 unit of available nitrogen incorporated into cell material will allow for the assimilation of 10 units of cell-carbon but will be accompanied by the volatilization of 20 units of CO_2-carbon. In this first stage, no nitrogen is lost because the demand exceeds the supply, but CO_2 is released, and the C:N ratio narrows. As the primary population dies and is itself decomposed, the nitrogen liberated will be assimilated by a secondary flora which then synthesizes 10 times more microbial carbon and volatilizes 20 times more CO_2-carbon than nitrogen made available. The C:N ratio is narrowed further. This process is repeated until the equilibrium C:N ratio is attained, ca. 10:1. At this point, the organic nitrogen that becomes mineralized is no longer necessary for microbial growth, and it remains in the mineral form. Henceforth, nitrogen and carbon mineralization run parallel, and the humus C:N ratio has at this stage reached the value determined largely by the chemistry of the microbial cell.

Natural materials rich in lignin are less readily utilized by microorganisms than lignin-poor products. It is not uncommon to find that the rates of decay of plant debris are proportional to their content of lignin. In like fashion, mineralization of various chemical fractions prepared from oat straw is related directly to the percentage of lignin in the fractions (21). The suggestion has therefore been made that the quantity of lignin in plant residues is of greater importance in predicting decomposition velocity than the C:N ratio (22). The resistance of wood and sawdust to microbial attack is probably linked to the abundance of lignin in such materials.

Young, succulent tissues are metabolized more readily than residues of mature plants. As the plant ages, its chemical composition changes; the content of nitrogen, proteins, and water-soluble substances falls, and the proportion of cellulose, lignin, and hemicelluloses rises. Although aging makes the vegetation more resistant to decay, the changes with age of many individual constituents have prevented a final explanation of the precise reason for the effect. A large part of the resistance associated with aging probably is a consequence of the abundance of lignin, but other factors may also be operative.

Changes during Organic Matter Decomposition

In studies of decomposition, the entire plant residue, extracted tissue constituents, or pure organic compounds may be utilized. The various techniques each have their values since every material is metabolized in a different way and by dissimilar populations.

As a result of the development of a mixed flora on chemically complex natural products, some components quickly disappear while others are less susceptible to microbial enzymes and persist. The water-soluble fraction contains the least resistant plant components and is thus the first to be metabolized. As a result, in those green manures in which 20 to 40 per cent of the dry matter is water-soluble, decomposition proceeds rapidly. Cellulose and hemicelluloses, on the other hand, disappear not as quickly as the water-soluble substances, but their persistence is not too great. The oxidation of cellulose and hemicelluloses in rotting plants proceeds at roughly parallel rates. The lignins are highly resistant and consequently become relatively more abundant in the residual, decaying organic matter.

In succulent tissue and in plowed-under green manures, the bulk of the organic matter lost during decay is derived from the cellulosic, hemicellulosic, and water-soluble constituents. In contrast, the major part of the weight loss in woody materials results from the disappearance of cellulose. The magnitude of dry matter loss is reduced under anaerobiasis, but here too the percentage of sugars, water-soluble constituents, and cellulose declines and the percentage of lignin rises with time (5). The metabolism of the highly available carbohydrates of the plant residue is accompanied by a qualitative alteration in the chemical composition of the remaining portion since the character of the organic matter is now dominated by the newly formed microbial cells and by those plant fractions exhibiting the greatest resistance to attack, for example, aromatic substances related to and possibly derived from lignin.

Other modifications take place in the organic matter as it undergoes decomposition. With straw, for example, the original bright coloration is modified to a dark gray, a change requiring 1 to 2 months in the field. The volume occupied by the straw decreases, and the strength of the fibers diminishes, probably because of the digestion of the wall structure of the fibrovascular bundles (17). The data presented in table 3 demonstrate that the hydroxyl content of the remaining residue declines while the carboxyl content and cation exchange capacity rise as rotting progresses. Residues remaining after prolonged decomposition of cellulose or glucose contain little lignified carbon whereas tissues rich in lignin yield a decayed fraction containing a high concentration of lignin-like substances (21).

When carbonaceous substrates are incorporated into the soil, there is an immediate and marked drop in the O_2 and an increase in the CO_2 content of the soil air; at the same time, the oxidation-reduction potential (E_h) is shifted to a more reduced condition. The rate and magnitude of the increase in reducing power varies with the substrate added. A similar fall in oxidation-reduction potential and disappearance of dissolved O_2 takes place in flooded soil. If a readily available carbohydrate is added to the waterlogged field, the drop in oxidation-reduction potential is accelerated, yet, should the sample receiving the organic compounds be sterilized immediately, no difference in potential would be detected between treated and control

TABLE 3

Changes in Properties of Oat Straw during Decomposition
(6)

Days of Incubation	Lignin	Hydroxyl	Chemical Properties, meq/100 g	
			Carboxyl Content	Cation Exchange Capacity
	%	%		
0	19.3	7.40	28	25
14	21.8	5.94	24	26
40	28.0	8.03	81	42
88	30.8	5.29	95	47
135	34.3	5.48	113	58
180	39.4	5.59	142	60
244	38.3	4.69	139	81
355	37.6	4.62	139	82

samples, regardless of flooding. Consequently, microorganisms cause the change in E_h through the consumption of O_2 and the liberation of reduced products.

The quantity and type of clay in a soil have a bearing upon carbon mineralization because clays adsorb many organic substrates, extra-cellular carbohydrate-splitting enzymes produced by microorganisms, and even bacterial cells. Bentonite has a marked carbon-retaining capacity, and decomposition is suppressed in its presence, but other clays have similar effects (2). The addition of kaolinite or illite to culture media inoculated with soil enrichments has no protective action against decomposition. Montmorillonite, however, retards microbial degradation of casein, gelatin, cellulose dextrins, soybean leaf meal, alfalfa meal, and hydroxyethylcellulose, but montmorillonite is ineffective in depressing the mineralization of a number of other substances (16).

It has been pointed out that treatment of soil with plant residues enhances the rate of humus breakdown. The greater the addition rate, the greater the loss of humus. Not only is there a decrease in native organic matter but sometimes there is a net loss in carbon; i.e., less carbon is occasionally present in amended soils after 4 to

8 months than in the original sample. These facts may explain some of the field observations of lack of organic carbon accumulation following the plowing down of green manure crops. The more readily decomposable residues would probably produce the greater acceleration in humus decay (7, 11).

Anaerobic Carbon Mineralization

The main products of aerobic carbon mineralization are CO_2, water, and cells. In the absence of O_2, organic carbon is incompletely metabolized, intermediary substances accumulate, and abundant quantities of CH_4 and smaller amounts of H_2 are evolved. At the same time, the energy yield during anaerobic fermentation is low, resulting in the formation of fewer microbial cells per unit of organic carbon degraded. Consequently, organic matter breakdown is consistently slower under total anaerobiasis than in environments containing adequate O_2; the rate in waterlogged soils is intermediate between the two extremes.

TABLE 4

The Effect of Waterlogging on Various Microbiological Processes in Soil (30)

| Days | E_h | Bacteria/g $\times$ 10^3 | | ml Gas/100 g of Soil | | | |
		Aerobes *	Anaerobes *	O_2	CH_4	H_2	CO_2
	volts						
0	0.45	34,000	22,000	3.2	0.0	0.0	83
1	0.22	220,000	—	0.3	0.0	0.0	10
2	−0.05	110,000	23,000	0.0	0.0	0.2	172
4.5	−0.23	55,000	50,000	0.0	0.3	0.0	—
6				0.0	2.2	3.6	280
8	−0.25	53,000	170,000	0.0	14.7	2.1	—
10				0.0	21.4	0.0	226
13	−0.25	62,000	130,000				
23				0.0	60.3	13.2	—

* Includes facultative anaerobes.

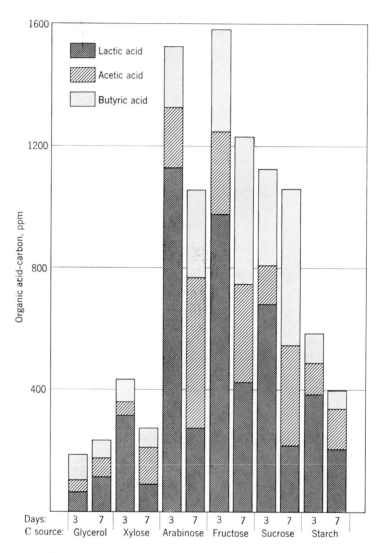

Figure 4. Production of organic acids from various carbon sources applied to waterlogged soil (28).

When a soil is waterlogged or completely flooded, there is a shift from aerobic to anaerobic transformations. This is reflected by the data of table 4. As O_2 disappears, CH_4 and H_2 appear in addition to CO_2. In practice, the amount of CH_4 is frequently great, but the quantity of H_2 is invariably small. In flooded paddy fields and in other waterlogged environments, much of the carbon mineralization is anaerobic although O_2 is present to some extent. In addition, O_2 may be formed biologically by the algae developing in the liquid phase (12). Where sufficient available carbohydrates are present, most of the O_2 is utilized before it penetrates too deeply in the liquid-mud layer, and the transformation at the lower depths is almost entirely anaerobic.

Organic acids accumulate because of the fermentative character of the microflora of wet soils. In flooded fields, the dominant acids are acetic and formic (29), a condition resembling that in well-drained soils. In contrast, however, lactic, acetic, and butyric acids are detected in the solution phase when simple carbohydrates are applied to flooded soils (figure 4). Lactic acid is the first major product of anaerobic fermentation, but it is soon transformed to other compounds, chiefly acetic and butyric acids. The latter two acids, though present initially in low concentration, increase in amount with prolonged incubation. The organic acids rather than the sugars serve as the substrates for the bacteria which produce the CH_4 in these habitats. Anaerobic carbon transformations are thus characterized by the formation of organic acids, CH_4, and CO_2 as major end-products.

Flora

The amount, type, and availability of organic matter will determine the size and composition of the heterotrophic population that a soil will contain. The nature of the flora will vary with the chemical composition of the added substrates, certain microbial groups predominating for a few days, others maintaining high population levels for long periods. Each individual organism has a complex of enzymes which permits it to oxidize a fixed array of chemical compounds, but no others. If the proper substances are present in an accessible state, then the microorganism will proliferate, providing that it can cope with the competition of other organisms having similar enzymatic potentials.

The microorganisms preferentially stimulated by the components of added carbonaceous substances make up the primary flora. A secondary flora also develops, one growing upon compounds produced by the primary agents or growing upon the dead or living cells of the initial flora. This succeeding group of organisms has a different biochemical make-up from those appearing initially. The population responding to organic carbon amendments thus feeds upon (a) the organic substrates added, (b) intermediates formed during decomposition, and (c) the protoplasm of microorganisms active in the degradation of a or b.

When succulent green manures are incorporated into the soil, the abundance of bacteria around and within the buried tissues increases rapidly. A rise in bacterial numbers only occurs directly upon the plant substance, the populations here reaching 10^{10} per gram in the first week while the viable counts of bacteria in the adjacent soil are not markedly altered. By the seventh day, the bacterial numbers begin to decline, falling to a point where the counts are essentially the same as in unamended soil. There is a concomitant rise followed by a subsequent diminution in the numbers of protozoa, the changes paralleling the bacterial fluctuations (25). Plate counts of fungi and actinomycetes, however, seem to be little affected by turning under green manures.

Mature crop residues, having a distinctly different chemical composition from green manures, support a flora better adapted to utilize resistant carbonaceous compounds. This population is largely fungal although bacteria and actinomycetes also are stimulated to some extent. In their study of the response of the microflora to crop residues, Dawson and coworkers (8) demonstrated significant increases in fungi, bacteria, and actinomycetes; the effects on the three groups were significantly correlated with one another. The use of a mulch likewise increased the populations of fungi, bacteria, and actinomycetes, the response being proportional to the amount of straw.

Microscopic studies of the microflora in situ have demonstrated that the addition of simple sugars results in rapid bacterial proliferation while starch benefits the actinomycetes and cellulose affects fungal development in particular. Substrates rich in proteins or amino acids such as blood meal or peptone stimulate the spore-forming bacilli (19, 32). The flora concerned in humus decomposition differs from that concerned with the breakdown of freshly added plant materials, and these floral differences are the basis for the separation between zymogenous and autochthonous organisms.

The relationship between microbial numbers and CO_2 evolution has still not been fully resolved. Because the abundance of microorganisms depends upon the presence of available carbonaceous and energy materials, a correlation between microbial numbers and CO_2 release might be expected and is sometimes observed. Yet, reports to the contrary are not lacking. If the carbon source were homogeneous and the population composed of a single species, a definite relationship might be clear. But, with the diversity of microbial types and the variety of carbon sources, a poor correlation between numbers and CO_2 formation is not surprising. Moreover, even in the development of bacteria in pure culture, there is no clear relation between population density and activity in the late stages of growth. In unamended soils, the bacteria are largely not in the active phases of growth, and CO_2 production is thus rarely proportional to the size of the viable population. Only with rapid increases in microbial numbers is a clear association to be expected.

REFERENCES

1. Acharya, C. N. 1935. *Biochem. J.,* 29:1116–1120.
2. Allison, F. E., M. S. Sherman, and L. A. Pinck. 1949. *Soil Sci.,* 68:463–478.
3. Bartholomew, W. V., and A. G. Norman. 1946. *Soil Sci. Soc. Am., Proc.,* 11:270–279.
4. Bingeman, C. W., J. E. Varner, and W. P. Martin. 1953. *Soil Sci. Soc. Am., Proc.,* 17:34–38.
5. Boruff, C. S., and A. M. Buswell. 1930. *Ind. Eng. Chem.,* 22:931–933.
6. Broadbent, F. E. 1954. *Soil Sci. Soc. Am., Proc.,* 18:165–169.
7. Broadbent, F. E., and W. V. Bartholomew. 1948. *Soil Sci. Soc. Am., Proc.,* 13:271–274.
8. Dawson, R. C., V. T. Dawson, and T. M. McCalla. 1948. *Neb. Agric. Expt. Sta. Research Bulletin 155.*
9. Dyal, R. S., F. B. Smith, and R. V. Allison. 1939. *J. Am. Soc. Agron.,* 31:841–850.
10. Giddens, J. 1957. *Soil Sci. Soc. Am., Proc.,* 21:513–515.
11. Hallam, M. J., and W. V. Bartholomew. 1953. *Soil Sci. Soc. Am., Proc.,* 17:365–368.
12. Harrison, W. H., and P. A. S. Aiyer. 1913. *Mem., Dept. Agric. India, Chem. Ser.,* 3:65–106.
13. Hende, A. van den, A. Cottenie, and R. de Vlieghere. 1952. *Trans. Intl. Soc. Soil Sci., Comm. II and IV,* 2:37–47.
14. Katznelson, H., and I. L. Stevenson. 1956. *Canad. J. Microbiol.,* 2:611–622.
15. Lees, H., and J. W. Porteous. 1950. *Plant and Soil,* 2:231–241.
16. Lynch, D. L., and L. J. Cotnoir. 1956. *Soil Sci. Soc. Am., Proc.,* 20:367–370.
17. McCalla, T. M. 1943. *Soil Sci. Soc. Am., Proc.,* 8:258–262.

18. Millar, H. C., F. B. Smith, and P. E. Brown. 1936. *J. Am. Soc. Agron.*, 28: 914–923.
19. Mollenhoff, H. H., F. B. Smith, and P. E. Brown. 1936. *Proc. Iowa Acad. Sci.*, 43:117–121.
20. Newman, A. S., and A. G. Norman. 1941. *Soil Sci. Soc. Am., Proc.*, 6:187–194.
21. Peevy, W. J., and A. G. Norman. 1948. *Soil Sci.*, 65:209–226.
22. Pinck, L. A., F. E. Allison, and M. S. Sherman. 1950. *Soil Sci.*, 69:391–401.
23. Rovira, A. D. 1953. *Nature*, 172:29–30.
24. Schwartz, S. M., J. E. Varner, and W. P. Martin. 1954. *Soil Sci. Soc. Am., Proc.*, 18:174–177.
25. Smith, N. R., and H. Humfield. 1930. *Proc. Comm. III, 2nd Intl. Cong. Soil Sci.*, Leningrad, pp. 181–182.
26. Stevenson, I. L., and H. Katznelson. 1958. *Canad. J. Microbiol.*, 4:73–79.
27. Stotzky, G., and J. L. Mortensen. 1957. *Soil Sci.*, 83:165–174.
28. Subrahmanyan, V. 1929. *J. Agric. Sci.*, 19:627–648.
29. Takai, Y., and T. Koyama. 1956. *J. Sci. Soil Manure*, 26:509–512.
30. Takai, Y., T. Koyama, and T. Kamura. 1956. *Soil and Plant Food*, 2:63–66.
31. Waksman, S. A. 1929. *J. Am. Soc. Agron.*, 21:1–18.
32. Winogradsky, S. 1924. *Compt. Rend. Acad. Sci.*, 178:1236–1239.

10

Microbiology of Cellulose

A prominent carbonaceous constituent of higher plants and probably the most abundant organic compound in nature is cellulose. Because a large part of the vegetation added to soil is cellulosic, the decomposition of this carbohydrate has a special significance in the biological cycle of carbon. As a result, considerable attention has been given to the microorganisms participating in the decomposition of this substance.

In structure, cellulose is a carbohydrate composed of glucose units bound together in a long, linear chain by β-linkages at carbon atoms 1 and 4 of the sugar molecule. Most evidence suggests that there are between 1400 and 10,000 glucose residues in the molecule, but the number of sugar units per chain and the molecular weight of cellulose vary with the plant species. Molecular weight determinations give values ranging from 200,000 to almost 2 million.

Cellulose occurs in seed-bearing plants, in the algae, and in many of the fungi. The polysaccharide is localized in the cell wall where it is found not as simple chains but rather as submicroscopic rod-shaped units known as micelles. The micelles in turn are further arranged into a larger structure, the microfibril, which may contain 10 to 20 micelles. In the cell wall, the cellulose probably is organized into discrete units separated by a space, which in mature tissue is often filled with lignin. A number of polysaccharides are also associated with the cellulose of the plant cell wall. These include xylans, mannans, and polyuronides, but arabans and galactans are sometimes found in small quantities. The polysaccharides that are structurally linked with the cellulose of the cell wall have been termed *cellulosans*.

The cellulose content of higher plants is never fixed, and the concentration changes with age and type of plant. The carbohydrate is especially prominent in woody substances and in straw, stubble, and leaves. Succulent tissues are commonly poor in cellulose, but the concentration increases as the plant matures. In young grasses and legumes, for example, cellulose may account for as little as 15 per cent of the dry weight, but the figure may be greater than 50 per cent in woody materials. A concentration range of 15 to 40 per cent includes most of the common crop species, the lower extreme being typical of younger plants.

Both starch and cellulose are polymers of the same building block, glucose, but the individual peculiarities of the two molecules permit ready microbial attack of the former substance while the latter is far more resistant to microbiological and enzymatic breakdown. Further, because of their structural differences, the two carbohydrates stimulate entirely different populations.

Factors Governing Decomposition

The rate at which cellulose is metabolized is governed by a number of environmental influences, and soils varying in their physical and chemical characteristics possess markedly different cellulolytic capacities. The major environmental factors affecting the transformation are the available nitrogen level, temperature, aeration, moisture, pH, the presence of other carbohydrates, and the relative proportion of lignin in the residue. Modifications in the physical and chemical characteristics of the habitat can alter either the composition of the microflora or the cellulose-degrading activity of individual organisms.

The application of inorganic nitrogen enhances cellulose breakdown in soil, either ammonium or nitrate salts serving as suitable sources of the element. The rate of decomposition is proportional to the concentration of nitrogen added, but at high application rates, where there is more inorganic nitrogen than needed, cellulose decomposition does not respond to supplemental increments (figure 1). The point at which additional quantities are no longer beneficial is at a ratio of ca. 1 part of inorganic nitrogen for each 35 parts of cellulose. Manure and organic nitrogen compounds such as urea, amino acids, peptone, and casein also increase the conversion rate (1). The effect of animal manure seems to result from its nitrogen contribution because a similar stimulation is noted when equivalent quantities of am-

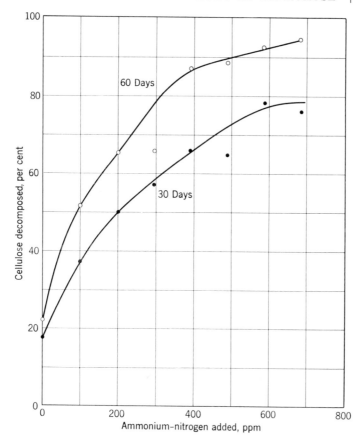

Figure 1. The requirement for nitrogen in cellulose decomposition. Cellulose added to soil at rate of 1.5 per cent (1).

monium salts are used. The existence of a response to this element suggests that the nitrogen level in soil is limiting. Indeed, it has been proposed that the supply of available nitrogen can be estimated from the quantity of CO_2 evolved when soils are treated with cellulose.

That available nitrogen is a critical factor is apparent from the correlations observed between the cellulose degradation rates and the nitrogen-mineralizing capacity and nitrate content of soil (17). The finding that approximately 1 unit of nitrogen is required for each 35 units of cellulose oxidized suggests that 3 parts of nitrogen are incorporated into microbial protoplasm for 100 parts of cellulose decomposed. Assuming that microbial cells contain 5 to 10 per cent nitrogen on a dry weight basis, then 30 to 60 parts of biologically active tissue are synthesized during the aerobic degradation of 100 parts of cellulose. In nature, of course, nutrient elements are continuously recycled as the microorganisms themselves are decomposed; therefore, far more of the polysaccharide is degraded than the available nitrogen supply could account for.

There is no correlation between cellulose mineralization and the level of available phosphorus nor is there a stimulation if phosphorus is added to soils low in available phosphate (17, 18). Apparently, the supply of this mineral is rarely inadequate for microbiological cellulose digestion.

The biological utilization of cellulose can proceed from temperatures near freezing to a point which is approximately the maximum for life, essentially from 5 to 65°C. Each of the variety of cellulolytic organisms is affected differently by temperature. Mesophiles dominate at moderate temperatures while a thermophilic microflora adapted to hotter localities can bring about a rapid cellulose dissimilation above 45°C. In addition to temperature-induced changes in the composition of the flora, warming increases the velocity of substrate turnover because of the direct effect of temperature upon enzyme action.

Aeration likewise governs the composition of the active flora, aerobes dominating oxygenated environments and anaerobic bacteria being favored by decreasing partial pressures of O_2. Because of the energetics of anaerobic processes, the rate of cellulose metabolism in environments deficient in O_2 is significantly reduced by comparison with aerated habitats. Oxygen disappears at high soil moisture levels so that poor drainage is associated with proliferation of the anaerobic cellulolytic bacteria while the numbers of fungi and actinomycetes utilizing cellulose decline. At moderate moisture levels, conditions are conducive to growth of the cellulolytic fungi and aerobic bacteria although certain strains tolerate suboptimal moisture.

In environments of neutral to alkaline pH, many microorganisms are capable of growing and liberating the appropriate enzymes for the hydrolysis of the polysaccharide; at acid reaction, the disappearance of cellulose is mediated largely by filamentous fungi. Although the process is rapid below pH 5.0 and occasionally below 4.0, soils with lower hydrogen ion concentrations degrade cellulose more readily (18). Coincident with man-made changes in pH by liming, there is a shift in the composition of the active flora, one which will be discussed below.

Many microorganisms grow poorly in media containing purified cellulose as the sole source of carbon, yet, on sterile plant material, the same organisms vigorously utilize the polysaccharide. For example, bacteria decompose the cellulose of corn stalks more rapidly than a purified cellulose prepared therefrom. Apparently, xylans and other carbohydrates within the corn stalks favor cellulose metabolism, and the removal of these xylans upon purification of the cellulose is accompanied by a diminished rate of decay (5). Addition of readily metabolizable substances to soil likewise accelerates cellulose decomposition (2). Since cellulose is only poorly available at best, large populations develop slowly; hence, the disappearance of purified cellulose is not rapid. If a population can develop to large size at the expense of some more available carbonaceous nutrient, the flora may adapt to the cellulose once the supply of the second carbohydrate becomes limiting, the net effect being an increase in cellulose hydrolysis.

The phenomenon of greater decay in the presence of other carbohydrates occurs in natural materials, and it should not be confused with the decreased cellulose breakdown noted in pure culture when simple compounds are present. The sparing action in the latter instance is the result of a preferential digestion of the more readily utilized substrate.

TABLE 1

Decomposition by *Pseudomonas ephemerocyanea* of Jute Preparations Containing Different Quantities of Cellulose and Lignin (6)

Preparation	Cellulose Content	Lignin Content	% of Cellulose Decomposed
	%	%	
A	99.2	0.0	100.0
B	95.5	3.3	95.6
C	89.2	6.3	83.1
D	82.7	11.9	37.9
E	75.6	12.6	17.7

Incubation period of 21 days.

Lignin, a plant constituent known to influence microorganisms, is found in the cell wall in close proximity to cellulose. To determine the effect of the lignin content of plant tissue, plant fractions possessing differing relative proportions of lignin and carbohydrates have been prepared. In the isolated fractions containing the largest quantities of lignin, cellulose is most slowly oxidized (table 1). Lignin is itself not toxic because its addition to cellulolytic cultures results in no inhibitions. The influence of lignin in reducing the susceptibility of cellulose to decomposition is probably a physical effect resulting from the close structural interlinkage between cellulose and lignin in the cell wall. In the rotting of natural materials, there is an analogous diminution in cellulose losses in residues of plant species having a high lignin content in comparison with organic matter low in lignin.

Aerobic Mesophilic Microflora

Cellulolytic microorganisms are common in field and forest soils, in manure, and on decaying plant tissues. The physiological heterogeneity of the responsible microflora permits the transformation to take place in habitats with or without O_2, at acid or at alkaline pH, low or high moisture levels, and from temperatures just above freezing to the extremes of the thermophilic range. The cellulose-utilizing population includes aerobic and anaerobic mesophilic bacteria, filamentous fungi, basidiomycetes, thermophilic bacteria, actinomycetes, and certain protozoa. Although many of these organisms have been studied only in pure culture, the action in nature is clearly the result of a complex population. At best, it is difficult to compare pure cultures with the mixed populations active in vivo since, in the latter circumstance, there is an intense microbiological competition for nutrients and sequential changes in the composition of the microflora with time.

A diverse group of fungi utilizes cellulose for its carbon and energy sources (table 2). Following treatment of soil with cellulose, there is a significant increase in the numbers of fungi, particularly if the nitrogen supply is adequate. Plate counts of filamentous fungi in excess of 10^6 per gram of soil during the decomposition of straw plus $NaNO_3$ are not uncommon. Strongly cellulolytic fungi are represented by species of the genera *Aspergillus, Chaetomium, Curvularia, Fusarium, Memnoniella, Phoma, Thielavia,* and *Trichoderma.* It has been proposed that fungi are the main agents of cellulose degradation

TABLE 2

Some Microbial Genera Capable of Utilizing Cellulose

Fungi		Bacteria		Actinomycetes
Alternaria	*Polyporus*	*Achromobacter*	*Clostridium*	*Micromonospora*
Aspergillus	*Rhizoctonia*	*Angiococcus*	*Cytophaga*	*Nocardia*
Chaetomium	*Rhizopus*	*Bacillus*	*Polyangium*	*Streptomyces*
Coprinus	*Trametes*	*Cellfalcicula*	*Pseudomonas*	*Streptosporangium*
Fomes	*Trichoderma*	*Cellulomonas*	*Sorangium*	
Fusarium	*Trichothecium*	*Cellvibrio*	*Sporocytophaga*	
Myrothecium	*Verticillium*		*Vibrio*	
Penicillium	*Zygorhynchus*			

in humid soils while bacteria are of greater significance in semi-arid localities. In the destruction of forest litter, wood, and woody tissues, cellulolytic basidiomycetes are especially prominent, but the basidiomycetes have received scant attention because they thrive poorly on conventional media. Indeed, many fungi seem able to decompose cellulose. This is in great contrast to the bacteria, a group in which possession of the requisite enzymes is a comparative rarity.

Aerobic, mesophilic bacteria metabolizing cellulose are never abundant in unamended soils, the population density extending from less than 100 to usually no more than 50,000 per gram. The number is far greater in manured fields and in proximity to plant roots (23). Bacterial genera that contain representatives digesting cellulose are listed in table 2. The taxonomy of these organisms is still in a state of change so that certain names may disappear as new epithets are created. van Iterson (25) was the first to study individual aerobic bacteria involved in cellulose degradation. He described a non-spore-forming aerobe which reputedly acted in association with a pigmented micrococcus to give a yellowish brown discoloration to disintegrating filter paper. Several years later, Hutchinson and Clayton (9) isolated an aerobic, cellulolytic bacterium which morphologically appeared as a long, flexuous rod with pointed ends. Their name for the bacterium, *Spirochaeta cytophaga*, has been subsequently changed, and the organism is now classified as the type species of the genus *Cytophaga* (figure 2). Other *Cytophaga* species have been subsequently described. The cytophagas are important in the aerobic decomposition of the polysaccharide and are abundant in soils receiving straw or manure. Members of the genus *Sporocytophaga* also oxidize cellulose; these differ from *Cytophaga* species by their capacity

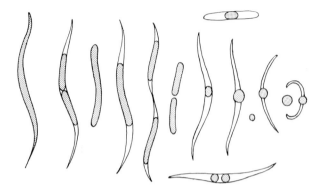

Figure 2. Morphological stages in the development of a cytophaga (7).

to form microcysts. In addition to *Cytophaga* and *Sporocytophaga*, other myxobacteria classified as species of *Angiococcus* and *Polyangium* will develop upon cellulose.

Occasional species of *Achromobacter*, *Pseudomonas*, *Vibrio*, and *Bacillus* utilize cellulose, but this physiological attribute is uncommon to most species of the four genera. *Bacillus* contains aerobic, spore-forming, gram positive rods while the first three genera include non-spore-forming, gram negative aerobes. *Cellulomonas*, on the other hand, is a cellulolytic genus made up of short, gram negative rods commonly producing yellow, water-insoluble pigments; these organisms are straight or somewhat curved, but occasional pleomorphic forms are found. Two additional cellulolytic genera were proposed by Winogradsky (29): *Cellvibrio*, to include long, slender rods that exhibit a slight curving, and *Cellfalcicula*, characterized by spindle or sickle-shaped cells. The last three genera contain species of great physiological similarity in terms of cellulose utilization.

Actinomycetes that grow upon cellulose have received little attention despite their presence during the decay of cellulosic materials. Many *Streptomyces* isolates develop, frequently with conspicuous pigments, on cellulose agar supplemented with inorganic nutrients. Often, a clear zone appears around the colony, the halo indicating that the responsible enzyme is functioning at a distance from the organism producing it. The halo effect is characteristic of extracellular catalysts. In addition to *Streptomyces*, species of *Micromonospora*, *Streptosporangium*, and *Nocardia* are cellulolytic. When dilutions are plated on a dextrin medium, cellulose-utilizing actinomycetes are observed in numbers as great as 500,000 per gram of soil (4). Nevertheless, though many actinomycetes have the necessary complement of enzymes, they are much slower in attacking the polysaccharide than most fungi and true bacteria.

Several protozoa in pure culture are capable of cellulose breakdown, e.g., species of *Hartmanella* and *Schizopyrenus* (24). Protozoa in the intestinal contents of several higher animals also can cleave the cellulose molecule.

A prominent factor governing the composition of the aerobic, mesophilic flora decomposing cellulose is the pH of the environment. In soils of near neutral reaction, ca. pH 6.5 to 7.0, the active population contains both vibrios and fungi. In soils of slightly greater acidity, about pH 5.7 to 6.2, there are fewer vibrios and more cytophagas. In land more acid than pH 5.5, the flora is dominated by the filamentous fungi. Even when tested in pure culture, the cellulolytic vibrios have their optimum at pH 7.1 to 7.6 and will not grow below pH 6.0 while the cytophagas develop at slightly higher hydrogen ion concentrations (10). Thus, the fungi are active in acid habitats while both the fungi and the bacteria are the causative organisms at reactions greater than pH 6.0. Consequently, the addition of the pure polysaccharide or of cellulosic crop residues to soils of pH greater than ca. 6.0 results in a marked increase in the abundance of fungi and bacteria. In aerated soils of high hydrogen ion concentrations, only the filamentous fungi respond to such treatments (table 3).

Several of the cellulose-hydrolyzing bacteria seem to have a unique nutrition: they are reported to be unable to grow in media containing simple sugars as carbon sources. Thus, *Cellvibrio, Cellfalcicula*, cellulolytic cocci of the bovine rumen, and a number of anaerobes are apparently obligate cellulose decomposers, using few or none of the simple sugars. Glucose is frequently not a suitable carbohydrate whereas growth is normal upon cellulose. A similar nutritional pattern had been reported for *Cytophaga hutchinsonii*, but Stanier (20) demonstrated that it is not an obligate cellulose-decomposing bacterium. *C. hutchinsonii* fails to grow in heat-sterilized, glucose-containing media, but it will proliferate readily in a glucose–mineral salts medium provided the sugar is sterilized by filtration; i.e., the reputed lack of glucose oxidation is a result of toxic products produced during autoclaving.

Cellulose is not an obligate carbon source for fungi and actinomycetes. These microorganisms have a broad nutritional base, and they utilize many carbonaceous materials. Indeed, the growth on

TABLE 3

Effect of Cellulose and Nitrogen on the Microbial Population in Soil (27)

Soil	Treatment	No./g of Soil × 10³		
		Fungi	Bacteria	Actinomycetes
Unlimed, pH 5.1	None	115.7	3,900	1,260
	N	115.7	3,900	1,260
	Cellulose	160	3,600	600
	Cellulose + N	4,800	2,480	400
Limed, pH 6.5	None	25.4	7,700	2,760
	N	25.4	7,700	2,760
	Cellulose	47	17,400	2,200
	Cellulose + N	290	47,000	3,200

Cellulose was added at a rate of 1 per cent and nitrogen as the nitrate salt (0.1 per cent).

Incubation period of 17 days.

cellulose is frequently slower than that upon other compounds. In contrast with the aforementioned bacterial genera, *Bacillus, Pseudomonas,* and *Vibrio* strains develop in a variety of laboratory media and readily metabolize glucose and other simple sugars. There is no obligate requirement for any one carbohydrate for these bacteria.

Cellulose is degraded more rapidly in mixed than in pure culture, even when the associated organisms are unable by themselves to attack the polysaccharide. The secondary population probably favors the primary flora by removing the breakdown products and thereby preventing the metabolic wastes from causing inhibitions. *Cytophaga,* for example, produces organic acids which reduce the hydrolysis of cellulose in laboratory culture; if an organism is present which further degrades the organic acids, the toxicity is relieved (3).

Anaerobic Mesophilic Microflora

Several microorganisms are capable of decomposing cellulose in the total absence of molecular oxygen, and the polysaccharide disappears under anaerobiasis whether supplied as the purified chemical or in the form of plant materials. The production of large quantities of ethanol and organic acids such as acetic, formic, lactic, and butyric is typical of the anaerobic cleavage of the cellulose molecule. When a soil becomes anaerobic, the decomposition proceeds through the action of bacteria which do not require O_2 for respiration. Fungi or actinomycetes are not significant in anaerobic environments. Differing from the transformation in air, the anaerobic conversion is not detectably affected by added inorganic nitrogen. Since anaerobic decomposition supplies little energy, the bacteria must degrade large quantities of the substrate in order to assimilate a small amount of carbon. Consequently, there is a proportionally small demand for nitrogen for assimilation into microbial tissue, less than the amount usually present in plant residues.

The isolation and maintenance of pure cultures of cellulolytic anaerobes is difficult, and many early investigators undoubtedly never had pure cultures. At present, several types of anaerobic cellulose decomposers are known: spore-forming mesophiles, spore-forming thermophiles, non-spore-forming rods, cocci, and several actinomycetes and fungi that grow anaerobically. At best, cellulolysis without O_2 is slow, regardless of the group concerned. The anaerobic bacteria are rarely numerous in unamended, well-drained soils although peats, marshes, and manure often support a sizable population. Commonly, from 10^2 to 10^3 anaerobic cellulose-fermenting bacteria are found per gram of non-flooded soil. On the other hand, the presence of a fermentable substrate or the exclusion of air stimulates this flora. The low numbers detected in well-drained soils probably represent the spores of the predominant bacteria. Differing from the aerobic bacteria, these organisms are not sensitive to acidity, and they have been found in soils of pH 4.3.

The most common anaerobic cellulose fermenters in nature appear to be members of the genus *Clostridium*. These bacteria are found in soil, compost, manure, river mud, and sewage. Some species are relatively specific for cellulose, but others attack a diverse group of carbohydrates. Many *Clostridium* spp. are cellulolytic, a capacity not too rare in the genus. To isolate such clostridia, a soil suspension is pasteurized at 80°C for 10 minutes, and dilutions are made into cellulose media which are then incubated anaerobically. The method takes advantage of the heat resistance of the spores and the anaerobic and cellulolytic nature of the vegetative cell. The technique is, therefore, a relatively specific means of obtaining isolates of the genus.

Non-spore-forming cellulolytic anaerobes can be demonstrated in soil or in sewage sludge, but they are not abundant. One, a non-sporulating rod, digests cellulose more readily than the spore formers. Certain fungi such as *Merulius* and *Fomes* have the capacity to develop slowly on cellulose in the absence of O_2, and these may play some role in soil. At least one actinomycete, a micromonospora, grows anaerobically, albeit slowly, in cellulosic media. This strain is atypical among the micromonosporas both because it is an obligate anaerobe and because it produces propionic acid (8, 16).

The animal digestive system also has an active cellulolytic population, but the predominant organisms differ from those in soil. In the rumen of cows and sheep, anaerobic cellulolytic cocci are found in abundance, sometimes in numbers ranging from 10^7 to 10^9 per milliliter of rumen fluid. The gram positive cocci seem to be the major organisms concerned in cellulose hydrolysis within the bovine rumen. Of many carbohydrates tested, these strains utilize only cellulose. Here too, therefore, is a group of obligate cellulose utilizers. Gram negative cellulolytic rods have also been obtained from the bovine rumen. The anaerobic decomposition of cellulose in soil is always slow when compared with the far more rapid process in the rumen. In the former environment, the predominant anaerobic organisms are the spore-forming rods; in rumen, the flora consists largely of non-spore-forming cocci.

Thermophilic Decomposition

Thermophilic cellulolytic bacteria can be readily obtained from soil and manure. For the demonstration of the presence of thermophilic microorganisms, inocula of soil or manure are placed in a medium containing filter paper as a cellulose source, inorganic salts, and $CaCO_3$, and the enrichment is incubated at $65°C$. In the decomposition, the filter paper disintegrates and frequently assumes a brownish-yellow color. Since such thermophilic bacteria do occur in soil, cellulose breakdown will take place at elevated temperatures. Despite the widespread distribution of thermophiles, it is likely that their role in cellulose decomposition in nature is minor. An exception is the compost heap, however, in which thermophiles are active agents in the decay.

Both aerobic and anaerobic microorganisms can function in thermophilic transformations. Because of the high temperatures concerned, the cellulolysis is especially vigorous. For example, about one-third of the cellulose in birch can be fermented by thermophilic enrichment cultures at 61°C in a period of two weeks (29). Two thermophilic anaerobes are active upon the polysaccharide. The species bearing ovoid spores, *Clostridium thermocellum*, forms acetic acid, ethanol, CO_2, and H_2. *Clostridium thermocellulaseum*, on the other hand, has spherical spores and accumulates reducing sugars. These bacteria are straight or somewhat curved, gram negative rods that typically produce endospores. Both are obligate anaerobes, requiring low oxidation-reduction potentials for proliferation. The optimum temperature for cellulose degradation by thermophilic clostridia is from 55 to 65°C with little activity below 50°C and no growth above 68°C. The optimal pH is in the vicinity of neutrality (14).

Biochemistry of Cellulose Decomposition

Aerobic bacteria generally convert cellulose to two major products, CO_2 and cell substance. There are no significant accumulations of carbonaceous intermediates, and the concentration of organic acids rarely reaches an appreciable level. The major products of the fungal and actinomycete decomposition of the polysaccharide are CO_2 and cell-carbon, but certain groups probably release small amounts of organic acids. The initial hydrolysis of cellulose is probably the rate-limiting reaction in the microbiological oxidation of the carbohydrate so that intermediates which normally would appear when aerobes are utilizing readily available sugars never accumulate.

The conversion is entirely different with mesophilic and thermophilic anaerobes. These bacteria are incapable of metabolizing even simple substrates to completion, and a number of organic compounds are released as end-products. The main substances that accumulate in the absence of O_2 with these genera are CO_2, H_2, ethanol, and acetic, formic, succinic, butyric, and lactic acids (table 4). Early microbiologists reported the finding of a third gas during the bacterial fermentation, CH_4, but modern investigations of cultures whose purity is beyond doubt have established that none of the cellulolytic anaerobes produce CH_4. In enrichment cultures as in soil, however, the anaerobic dissimilation of carbohydrates is accompanied by the evolution of much CH_4. Methane is not produced by the bacteria

TABLE 4

Products of the Anaerobic Decomposition of Cellulose

Bacterium	Products
Mesophiles	
Clostridium cellobioparus	CO_2, H_2, ethanol, acetic, lactic, and formic acids
Clostridium dissolvens	CO_2, H_2, ethanol, acetic, lactic, and butyric acids
Bacteroides succinogenes	CO_2, acetic, and succinic acids
Ruminococcus flavefaciens	Acetic, formic, and succinic acids
Thermophiles	
Clostridium thermocellum	CO_2, H_2, ethanol, acetic, lactic, formic, and succinic acids

utilizing the polysaccharides but rather by a secondary bacterial population which metabolizes the organic acids liberated by the primary microflora.

The initial step in cellulose destruction is the enzymatic hydrolysis of the polymer. The enzyme, or enzyme complex, has been given the name of *cellulase*. Cellulase catalyzes the conversion of insoluble cellulose into simple, water-soluble products. One of the factors limiting knowledge of the responsible enzymes is the poor solubility of the substrate. To overcome this difficulty, soluble cellulose derivatives are frequently utilized, but they may be far different from the material decomposed in nature. The hydrolysis effected by cellulase ultimately leads to the liberation of mono- or disaccharides, a reaction characteristic of the entire cellulolytic flora. The steps subsequent to the initial cellulose hydrolysis vary with the individual organisms concerned, the simple sugars being metabolized to CO_2 by the aerobes and to organic acids and alcohols by the anaerobes.

The microbial cell is impermeable to the cellulose molecule so the organism must excrete extracellular enzymes in order to make the carbon source available. The extracellular catalyst acts hydrolytically, converting the insoluble material to soluble sugars which penetrate the cell membrane. Once inside the cell, the simple sugars are oxidized and provide energy for biosynthetic reactions. The zone of clearing in agar media which contain the polysaccharide is a result of the extracellular enzyme acting at a distance from the colony that formed it.

Purified cellulase catalyzes the hydrolysis of an entire class of compounds known as β-1,4-glucosides.

glucose

β-1,4-glucoside structure

Included in the group of β-1,4-glucosides are cellobiose, cellotriose, cellotetraose, and cellulose, the molecules containing two, three, four, and many glucose units, respectively. Cellulase acts on molecules as simple structurally as cellotriose and also on the highly polymerized cellulose chain. Cellobiose does not seem to be susceptible to enzymatic cleavage by cellulase (21), but, with this outstanding exception, the enzyme hydrolyzes β-1,4-glucosidic linkages. Under no condition, however, can the purified enzyme catalyze a rapid depolymerization of the cellulose molecule. Cellulase is adaptive in most microorganisms; i.e., it is synthesized only in the presence of its specific substrates, cellulose or cellulose derivatives. In *Trichoderma viride*, for example, the enzyme is formed when the fungus is grown upon cellulose or cellobiose, but not when the organism is cultured upon a large number of other compounds (13). Since the cell is not permeable to cellulose, it is interesting to speculate on the mechanism by which an external substrate such as cellulose can cause the organism to synthesize an enzyme.

It is possible to separate the reactions concerned in the initial hydrolysis from those involved in the subsequent metabolic conversions. This is accomplished by means of selective treatments which destroy only part of the enzyme systems involved. Thus, if growth is prevented by the use of an antiseptic, cellulose hydrolysis contin-

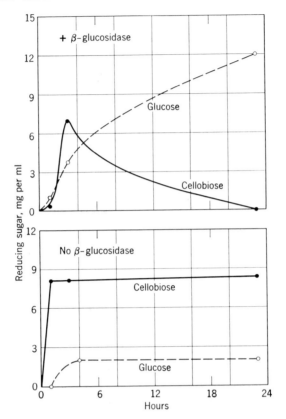

Figure 3. Formation of cellobiose and glucose from cellulose by the cellulase of *Trichoderma viride* (11).

ues, and cellobiose and glucose accumulate. By use of other selective techniques, particularly partial heat inactivation, cellobiase (β-glucosidase) but not cellulase can be destroyed; under these circumstances, there is a build-up of cellobiose (figure 3).

There are two possible mechanisms for the substrate cleavage. Cellulase may cause a random splitting of the long cellulose molecule or, alternatively, cellobiose units may be removed from the terminal ends of the chain. The latter hypothesis requires that cellobiose be the only product. The report that cellotriose and cellotetraose have been detected favors the hypothesis of random cleavage rather than the concept of end-group attack. It is possible, however, that cellotriose and cellotetraose are formed from cellobiose rather than from cellulose by the enzyme transglycosidase.

2 cellobiose   glucose   (I)

cellotriose

Whitaker (28) has pointed out that there is little C^{14} in the cellotriose and cellotetraose formed when *Myrothecium verrucaria* cellulase depolymerizes a cellulose dextrin in the presence of cellobiose-C^{14}. Such evidence minimizes the contribution of reactions similar to equation I to the formation of the triose and the tetraose. Consequently, random cleavage of the polysaccharide molecule seems to be the likeliest hydrolytic mechanism.

Glucose is the final product of the enzymatic hydrolysis. If the microorganism produces cellobiase in addition to the cellulase, the glucose undoubtedly is formed directly from the cellobiose. The classical cellobiase is essentially a β-glucosidase, that is, an enzyme which hydrolyzes β-glucosides. For cellobiose, the reaction results in the production of glucose.

$$\text{cellobiose} \rightarrow 2 \text{ glucose} \qquad (II)$$

Occasionally, glucose may be formed in the absence of β-glucosidase activity. Hence, there must be alternative mechanisms for cellobiose degradation.

On the basis of their studies with soluble cellulose derivatives, Levinson, Mandels, and Reese (11) suggested that cellulose hydrolysis to the cellobiose level requires two steps. One is a reaction catalyzed by an enzyme, C_1, which yields long, linear chains composed of many glucose units. The enzyme of the second step, C_x, hydrolyzes the cellulose derivatives formed by C_1. The existence of two separate enzymes, C_1 and C_x, may explain the observation that certain microorganisms digest partly degraded cellulose materials but cannot hydrolyze native cellulose; i.e., C_1 is the catalyst for the degradation of native cellulose and leads to the formation of shorter chains of glucose units. These are then hydrolyzed by C_x to cellobiose.

$$\text{native cellulose} \xrightarrow{C_1} \begin{array}{c} \text{long} \\ \text{glucose} \\ \text{chains} \end{array} \xrightarrow{C_x} \text{cellobiose} \qquad \text{(III)}$$

Both of the enzymes making up the classical cellulase are extracellular while, should cellobiose be assimilated, its cleavage and subsequent metabolism must be intracellular. By the nature of the reaction it catalyzes, C_x can be termed a β-polyglucosidase in contrast to β-glucosidase which acts on cellobiose and related simple molecules. By extension of the proposed reaction sequence of equation III, many organisms which cannot attack cellulose may produce C_x and hence hydrolyze β-1,4-glucosidic linkages, but only those few organisms elaborating C_1 can decompose native cellulose. The latter are the true cellulolytic microorganisms.

The hypothesis of a two-component cellulase system has not gone unchallenged. Studies by Thomas and Whitaker (22) of a purified preparation of the cellulase produced by *Myrothecium verrucaria* indicate the presence of a single enzyme which functions in the decomposition. Other investigators report two or more components in purified cellulase preparations derived from fungi (15, 19). Hence, it is not yet clear whether cellulase is composed of several constituents or whether it is a single enzyme.

An important factor concerned in the biochemistry of cellulose breakdown in soil is the effect of clay minerals. Because of their chemical nature, cellulosic compounds can be adsorbed by clay minerals, the polysaccharide derivatives of higher molecular weight generally being adsorbed to a lesser degree than the short-chain compounds. But possibly of greater importance is the partial inactivation of cellulase by certain clays, an effect which has great significance because the enzyme or enzyme system is extracellular, and therefore it can be altered in its activity by clays. The enzyme inactivation and the substrate adsorption phenomena may account, at least in part, for the protective action of montmorillonite clay on cellulosic materials subjected to microbial decomposition (12).

REFERENCES

Reviews

Hungate, R. E. 1950. The anaerobic mesophilic cellulolytic bacteria. *Bacteriol. Rev.*, 14:1–49.

Imschenezki, A. A. 1959. *Mikrobiologie der Cellulose.* Akademie-Verlag, Berlin.

Norman, A. G., and W. H. Fuller. 1942. Cellulose decomposition by microorganisms. *Adv. Enzymol.*, 2:239–264.

Reese, E. T. 1956. Enzymatic hydrolysis of cellulose. *Applied Microbiol.*, 4: 39–45.

Siu, R. G. H. 1951. *Microbial decomposition of cellulose.* Reinhold Publishing Corp., New York.

Siu, R. G. H., and E. T. Reese. 1953. Decomposition of cellulose by microorganisms. *Botan. Rev.*, 19:377–416.

Literature cited

1. Anderson, J. A. 1926. *Soil Sci.*, 21:115–126.
2. Broadbent, F. E. 1947. *Soil Sci. Soc. Am., Proc.*, 12:246–249.
3. Fahraeus, G. 1949. *Lantbruks-Hogskol. Ann.*, 16:159–166.
4. Fuller, W. H., and A. G. Norman. 1942. *Soil Sci. Soc. Am., Proc.*, 7:243–246.
5. Fuller, W. H., and A. G. Norman. 1943. *J. Bacteriol.*, 46:281–289.
6. Fuller, W. H., and A. G. Norman. 1943. *J. Bacteriol.*, 46:291–297.
7. Gray, P. H. H. 1957. *Canad. J. Microbiol.*, 3:897–903.
8. Hungate, R. E. 1946. *J. Bacteriol.*, 51:51–56.
9. Hutchinson, H. B., and J. Clayton. 1918. *J. Agric. Sci.*, 9:143–173.
10. Jensen, H. L. 1931. *J. Agric. Sci.*, 21:81–100.
11. Levinson, H. S., G. R. Mandels, and E. T. Reese. 1951. *Arch. Biochem. Biophys.*, 31:351–365.
12. Lynch, D. L., and L. J. Cotnoir. 1956. *Soil Sci. Soc. Am., Proc.*, 20:367–370.
13. Mandels, M., and E. T. Reese. 1957. *J. Bacteriol.*, 73:269–278.
14. McBee, R. H. 1950. *Bacteriol. Rev.*, 14:51–63.
15. Norkrans, B. 1957. *Physiol. Plant.*, 10:454–466.
16. Pochon, J., and M. Bay. 1951. *Ann. Inst. Pasteur*, 81:179–186.
17. Ruschmeyer, O. R., and E. L. Schmidt. 1958. *Applied Microbiol.*, 6:115–120.
18. Schmidt, E. L., and O. R. Ruschmeyer. 1958. *Applied Microbiol.*, 6:108–114.
19. Sison, B. C., W. J. Schubert, and F. F. Nord. 1958. *Arch. Biochem. Biophys.*, 75:260–272.
20. Stanier, R. Y. 1942. *Soil Sci.*, 53:479–480.
21. Thomas, R. 1956. *Austral. J. Biol. Sci.*, 9:159–183.
22. Thomas, R., and D. R. Whitaker. 1958. *Nature*, 181:715–716.
23. Timonin, M. I., and R. H. Thexton. 1950. *Soil Sci. Soc. Am., Proc.*, 15: 186–189.
24. Tracey, M. V. 1955. *Nature*, 175:815.

25. van Iterson, C. 1904. *Cent. Bakteriol.,* II, 11:689–698.
26. Virtanen, A. I. 1939. *Proc. 3rd Intl. Cong. Microbiol.,* New York, pp. 747–748.
27. Waksman, S. A., and O. Heukelekian. 1924. *Soil Sci.,* 17:275–291.
28. Whitaker, D. R. 1956. *Canad. J. Biochem. Physiol.,* 34:488–494.
29. Winogradsky, S. 1929. *Ann. Inst. Pasteur,* 43:549–633.

11

Microbiology
of the Hemicelluloses

Polysaccharides known as hemicelluloses are one of the major plant constituents added to soil, second only in quantity to cellulose, and they consequently represent a significant source of energy and nutrients to the microflora. Further, as the hemicelluloses make up a large portion of plant tissue, the rate of decomposition of structurally associated organic materials will be greatly affected by the disappearance of the hemicelluloses. Because of their abundance and susceptibility to microbiological degradation, they are important in the dry weight loss of crop residues. Yet, although the degradation of cellulose in natural habitats and in culture systems has been extensively investigated, little attention has been given to the attack on the hemicellulosic components; therefore, information on the transformation in soil, the microorganisms concerned, or the biochemical mechanism of hemicellulose breakdown is still fragmentary.

Towards the close of the nineteenth century, Schulze coined the term *hemicellulose,* an unfortunate choice, for the molecule bears no structural relationship to cellulose. The hemicelluloses are a class of water-insoluble polysaccharides extracted from plants by dilute alkali; upon hydrolysis with hot, dilute mineral acid they yield hexoses (six-carbon sugars), pentoses (five-carbon sugars), and frequently uronic acids. Other names have been suggested to replace the inappropriate term hemicelluloses, e.g., pentosans, hexosans, polyoses, or non-cellulosic cell-wall polysaccharides. Because chemical hydrolysis of many hemicelluloses yields a large proportion of a single sugar, the polysaccharide is often classified on the basis of its main sugar

183

component: xylan and araban for polymers of the two pentose sugars and mannan and galactan for the hexose polysaccharides. The
fact that alkali extracts of plant tissues contain uronic acids as well
as simple sugars led Norman to propose a division of the hemicelluloses into those containing uronic acids, the *polyuronide hemicelluloses,* and those hemicelluloses largely devoid of uronic acid units,
the *cellulosans.* The latter are intimately associated with the cellulose of the plant, hence the designation, but they have no structural
kinship to cellulose. The major cellulosan, i.e., the most abundant
hemicellulose polysaccharide serving as an integral part of the cellulosic architecture of plants, appears to be xylan.

Chemistry

The polyuronides can be viewed as polysaccharides containing
uronic acid residues in greater or lesser quantities as part of the
structure of the molecule. Not all of the polyuronides, however, are
designated as hemicelluloses, and some of the water-soluble polyuronides and substances such as the pectic materials, plant gums, and
mucilages are considered commonly to be outside of this class of compounds. It is likely that the polyuronide hemicelluloses do not occur
in a free form but rather are intimately linked with other components
of the cell wall of higher plants, possibly in the form of lignin-poly-
saccharide complexes.

Chemical hydrolysis of the polyuronide hemicellulose with hot,
dilute mineral acids cleaves the molecule, and sugars and uronic acids
are liberated (figure 1). Analysis of the products of hydrolysis reveals the existence of two major polysaccharide types, both containing a pentose sugar and a uronic acid moiety. In one, the repeating
constituents are xylose and glucuronic acid whereas the second contains arabinose and galacturonic acid. The first type of polyuronide
hemicellulose is the more prevalent among members of the plant kingdom, and the predominant unit in the molecule is xylose. The molar
ratio of xylose and glucuronic acid moieties varies according to the
natural material, figures of 7 to 19 xylose residues for each glucuronic
acid having been reported for a number of plants.

Xylose polymers occur in two forms in nature; one is associated
with glucuronic acid in the polyuronide hemicellulose and the other is
found as the simple polymerized chain of pentose units, the xylan.
The latter is a high molecular weight polymer of xylose units. The

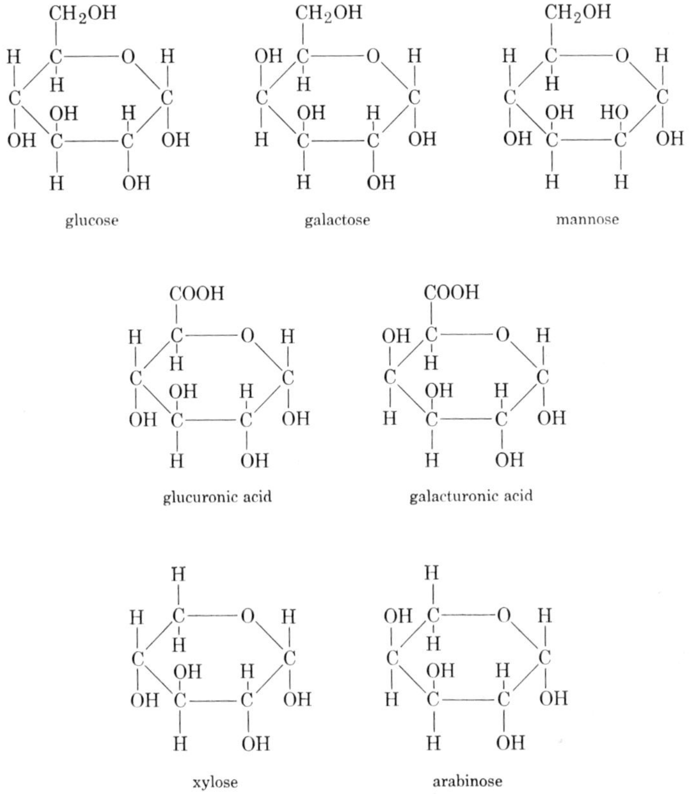

Figure 1. Structure of sugar constituents of hemicelluloses.

empirical formula of xylan is $(C_5H_8O_4)_n$, and it is a polysaccharide of D-xylose units, which have the structure $C_5H_{10}O_5$. Xylans may also contain traces of L-arabinose and sometimes D-glucuronic acid. For example, the esparto grass xylan contains one arabinose for each 18 to 20 xylose units. Present evidence indicates that the xylose units are probably bound together in the form of a branched molecule with a single branch for each 18 to 20 xylose residues. Estimates of the molecular size give results indicating the presence of 50 to 150 pentose units in the xylan chain.

Another hemicellulose not containing uronic acid in its structure is mannan, a polymer of D-mannose units. The mannan of ivory nut consists of a long chain of mannose residues with the individual sugars bound together by β-1,4-linkages; the carbohydrate seems to contain about 70 to 80 mannose units. The mannan of yeast, on the other hand, is a long polymer of mannose sugars with short, radiating side chains, and in this polysaccharide approximately 500 mannose units are linked together. In several organisms, there are found glucomannans which yield both D-mannose and D-glucose upon acid hydrolysis, and other mannose-containing polysaccharides have small amounts of D-galactose. Arabans, polysaccharides in which the repeating unit is arabinose, occur in some higher plants, where they are usually associated with the pectic substances of the primary cell wall.

Decomposition

When a plant residue is added to soil, its hemicellulose fraction disappears initially at a rapid rate, but the subsequent degradation appears to be more slow. The change in decomposition rate is probably a result of the chemical heterogeneity of the hemicellulose fraction, some portions decaying slowly, others rapidly. The effect may also be attributed in part to the presence within the microorganisms of hemicellulosic constituents which are formed in soil during the period of decay. Such a microbiological synthesis would be reflected in an apparently slow disappearance of the total hemicelluloses although the plant-derived carbohydrates may be in fact transformed quickly. The data of Schmidt et al. (16) substantiate this contention by the demonstration that the hyphae of a number of fungi contain hemicellulosic polysaccharides. From 0.68 to 1.43 per cent of the mycelial weight of *Aspergillus* and *Penicillium* was shown to be pentosan-like even when the growth medium was free of pentose sugars. These observations make it likely that a significant but as yet unknown portion of the hemicellulosic material found in humus is derived from the synthetic activities of the microbial population.

During the first few days of attack on plant tissue, hemicelluloses disappear more rapidly than cellulose. The data of table 1, illustrating the aerobic breakdown of oat straw, demonstrate clearly the differential oxidation of the two dominant polysaccharides. A single example will suffice to show the relative rates of decomposition of cellulose and hemicelluloses under aerobic and anaerobic conditions. Acharya (1), in his study of the rotting of rice straw, found that hemicelluloses disappear more readily under anaerobiasis than cellulose; e.g., only 9.8 per cent of the cellulose was metabolized after 1 month whereas 26.8 per cent of the hemicelluloses had been destroyed. In

TABLE 1

Microbial Decomposition of Some Constituents of
Oat Straw (11)

| Days | % of Constituent Oxidized | |
	Hemicellulose	Cellulose
0–4	43.5	2.3
4–8	6.5	9.1
8–16	5.4	25.0

the presence of air, on the other hand, 62.4 per cent of the hemicelluloses and 56.2 per cent of the cellulose were mineralized in the same period.

The metabolism of hemicelluloses is governed by the physical and chemical characteristics of the habitat, and pH and temperature affect this process in a manner similar to their effects upon the decomposition of plant residues. Persistence is greater in the absence than in the presence of O_2, and the disappearance is most marked when the environment is aerobic, less in waterlogged habitats, and least under conditions of complete anaerobiasis. Important also is the availability of mineral nutrients, especially nitrogen, for which there is a great demand by the microflora. Likewise, age of plants has a distinct bearing upon the decay, and the hemicelluloses of more mature plants are degraded more slowly than those in younger tissue. In part, the effect of crop maturity may result from an alteration in the structure of the polysaccharide, but it may at the same time reflect a change with age in the physical or chemical relationships among the various carbonaceous constituents.

Microorganisms

Many microorganisms of the soil utilize hemicelluloses for growth and cell synthesis. Fungi, actinomycetes, and both aerobic and anaerobic bacteria are represented in the active population. More microbial species are active in destroying hemicelluloses than cellulose. The responsible flora contains a broad cross section of taxonomic, morphological, and physiological groups, and the organisms do not exhibit the substrate specificity that is associated with a portion of the cellulolytic population. Thus, in addition to polysaccharides, these microorganisms use organic acids and many simple sugars. The populations concerned in the utilization and destruction of the hemicelluloses of different plants may be expected to differ from one another because of the great chemical dissimilarities of the various hemicelluloses and because the associated components of the plant tissues undoubtedly have a modifying effect upon the composition of the microflora.

During aerobic decomposition of organic remains, an abundant population capable of hemicellulolytic action develops. In the initial stage of rapid hemicellulose disappearance, the quantity of fungus mycelium increases significantly as this group assumes a dominant role in the oxidation (12). For example, when purified xylan is used as substrate and the changes in biological equilibrium are measured by the Rossi-Cholodny buried slide method, the segment of the flora responding most rapidly is seen to be the fungi whereas the bacteria as a class are not generally as vigorous (10). It is possible, however, that the bacteria may be significant by working in association with the fungi since the disappearance is greater through the agency of a mixed population than of individual pure cultures. The presence of hemicelluloses also leads to a more rapid metabolism of cellulose because the greater availability of the former allows a larger population to develop, a portion of which uses the more biologically resistant cellulose (12).

A method of estimating the abundance of hemicellulolytic organisms has been presented by Pochon and Augier (14). The procedure entails the inoculation of dilutions of a soil suspension into tubes containing a hemicellulose–nitrate–inorganic salts medium. The results obtained by this technique indicate that soils of neutral reaction have a larger population capable of using these polysaccharides than acid soils.

Various fungi, bacteria, and actinomycetes in pure culture can decompose hemicelluloses, frequently using them as the sole sources of carbon and energy. The capacity to degrade these carbohydrates is present in the major fungal groups—the imperfect fungi, the Phycomycetes, Ascomycetes, and the Basidiomycetes. Waksman (21) carried out an extensive investigation of the ability of individual cultures to bring about the decomposition of a number of plant tissues. When the substrate was wheat straw, *Trichoderma* sp. decomposed in 48 days 200.5 of the 707.5 mg of hemicellulose initially present while a soil infusion oxidized 379.3 mg aerobically and 177.7 mg in the absence of O_2. *Trichoderma* sp. also oxidized the hemicelluloses of mature oak leaves, but it was less active than *Streptomyces* sp. and the basidiomycete, *Polyporus* sp. Species of *Aspergillus* inoculated onto sterile plant tissue decomposed 31 to 53 per cent of the pentosan of ground field corn in 142 days at 28°C, and the extent of decomposition fell within the same range when the organisms were *Penicillium*, *Cunninghamella*, and *Rhizopus* spp. (16). Many fungal genera degrade a pentosan of wheat, the most active being *Alternaria*, *Aspergillus*, *Fusarium*, *Trichoderma*, and *Trichothecium* (17). With several of the strains tested, a zone of clearing appears surrounding the fungus colony growing on the normally opalescent agar medium. The cleared area suggests the liberation of extracellular enzymes needed for the hydrolysis of the carbohydrate.

TABLE 2

Microorganisms That Utilize Hemicelluloses

Organism	Substrate	Reference
Bacteria		
Anaerobes	Galactan, mannan	(23)
Bacillus	Xylan	(7)
Bacillus, Achromobacter	Oat hemicellulose	(12)
Bacillus, Pseudomonas	Wheat pentosan	(17)
Cytophaga, Sporocytophaga	Hemicellulose	(5)
Lactobacillus	Xylan	(4)
Vibrio	Mannan, xylan	(2)
Actinomycetes		
Actinomycetes	Galactan, mannan, xylan	(22)
Streptomyces	Wheat pentosan	(17)
Streptomyces	Oak hemicellulose	(21)
Fungi		
Alternaria, Fusarium, Trichothecium	Hemp polyuronide	(6)
Aspergillus, Rhizopus, Zygorhynchus	Galactan, mannan, xylan	(22)
Chaetomium, Helminthosporium Penicillium	Wheat pentosan	(17)
Coriolus, Fomes, Polyporus	Araban, galactan, mannan	(8)

The presence of hemicellulolytic bacteria in soil, manure, and decomposing straw has been demonstrated by Norman (12), who isolated seventeen mesophilic and three thermophilic strains. Five of the mesophiles were characterized as strains of *Achromobacter ubiquitum* while the remaining twelve were aerobic, spore-forming rods. These isolates carried out a slow degradation of sterile straw, the slow rate suggesting a secondary role for the bacteria in natural environments. Other active cultures that have been described include strains of *Bacillus, Cytophaga, Pseudomonas, Sporocytophaga,* and *Streptomyces.* A summary of the organisms known to have hemicellulolytic capacities is presented in table 2. The list is far from complete, but it does serve to suggest that the production of the necessary enzymes is not a rare physiological attribute.

Specific Hemicelluloses

One of the hemicellulosic-type compounds that has received considerable attention is xylan, the polymer of the pentose D-xylose. The breakdown of xylose-containing carbohydrates is important in the disappearance of many plant residues from the soil because these polysaccharides make up a large proportion of the total carbohydrate content of grasses and woody plants. Soil contains a large number of fungi, bacteria, and actinomycetes capable of xylan degradation, and pure culture representatives of this flora have been shown to utilize the purified carbohydrate as well as the xylan in natural products. Dominant during the preliminary stages of the decomposition in acid soils are the filamentous fungi whereas the initial population in neutral to alkaline environments and in the rotting of straw and manure appears to consist of strains of *Bacillus.* Other potential xylan-utilizing bacteria are strains of *Achromobacter* and *Sporocytophaga.* At temperatures of 60 to 65°C, the rapid xylan metabolism results from the activities of thermophilic, aerobic, spore-forming bacilli.

A method has been proposed for estimating xylan-hydrolyzing activity, one requiring the incubation of a soil-buffer mixture with wheat straw xylan. Toluene is added to prevent appreciable microbial proliferation, and the reaction is studied by measuring the formation of reducing sugars. Determined in this manner, the xylanase content of soil varies with the crop and the supply of organic materials (figure 2); the enzyme is especially concentrated in plots treated with barnyard manure. The presence of a xylan-containing crop such as wheat

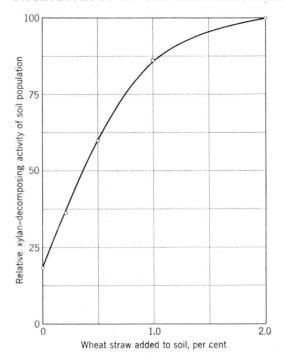

Figure 2. Effect of the addition of straw on the xylanase activity in soil (18).

results in an enhanced xylanase activity in soil when compared with locations supporting a crop containing little or no xylan (18).

Mannan, the polysaccharide composed of mannose in polymeric combination, is also rapidly metabolized. This fact can be confirmed experimentally by inoculating an aliquot of soil into an inorganic salts medium containing mannan as sole carbon source and observing the rate of microbiological growth proceeding at the expense of the carbohydrate. Among the organisms shown to utilize mannan in plant tissue or purified mannan polysaccharides are bacteria of the genus *Vibrio*, a number of actinomycetes, and fungi placed in the genera *Aspergillus, Penicillium, Rhizopus, Trichoderma,* and *Zygorhynchus*.

Galactans are suitable carbon sources for a number of basidiomycetes, aerobic and anaerobic bacteria, actinomycetes, and the fungi *Aspergillus, Cunninghamella, Humicola, Penicillium, Rhizopus, Trichoderma,* and *Zygorhynchus*. Both fungi and actinomycetes use purified galactan in media where it is the sole organic nutrient, and the same organisms likewise cause the breakdown of galactan in Irish moss when the plant material is added to inorganic nutrient solutions. Whether the organism be a fungus, actinomycete, or bacterium, galactans frequently tend to be less readily dissimilated than mannans and xylans (table 3), but such observations on relative rates are based largely upon pure culture studies. It has been demonstrated, however, that the release of CO_2 from carbohydrate-amended soils is most rapid with starch and slowest with galactan while mannan, xylan, and a pentosan derived from seaweed occupy intermediary positions (3).

A polysaccharide that has been investigated intensively because of its routine use in microbiology laboratories is the gel-forming substance in agar. This hemicellulose-like substance, often called gelose, is a galactose polymer possessing the property of forming rigid gels. It is found in and can be extracted from several types of red algae by treatment with hot water. The gelose molecule is composed of a linear chain of galactose units bound together by β-1,3-linkages. Some recent evidence suggests that the basic repeating unit is a disaccharide of D-galactose and 3,6-anhydro-L-galactose (24). Organisms which liquefy agar are readily demonstrable by the zones of liquefaction or pits produced in the gel; other bacteria cause no true liquefaction but produce rather a zone of softening. Regardless of visual symptoms,

TABLE 3

Microbiological Decomposition of Polysaccharides in Liquid Media (22)

Microorganism	% of Substrate Decomposed		
	Mannan	Xylan	Galactan
Aspergillus sp.	94	55	37
Penicillium sp.	98	55	34
Rhizopus sp.	96	19	34
Streptomyces 26	47	38	29
Streptomyces 40	93	35	29
Streptomyces 50	49	18	6.8
Trichoderma sp.	29	56	37

Incubation period of 42 days.

all strains apparently cause a marked decrease in viscosity of the substrate.

Agar digesters of the soil have been divided into three major types: (*a*) those with liquefy agar rapidly—similar to *Vibrio agarliquefaciens* and *Vibrio andoi;* (*b*) organisms that soften agar—gram negative, peritrichous, non-spore-forming bacteria which elaborate yellow pigments; and (*c*) bacteria which weakly hydrolyze the agar—similar to *Achromobacter pastinator* (19). Marine sediments are an especially rich source of agar decomposers, and the numbers here range up to 50,000 to 200,000 per gram of mud. Among the active bacterial genera obtained from various habitats are found strains of *Vibrio, Flavobacterium, Bacillus, Pseudomonas, Achromobacter,* and *Cytophaga.*

It is apparent that soils are endowed with a large microbial population concerned in the degradation of hemicelluloses and related polysaccharides. This hemicellulolytic microflora is not restricted to a few species or genera, for it includes a variety of fungi, bacteria, and actinomycetes. The activity of any single isolate, however, will depend not only upon the environmental conditions but also upon the chemical nature of the polysaccharide molecule being utilized to provide energy and carbon for cell synthesis.

Biochemistry of Hemicellulose Decomposition

Because the hemicelluloses have high molecular weights and fail to pass through the microbial cell membrane, they must be converted into simpler compounds prior to utilization as carbon sources. The active flora must therefore first hydrolyze the polysaccharide by means of extracellular enzymes to shorter carbohydrate fragments which the cell can assimilate. The sole peculiarity of members of the hemicellulolytic population is thus their ability to catalyze the initial hydrolysis. Following the preliminary breakdown, however, a secondary population will develop upon the metabolic products. The latter group of organisms responds to the compounds liberated from the long polymers by the hemicellulolytic flora.

The enzymes catalyzing hemicellulose breakdown are broadly termed *hemicellulases.* Since many hemicellulosic constituents are found in biological systems, there are undoubtedly several hemicellulose-decomposing enzymes, but because of the limited information on the chemistry of the substrates, little is known concerning the differences between the individual catalysts.

In its development on polysaccharides, the hemicellulolytic isolate produces simple sugar units from the polymer. Similarly, purified preparations of hemicellulases act upon their respective substrates with the liberation of the sugar or sugars which are the building blocks of the polysaccharide molecule. If the basic, repeating hexose or pentose unit is a reducing sugar, the course of the reaction may be followed by measurement of the appearance of reducing substances (figure 3). Thus, growth of *Vibrio andoi* on xylan, mannan, or agar is accompanied by the appearance of reducing compounds (2), and the bacterial hydrolysis of ivory nut mannan releases free mannose and a mannose trisaccharide (15). In the enzymatic hydrolysis of agar by the extracellular agarase of *Pseudomonas atlantica*, a homol-

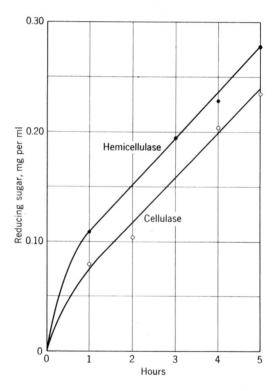

Figure 3. Production of reducing sugars during the enzymatic hydrolysis of hemicellulose and cellulose (20).

ogous series of galactose compounds are recovered, the basic structures of which contain a disaccharide of D-galactose and 3,6-anhydro-L-galactose (24). A similar conversion of the long polysaccharide structure to its simple constituents applies to the extracellular xylanase, which catalyzes the hydrolysis of xylan to xylobiose, xylotriose, and other short chains of xylose residues. The term xylanase is a misnomer because it implies that the sole substrate is xylan. In reality, the enzyme catalyzes the hydrolysis of a class of xylose polymers so that the term xylosidase would be more appropriate (7, 13). Similar class designations may be revealed by further study of the other enzymes catalyzing polysaccharide decomposition.

Since polysaccharide-splitting enzymes are extracellular, their activity in soil is affected by the diverse number of inanimate materials present. Such external influences are in addition to factors affecting growth of the responsible organisms and factors governing availability of the substrate. Therefore, it is interesting to note that hemicellulase has a reduced activity in the presence of montmorillonite clay (9). This may result from adsorption of the enzyme, the substrate, or both. Such inhibitory effects are of profound significance in altering the transformations catalyzed by the many extracellular enzymes required for the depolymerization of polysaccharides found in natural materials.

REFERENCES

Reviews

McIlroy, R. J. 1948. *The chemistry of the polysaccharides.* Longmans, Green and Co., New York.

Norman, A. G. 1937. *The biochemistry of cellulose, the polyuronides, lignin, etc.* Oxford Univ. Press, Oxford.

Polglase, W. J. 1955. Polysaccharides associated with wood cellulose. *Adv. Carbohydrate Chem.,* 10:283–333.

Wise, L. E. 1952. The hemicelluloses. In L. E. Wise and E. C. Jahn, eds., *Wood chemistry.* Reinhold Publishing Corp., New York, pp. 369–408.

Literature cited

1. Acharya, C. N. 1935. *Biochem. J.,* 29:1116–1120.
2. Aoi, K., and J. Orikura. 1928. *Cent. Bakteriol.,* II, 74:321–333.
3. Diehm, R. A. 1930. *Proc. Comm. III, 2nd Intl. Cong. Soil Sci.,* Leningrad, pp. 151–157.
4. Fred, E. B., W. H. Peterson, and A. Davenport. 1920. *J. Biol. Chem.,* 42: 175–189.
5. Fuller, W. H., and A. G. Norman. 1943. *J. Bacteriol.,* 45:565–572.

6. Fuller, W. H., and A. G. Norman. 1945. *J. Bacteriol.*, 50:667–671.
7. Inaoka, M., and H. Soda. 1956. *Nature*, 178:202–203.
8. Lutz, L. 1931. *Bull. Soc. Chim. Biol.*, 13:436–457.
9. Lynch, D. L., and L. J. Cotnoir. 1956. *Soil Sci. Soc. Am., Proc.*, 20:367–370.
10. Mollenhof, H. H., F. B. Smith, and P. E. Brown. 1936. *Proc. Iowa Acad. Sci.*, 43:117–121.
11. Norman, A. G. 1930. *Ann. Applied Biol.*, 17:575–613.
12. Norman, A. G. 1934. *Ann. Applied Biol.*, 21:454–475.
13. Pazur, J. H., T. Budovick, E. W. Shuey, and C. E. Georgi. 1957. *Arch. Biochem. Biophys.*, 70:419–425.
14. Pochon, J., and J. Augier. 1956. *Rapports, 6th Intl. Cong. Soil Sci.*, Paris, C:277–280.
15. Pringsheim, H. 1912. *Ztschr. Physiol. Chem.*, 80:376–382.
16. Schmidt, E. G., W. H. Peterson, and E. B. Fred. 1923. *Soil Sci.*, 15:479–488.
17. Simpson, F. J. 1954. *Canad. J. Microbiol.*, 1:131–139.
18. Sorensen, L. H. 1955. *Nature,* 176:74.
19. Stanier, R. Y. 1941. *J. Bacteriol.*, 42:527–559.
20. Van Sumere, C. F., C. Van Sumere–De Preter, and G. A. Ledingham. 1957. *Canad. J. Microbiol.*, 3:761–770.
21. Waksman, S. A. 1931. *Arch. Mikrobiol.*, 2:136–154.
22. Waksman, S. A., and R. A. Diehm. 1931. *Soil Sci.*, 32:97–117.
23. Waksman, S. A., and R. A. Diehm. 1931. *Soil Sci.*, 32:73–95.
24. Yaphe, W. 1957. *Canad. J. Microbiol.*, 3:987–993.

12

Lignin Decomposition

The third most abundant constituent of plant tissues and crop residues is commonly lignin. It is superseded in relative quantity only by cellulose and the hemicelluloses. Certain plants, the woody species in particular, contribute large amounts of lignin to the material to be degraded through the activities of the soil microflora. In forests alone, vast quantities of lignin are continually deposited upon the soil as wood waste, and these must be destroyed either by burning or by biological means.

The large amount of lignin annually entering the soil in plant residues does not accumulate, but rather it slowly and perceptibly disappears. Nevertheless, little is known of the microbiology and decomposition of lignin or of the environmental variables governing its loss. Three factors account for the inadequate state of knowledge: difficulties arising from the chemical complexity of the lignin molecule; difficulties in assaying for this substance; and problems related to the isolation of a purified lignin fraction suitable for use as a microbiological substrate. Much of the early research is of doubtful value because the conclusions were based upon unreliable methods for quantitatively estimating lignin in plant residues. In addition, a considerable portion of the early work on lignin breakdown is open to question since the drastic conditions used to isolate and purify the lignin fraction resulted in preparations decidedly different from those in the original tissue. These difficulties have now been largely overcome.

Within the plant, lignin is found in the secondary layers of the cell wall and also to some extent in the middle lamella. The lignin content of young plants is relatively low, but the quantity increases as the plant matures. Lignin probably never occurs free; usually it is combined with the polysaccharides. It is especially plentiful in woody plants, whereas its concentration is quite low in succulent tissue. Young, immature grasses and legumes commonly contain from 3 to 6 per cent lignin on a dry weight basis while chemical analyses of wood samples from a variety of trees give figures ranging from about 15 to 35 per cent.

Chemistry of Lignin

Lignins found in the many species, genera, and families of the plant kingdom are clearly different chemically from one another, and hence they cannot be considered as substances of uniform structure. Even in a single plant, the chemical composition may change to some extent with the stage of maturity. Prominent among the chemical properties of lignin is its strong resistance to acid hydrolysis, concentrated mineral acids having little effect on the molecule. It is also insoluble in hot water and neutral organic solvents but is solubilized by alkali. Solutions containing lignin give characteristic bands in the ultraviolet region of the light spectrum, with an absorption maximum in the vicinity of 280 mμ. The results of ultraviolet absorption studies show that lignin is a modified benzene derivative.

The lignin molecule contains only three elements—carbon, hydrogen, and oxygen—but the structure is aromatic rather than being of the carbohydrate type as typified by cellulose and the hemicelluloses. Chemical analysis reveals the presence of approximately 64 per cent carbon, 6 per cent hydrogen, and 14 per cent methoxyl groups ($-OCH_3$). These figures are only rough approximations since the composition varies with the source and the method of isolation. The molecule is a polymer of aromatic nuclei with either a single repeating unit or several similar substances as the basic building blocks. The basic unit in lignin seems to be a phenyl-propane (C_6-C_3) type of structure containing one methoxyl-carbon, C_6 representing the benzene ring linked to a C_3 propyl-type side chain. Thus, one aromatic ring is found for each ten carbons. The benzene nucleus contains a hydroxyl group in addition to the methoxyl. The methoxyl concentration varies with the species from which the lignin is derived, but generally about 21 per cent of the lignin in deciduous trees and 15 to 16 per cent of that in cereals and conifers is made up of methoxyl groups. Methoxyl disappearance has sometimes been used to indicate lignin breakdown, but this technique is not sufficiently critical as tissue constituents other than lignin contain methoxyl groups in their structure.

Estimates of the molecular weight of the repeating unit range from about 200 to 1000 depending upon the origin of the lignin and the technique of determining molecular weight. Choice of the technique is important since results obtained on a single preparation depend upon the method used. Determinations of the molecular weight of the lignin molecule itself vary from about 300 to 11,000. The latter figures divided by the molecular weight of the basic unit give the degree of polymerization, a value which clearly cannot be precisely defined.

Several models have been proposed to account for the information available on the structure of the lignin molecule (figure 1). Although these formulas are probably still only working models, they do illustrate the structural nature of the compound and the basic

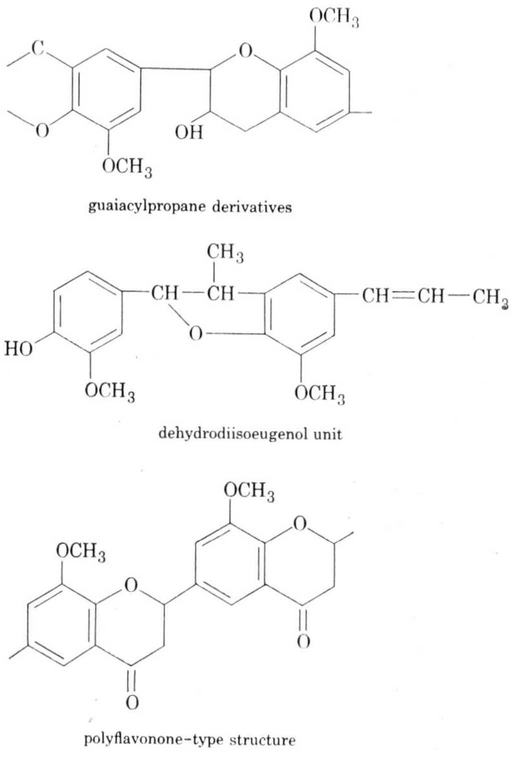

guaiacylpropane derivatives

dehydrodiisoeugenol unit

polyflavonone-type structure

Figure 1. Postulated structures for the repeating unit of lignin.

C_6-C_3 phenyl-propane building block, the presence of an aromatic nucleus, methoxyl groups, and an oxygen bridge. Detailed information on the chemistry of lignin can be found in the book by Brauns and in Siegel's review.

Decomposition

The outstanding microbiological characteristic of lignin is its resistance to enzymatic degradation. The decomposition of lignin proceeds either in the presence or in the absence of O_2, but the rate of loss in both circumstances is characteristically less than that observed for cellulose, hemicelluloses, and other carbohydrates. In short-term experiments, little loss is observed, but slowly, in a period of months, the lignin does disappear. Despite its resistance, this material quite clearly must be metabolized; otherwise it would have accumulated in vast quantities wherever plant remains are subjected to decay.

During decomposition, the microflora consumes the individual organic components of natural materials at different rates. Lignin is the last to show appreciable oxidation. Thus, as the complex organic substrates are metabolized and the water-soluble constituents, cellulose, and hemicelluloses disappear, the lignin content of the decaying residue rises. As a consequence, well-rotted materials have a high percentage of lignin. Because of the increase in relative abundance of the aromatic constituents, it would seem that lignin or lignin-like molecules are probably of significance in the formation of humus. For example, during the aerobic decomposition of corn stalks, two-thirds of the total dry matter is lost in 6 months but only about one-third of the lignin. Consequently, a residue initially containing 14.8 per cent lignin would contain approximately twice that amount one-half year later (figure 2). Such lignin, however, is modified to a certain extent. Among the chemical changes that have occurred in the molecule are a removal of some of the side chains of the aromatic nucleus and a decrease in the number of methoxyl groups. At the same time, the number of phenolic hydroxyls and carboxyls increases. The various new chemical groups that appear may in turn react with nitrogenous substances or other classes of compounds to give phenolic structures similar to those found in the organic fraction of soil. Hence, though a large part of native soil organic matter may be in some way derived from lignin, such constituents are not identical with the lignin of the original plant source.

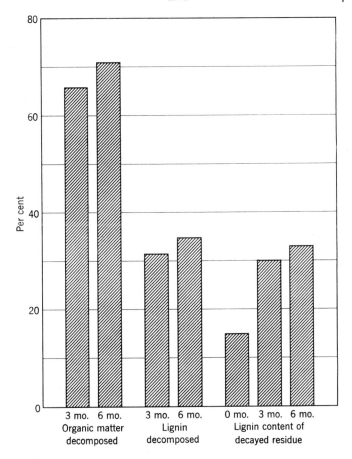

Figure 2. Changes in the lignin fraction of corn stalks during aerobic decomposition (2).

The rate and extent of lignin decomposition is affected by temperature, availability of nitrogen, anaerobiasis, and by constituents of the plant residue undergoing decay. Under optimum conditions in the laboratory and when the temperature is maintained in the vicinity of 30°C, it is common to find not more than one-third of the lignin metabolized in a period of six months and only about half to have been lost at the end of a year. Differences do exist in the microbial degradation of lignins found in different plants. For example, the lignins of alfalfa, oats, and corn stalks are more readily decomposed than the same constituents in wheat and rye straw or in the leaves and

TABLE 1

Decomposition of the Lignin in Oat Plants of Various Ages in the Presence and Absence of Inorganic Nitrogen (24)

Age of Plant	Lignin Content	Decomposition Period	Lignin Decomposed	
			No N	+NH$_4$
days	%	days	%	%
59	6.7	47	26.9	–
		125	54.2	–
86	11.7	47	27.8	25.0
		125	29.3	52.6
112	15.7	47	17.4	19.7
		125	22.5	46.6

needles of trees (21, 24). Some of the differences in rate may arise from structural dissimilarities between the lignins, but the association of the aromatic constituent with polysaccharides may alter its susceptibility in a manner analogous to the stimulation of cellulose decomposition by readily oxidizable carbohydrates. Here too, the presence of an accessible source of energy can provide nutrients to support a larger microflora that could bring about greater losses. Age of plant is another important variable. The lignin of young tissue disappears more rapidly than that in mature plants (table 1), but the explanation for the differences remains obscure. Part of the influence of maturity on lignin turnover may result from the supply of minerals in the tissue which is undergoing decay, but physical and chemical changes in the carbonaceous nutrients themselves cannot be discounted.

There has been some controversy in the past regarding losses of lignin under anaerobiasis, but it is now clear that the anaerobic conversion does occur. Nevertheless, the organisms concerned have not yet been identified. Bacteria are probably the responsible agents but, until the microorganisms are isolated and characterized, no unequivocal statement can be made. As with the aerobic transformation, the anaerobic decomposition is slower for lignin than for cellulose and the hemicelluloses. Anaerobic lignoclastic activity is invariably slow, and half of the substrate is still recovered after a year and a half (1, 4).

Temperature has a profound influence upon the rate and extent of breakdown. Little loss occurs at 7°C, and progressively higher temperatures favor the active microflora. At 37°C, the oxidation is extensive, and appreciable quantities disappear. Above the mesophilic temperature range, thermophiles participate in lignin destruction, and enrichment cultures of thermophilic bacteria degrade the lignin of finely ground wood in a relatively short period (22). Unfortunately, the thermophilic organisms involved in the oxidation of lignin also have never been isolated in pure culture.

Several chemical alterations occur during the decomposition of lignin (table 2). Since methoxyl groups are prominent in the molecule, it is not unexpected that they are metabolized as the lignin is degraded. Because of their exposed position, however, methoxyl groups are particularly prone to enzymatic cleavage, and they are oxidized more readily than the rest of the molecule. The rate of methoxyl decrease, when expressed as a percentage of the lignin remaining, is greatest under anaerobiasis, less in waterlogged circumstances, and least in aerobic environments. This suggests an enhancement of the preferential metabolism of methoxyls in the absence of O_2, i.e., a magnification of the differential breakdown between various portions of the

TABLE 2

Some Changes in the Lignin Fraction of Oat Straw during Decomposition (6)

Days of Incubation	Methoxyl Content	Carboxyl Content	Cation Exchange Capacity
	%	meq/100 g	meq/100 g
0	11.48	81	44
14	11.42	85	44
40	11.28	101	74
88	10.37	107	81
135	8.66	117	110
180	8.96	127	109
244	9.00	115	102
355	7.71	142	118
452	7.99	141	131

molecule (20). In investigations of the rotting of natural organic materials rather than fractions isolated therefrom, it is necessary to differentiate between methoxyl groups derived from lignin and those associated with carbohydrate fractions. A large part of the methoxyl loss may originate in the breakdown of the latter substrates. Parallelling the methoxyl cleavage during decomposition, there is an increase in the cation exchange capacity of the lignin; this may result in part from the loss of methoxyl groups, which would provide free hydroxyls to act in the retention of cations.

The lignin in most natural organic materials protects associated carbonaceous substances from destruction. The protective influence does not appear to arise from any toxicity of the lignin since lignin preparations do not retard microbiological decomposition (23). To study this phenomenon directly, delignified fractions of plant materials containing varying percentages of lignin and cellulose can be prepared. These may range from preparations composed almost entirely of cellulose to those with none of the lignin removed. If these substances are placed in culture media into which are inoculated pure cultures of various bacteria, the total amount of organic material degraded and the percentage of cellulose oxidized are inversely proportional to the lignin concentration, and the lowest carbon and cellulose loss occurs in the preparations with the highest percentage of lignin. In addition, the hemicelluloses in plants having a high lignin content are less susceptible to microbial digestion (1, 10). As a rule, natural products very rich in lignin such as sawdust or coir fiber are resistant to biological decay, woody materials with less lignin are somewhat more susceptible, while tissues low in lignin are most available to microorganisms. The lignin retardation is not physiological, at least not in the sense of a toxicity. Its effect in retarding the microbiological degradation of organic constituents of crop remains probably results from a physical or physico-chemical barrier set up by the close interlinkage between lignins and the hemicelluloses and cellulose of the plant cell wall, possibly by means of a lignin encrustation which mechanically separates the microorganism from the carbohydrate.

Microbiology

Research in lignin microbiology has been delayed by numerous problems, some of which have only been solved in recent years. It has been pointed out previously that a major obstacle encountered in these studies was the lack of a valid method for assaying quantitatively the amount of lignin in decaying organic remains. The problem of chemical determination has led to many erroneous conclusions and claims for the capacity of one or another organism to utilize lignin. A second difficulty arose in studies designed to test the ability of individual strains to attack purified lignins. Frequently, the extracted fractions contained solvents or polysaccharides which by themselves supported microbial growth. Alternatively, many of the prepared lignins were so drastically altered from the natural material that they were toxic to biochemical transformations not known to be affected by the presence of this tissue component. The so-called native lignin obtained by the method of Brauns (5) overcomes the latter shortcoming because no drastic treatments are involved in the isolation.

Some studies of microbiological lignin metabolism have used as a criterion of utilization the disappearance of methoxyl groups or of sodium lignosulfonate from culture media. However, the decrease in the concentration of substrate in the culture filtrate often can be accounted for by the adsorption of the organic molecule onto the mycelium or cells of the microorganism (7). There is also evidence that a number of filamentous fungi common in soil can synthesize lignin-like substances as part of their hyphae. Such lignin-like products have been found in *Cladosporium, Helminthosporium, Humicola, Dematium, Alternaria, Aspergillus, Metarrhizum,* and *Gliocladium* in amounts up to about one-fourth of the dry weight of the mycelium (19). The presence in microbial cells of compounds of this type, whether structurally similar to plant lignins or merely related to them in only certain properties, presents a problem to the microbiologist concerned with the oxidations carried out by a mixed flora.

Many of the Basidiomycetes are capable of degrading lignin, but the reaction is invariably slow. Because of the slow growth of the organisms, little is yet known of the cultural or environmental factors affecting the oxidation. The limited information presently available indicates that the microflora functioning in aerobic lignin decomposition at moderate temperatures consists largely of the higher fungi. In addition to the genera cited in table 3, *Agaricus, Armillaria, Coprinus, Cortinellus, Fomes, Ganoderma, Lenzites, Marasmius, Panus, Pleurotus, Polyporus, Polystictus, Poria, Stereum, Trametes,* and *Ustulina* contain active representatives.

TABLE 3

Decomposition of Lignin and Cellulose in Beech Leaves (17)

Fungus	Lignin Decomposed	Cellulose Decomposed
	%	%
Clavaria dendroidea	51.2	33.1
Clitocybe alexandri	32.3	6.4
Collybia longipes	30.9	59.1
Flammula carbonaria	35.9	56.0
Hypholoma fasciculare	43.1	59.1
Lepiota amianthina	53.3	43.2
Mycena polygramma	70.9	85.7
Pholiota mutabilis	53.9	73.4

Two methods have been in general use to demonstrate lignoclastic capacities. One entails a determination of the disappearance of lignin when portions of sterile plants are inoculated with pure cultures of suspected organisms. The other technique involves the use of isolated and purified lignin preparations. For example, *Poria subacida, Polyporus abietinus*, and *Polyporus versicolor* develop in media where the sole carbon and energy source is native lignin. With certain of these fungi, however, the organisms must be adapted to utilize the aromatic compound by prolonged cultivation in glucose-lignin media. The adaptation is accomplished by making each serial transfer into culture solutions with progressively lower concentrations of glucose. Once adapted, the fungi grow in media where carbon is supplied in the form of other lignin products, e.g., aspen lignin, calcium lignosulfonate, and alkali lignin (8, 11).

Most fungi which attack lignin also utilize cellulose (table 3). Commonly, the latter material is the more available of the two, and growth is sparse in lignin-containing media. In one study, for example, 44 of a total of 46 soil-inhabiting Basidiomycetes could degrade both lignin and cellulose. This population included species of *Clitocybe, Collybia, Mycena*, and *Marasmius*. Even in pure cultures of these fungi, periods of 6 to 7 months were required for half the lignin to be metabolized. On the other hand, some higher fungi are somewhat specialized for the consumption of lignin, for they decompose up to twice as much lignin as cellulose. Further, occasional fungi degrade the lignin of vegetable matter but are without effect on the cellulose (18).

Plant pathologists have divided the wood-destroying fungi into a brown-rotting group which affects the cellulose of wood but not the lignin and a group of white-rotting fungi which attacks both lignin and cellulosic constituents. *Polystictus, Armillaria, Polyporus, Stereum, Ganoderma, Pleurotus, Trametes, Fomes,* and *Ustulina* are classified as white-rotting fungi. Frequently, cellulose decomposition by the white-rotting organisms only becomes prominent late in the decay of the wood, after appreciable lignin has disappeared. Bavendamm (3) has proposed a simple and rapid technique to determine the lignoclastic capacity of fungi involved in rotting. He suggested the addition to agar media of compounds like tannic acid which, in the presence of a white rot fungus, resulted in the formation of brownish zones in the agar. Those pathogenic fungi not utilizing lignin, the brown rots, produced no zones of discoloration. The test presumably involves an oxidation of phenolic substances, a reaction which is correlated with lignin utilization. Many exceptions to this relationship exist although there may be some relation between lignin decomposing fungi and the Bavendamm tannic acid reaction (16).

A bacterium capable of degrading lignin has yet to be isolated in pure culture. Several claims have been made for specific bacteria, but the isolates apparently were developing upon the extractant rather than upon the lignin. ZoBell and Stadler (25), however, have demonstrated that the addition of purified lignin to lake water leads to a slow but highly significant increase in the bacterial flora of the water and a parallel utilization of O_2. The O_2 consumed in a 30-day period by enrichment cultures of the lignoclastic bacteria corresponds to an oxidation of up to 15 per cent of the purified lignin. The enrichments consist mainly of short, gram negative rods. It has already been pointed out that bacteria are concerned in the thermophilic decomposition of the lignin in ground wood and that the anaerobic digestion of lignin is possibly bacterial. There is thus considerable presumptive evidence implicating bacteria in the decomposition, but their role is undoubtedly secondary to the fungi.

Biochemistry of Lignin Decomposition

The biochemistry of lignin degradation, the mechanism of the enzymatic cleavage, and intermediates in the process have still to be

clearly established. The enzyme concerned, assuming a single catalyst, has sometimes been termed ligninase or lignase, but such nomenclature is still premature. From the rate of substrate turnover, it is
clear that end-products must be formed slowly, and these probably
are oxidized almost as rapidly as they appear. Because the molecule
is a polymer of aromatic nuclei, the likeliest intermediates are low
molecular weight aromatic substances similar to those shown in figure 3. Indeed, the formation of vanillin and vanillic acid during the
fungus rotting of spruce sawdust has been reported (13).

In order to simplify the difficulties inherent in studies of the enzymatic breakdown of the lignin molecule, simplified systems are used.

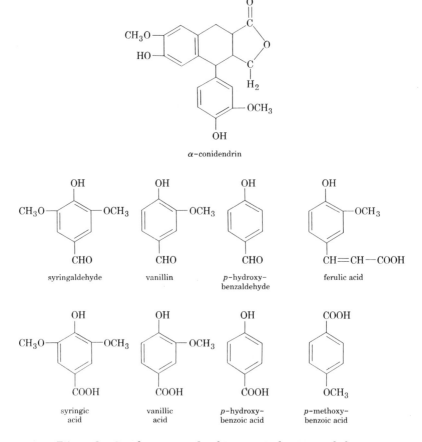

Figure 3. Simple compounds of interest in lignin metabolism.

It is assumed that the larger molecule is degraded to give products similar or identical with the simpler structures; thus, the culture fluid following growth of *Polyporus versicolor* acts upon both pine wood lignin and simple phenolic compounds such as conidendrin, syringaldehyde, and vanillin. In its action on the pine wood lignin, the extracellular enzyme preparation from *P. versicolor* seems to make the substrate more soluble. This enzyme system, therefore, may be functioning by converting the lignin to forms more available for subsequent digestion (9).

A common model system for the study of the biochemistry of lignin decomposition contains α-conidendrin (figure 3) as substrate. A *Flavobacterium* sp. utilizing α-conidendrin as sole source of carbon and energy has been isolated. The bacterium decomposes almost all of the α-conidendrin supplied in a period of 3 weeks with a resultant decrease in the methoxyl concentration in the medium. The decomposition seems to proceed via the formation of vanillic acid which is ultimately converted to protocatechuic acid (14, 15). Various soil fungi oxidize vanillin, vanillic acid, syringic acid, syringaldehyde, ferulic acid, *p*-hydroxybenzoic acid, and *p*-hydroxybenzaldehyde, frequently with the cleavage of the benzene ring. Vanillin and ferulic acid are converted to vanillic acid prior to ring rupture and, in a similar fashion, syringaldehyde is oxidized to syringic acid (12, 13). In the removal of the methoxyl, a hydroxyl group takes its place on the benzene nucleus. The final cleavage of the aromatic ring proceeds by one of several mechanisms which will be discussed subsequently.

In summary, lignin is probably depolymerized to give simple aromatic substances such as vanillin and vanillic acid or possibly other methoxylated aromatic structures. The enzyme system is undoubtedly extracellular. In the final stages, the remaining methoxyls are removed with the formation of hydroxy-benzene derivatives which are ultimately cleaved to give low molecular weight organic acids. On the other hand, a partial or complete methoxyl loss may precede liberation of the simple aromatic products.

REFERENCES

Reviews

Brauns, F. E. 1952. *The chemistry of lignin*. Academic Press, New York.
Campbell, W. G. 1952. The biological decomposition of wood. In L. E. Wise

and E. C. Jahn, eds., *Wood chemistry*. Reinhold Publishing Corp., New York. Vol. 2, pp. 1061–1116.

Gottlieb, S., and M. J. Pelczar, Jr. 1951. Microbiological aspects of lignin degradation. *Bacteriol. Rev.*, 15:55–76.

Siegel, S. M. 1956. The chemistry and physiology of lignin formation. *Quarterly Rev. Biol.*, 31:1–18.

Literature cited

1. Acharya, C. N. 1935. *Biochem. J.*, 29:1459–1467.
2. Bartlett, J. B., and A. G. Norman. 1938. *Soil Sci. Soc. Am., Proc.*, 3:210–216.
3. Bavendamm, W. 1928. *Zent. Bakteriol.*, II, 76:172–227.
4. Boruff, C. S., and A. M. Buswell. 1934. *J. Am. Chem. Soc.*, 56:886–888.
5. Brauns, F. E. 1939. *J. Am. Chem. Soc.*, 61:2120–2127.
6. Broadbent, F. E. 1954. *Soil Sci. Soc. Am., Proc.*, 18:165–169.
7. Day, W. C., S. Gottlieb, and M. J. Pelczar, Jr. 1953. *Applied Microbiol.*, 1:78–81.
8. Day, W. C., M. J. Pelczar, Jr., and S. Gottlieb. 1949. *Arch. Biochem.*, 23:360–369.
9. Dion, W. M. 1952. *Canad. J. Botany*, 30:9–21.
10. Fuller, W. H., and A. G. Norman. 1943. *J. Bacteriol.*, 46:291–297.
11. Gottlieb, S., W. C. Day, and M. J. Pelczar, Jr. 1950. *Phytopathol.*, 40:926–935.
12. Henderson, M. E. K. 1956. *J. Gen. Microbiol.*, 14:684–691.
13. Henderson, M. E. K., and V. C. Farmer. 1955. *J. Gen. Microbiol.*, 12:37–46.
14. Konetzka, W. A., M. J. Pelczar, Jr., and S. Gottlieb. 1952. *J. Bacteriol.*, 63:771–778.
15. Konetzka, W. A., E. T. Woodings, and J. Stove. 1957. *Bacteriol. Proc.*, 1957:135.
16. Ledingham, G. A., and G. A. Adams. 1942. *Canad. J. Research*, C, 20:13–27.
17. Lindeberg, G. 1946. *Arkiv Botanik*, 33A(10):1–16.
18. Lindeberg, G. 1947. *Proc. 4th Intl. Cong. Microbiol.*, Copenhagen, pp. 401–403.
19. Pinck, L. A., and F. E. Allison. 1944. *Soil Sci.*, 57:155–161.
20. Sircar, S. S. G., S. C. De, and H. D. Bhowmick. 1940. *Indian J. Agric. Sci.*, 10:152–157.
21. Tenney, F. G., and S. A. Waksman. 1929. *Soil Sci.*, 28:55–84.
22. Virtanen, A. I., and J. Hukki. 1946. *Suomen Kemistelehti*, 19B:4–13.
23. Waksman, S. A., and T. C. Cordon. 1938. *Soil Sci.*, 45:199–206.
24. Waksman, S. A., and I. J. Hutchings. 1936. *Soil Sci.*, 42:119–130.
25. ZoBell, C. E., and J. Stadler. 1940. *Arch. Hydrobiol.*, 37:163–171.

13

Microbiology
of Other Polysaccharides

The decomposition of two plant polysaccharide types, cellulose and the hemicelluloses, has already been considered. Together with lignin, these two carbohydrates comprise the bulk of the crop debris that undergoes decay. Several other polysaccharides, however, are found in plant tissues or in microorganisms, and their decomposition occupies a degree of prominence in soil. The metabolism of five additional polysaccharide types will be discussed in detail—starch, the pectic substances, inulin, gums, and chitin.

Starch

Starch is second only to cellulose as the most common hexose polymer in the plant realm. Starch serves the plant as a storage product, and as such it is the major reserve carbohydrate. This material occurs in large amounts in leaves carrying out photosynthesis, but the polysaccharide is distributed in the xylem, phloem, cortex, and pith of the stems of many species as well as in tubers, bulbs, corms, underground rhizomes, fruits, and seeds. Typically, the starch of higher plants accumulates in definite grains which may vary from 1 to 150 μ in diameter, the size depending upon the species. Microorganisms may also accumulate the polysaccharide.

Plant starches usually contain two components, amylose and amylopectin. The former has a linear structure built up of 200 to

500 or more glucose units linked together by an α-1,4-glucosidic bonding.

In amylopectin, the individual glucose units are likewise bound together by α-1,4-linkages, but the molecule is branched and has side chains attached through α-1,6-glucosidic linkages. In the highly branched structure of amylopectin, the distance between branch points is approximately 5 to 8 glucose residues. The two components of starch differ both physically and chemically, and they can be separated by a number of simple procedures. Starches commonly contain 70 to 80 per cent amylopectin and 20 to 30 per cent amylose, but exceptions are not uncommon; for example, the starch within the seeds of waxy corn contains no amylose, whereas that in wrinkled peas is essentially free of amylopectin.

Starch disappears rapidly when subjected to the activity of the soil population, and its decomposition proceeds at a greater rate than the microbiologically induced losses of cellulose and hemicelluloses. Likewise, it is decomposed more readily than mannan, galactan, xylan, and a seaweed pentosan (8). Under conditions of limiting O_2, a fermentation occurs with the formation of appreciable lactic, acetic, and butyric acids. The process of degradation goes on at a good pace even under total anaerobiasis. Measurements of starch decomposing activity can be made by a determination of the accumulation of reducing sugars when toluene-treated soils are incubated with starch. Toluene is an antiseptic so that the procedure presumably measures only the enzyme preformed by the microflora (9). The end-product of the soil-enzyme hydrolysis is glucose as the maltose formed from starch is rapidly hydrolyzed to yield the simple sugar.

Bacteria, fungi, and actinomycetes have the capacity to hydrolyze starch, and the physiological heterogeneity of the active flora suggests that the decomposition can take place in diverse environments. From 50 to 80 per cent of the bacteria and actinomycetes appearing on dilution plates can utilize the polysaccharide; therefore, soils frequently contain 10^6 to 10^7 or more starch hydrolyzers per

TABLE 1

Some Microbial Genera Utilizing Starch

Bacteria		Actinomycetes	Fungi
Achromobacter	Flavobacterium	Micromonospora	Aspergillus
Bacillus	Micrococcus	Nocardia	Fomes
Chromobacterium	Pseudomonas	Streptomyces	Fusarium
Clostridium	Sarcina		Polyporus
Cytophaga	Serratia		Rhizopus

gram. The organisms are particularly numerous in proximity to the plant root system, but their proportional incidence in the root zone is not significantly different from that in soil taken at a distance from the plant (13).

Some of the more ubiquitous genera implicated in starch utilization are listed in table 1. Among the bacteria are gram positive and gram negative genera, spore formers and non-spore formers, aerobes and obligate anaerobes as well as representatives of many physiologically different groups. Starch is generally an excellent carbon source for most actinomycetes, and strains of *Streptomyces, Nocardia,* and *Micromonospora* make use of the carbohydrate. Many filamentous fungi are also capable of excreting the appropriate hydrolytic enzymes; yeasts, on the other hand, rarely attack the polysaccharide. Organisms using starch as a carbon and energy source exhibit no particular substrate specificities, many attacking simple sugars, organic acids, pentosans, and sometimes cellulose. When pure starch is added to soil in the presence of sufficient mineral nitrogen, the diversity of microbial types becomes evident. After approximately 16 hours, the population is dominated by large rods, fungi, and actinomycetes, and these increase in abundance with time. Water-saturated samples develop an anaerobic population made up largely of species of *Clostridium* (18, 20).

Starch-hydrolyzing enzymes, the amylases, are characteristically extracellular and remain in the culture fluid after removal of the microorganism. Two amylases are commonly concerned in the microbial breakdown of starch, α- and β-amylase. β-Amylase acts upon both amylose and amylopectin, cleaving every second glucose-glucose bond from the terminal end of the molecule. Hence, maltose fragments are liberated from the straight chain of amylose, and significant quantities of other intermediates do not accumulate. β-Amylase is incapable of catalyzing the hydrolysis of branch points of amylopectin, however, and a residual dextrin fraction in addition to the disaccharide, maltose, remains. In contrast, the products formed by α-amylase in the depolymerization of amylopectin have a greater molecular weight than maltose. Both the enzymes act upon the 1,4-linkage, but the hydrolysis is retarded once the amylopectin branch point is encountered. Several other microbial enzymes hydrolyze the branch point positions. The maltose that is formed is converted to glucose by mediation of the enzyme α-glucosidase so that starch is transformed ultimately to glucose. The simple sugars are water-soluble and penetrate the cell, there to be used as energy sources for growth and protoplasmic synthesis. Diagrammatically, the process may be visualized as follows:

$$\underset{\text{(glucose)}_n}{\text{starch}} \xrightarrow{\text{amylase}} \underset{\text{(glucose)}_2}{\text{maltose}} \xrightarrow{\alpha\text{-glucosidase}} \text{glucose} \qquad (I)$$

Starch-hydrolyzing enzymes are usually adaptive, but the ability of microorganisms to form amylolytic enzymes depends upon the type of starch. Many amylolytic isolates are capable of growing upon the polysaccharide obtained from one plant but not from another, and some bacteria are highly specific for one or a few related starches (24). Because amylases are extracellular, the possibility exists that the enzymes are adsorbed and possibly inactivated by clays. There is evidence, however, that the decomposition of starch by the soil flora is not appreciably affected by the presence of various clays (17).

Pectic Substances

Pectic substances never make up a large portion of the dry matter of plants, commonly less than 1 per cent. The importance of these polysaccharides rests upon their relationship to the physical structure of the plant and to certain diseases produced by soil-borne and other pathogens. As the calcium and magnesium pectates, the pectic substances are found abundantly in the middle lamella, a tissue constituent located between individual cells. The primary and the secondary cell walls also contain polysaccharides of this type.

The pectic carbohydrates are complex polysaccharides composed of galacturonic acid units bound to one another in a long chain.

```
     COOH              H    OH            COOH
      |                 |    |             |
 —O⌐  C——O  H      H  C——C  ⌐—O⌐  C——O  H
    ╱ H    ╲  |     |╱  OH   H╲    ╱ H    ╲  |
   C   OH  H  C     C    H     C  C   OH  H  C
   |╲      ╱|      |╲    |    ╱|  |╲      ╱|
   H  C——C  ⌐—O⌐   C——O  H   H  C——C  ⌐—O—
      |    |          |    |          |    |
      H    OH        COOH             H    OH
```

The carboxyl of the galacturonic acid building block may be partially or completely esterified with methyl groups and may be partially or entirely neutralized by various cations. There are three types of pectic substances: (a) protopectin, a water-insoluble constituent of the cell wall; (b) pectin, a water-soluble polymer of galacturonic acid which contains methyl ester linkages; and (c) pectic acids, the water-soluble galacturonic acid polymers that are essentially devoid of methyl ester linkages. Each of these three classes represents a group of closely related substances. The pectic acids consist of long chains of galacturonic acids with the useful property of forming rigid pectate gels when treated with calcium salts. Pectins are polymerized molecules whose carboxyls are esterified with methyl groups, and protopectins are related to pectins but differ by their poor water-solubility. Pectic acids can be produced from pectins by treatment with dilute alkali, a conversion of $(RCOOCH_3)_n$ to $(RCOOH)_n$ where RCOOH designates the free galacturonic acid.

Bacteria, fungi, and actinomycetes are capable of acting upon and hydrolyzing pectin, protopectin and pectic acid, using the polysaccharides as carbon and energy sources to support proliferation. As a rule, pectic substances are readily decomposed by microorganisms in soil and in culture media. The diversity of microbial types and the ability of active genera to colonize a variety of soils and substrates can be taken as an indication that pectolytic microfloras are large. Soils generally contain 10^5 to 10^6 pectolytic microorganisms per gram, many of which are actinomycetes (26), although lower counts are occasionally observed. Microorganisms utilizing pectic substances are common not only in soil but in the root zone, and counts in excess of 10^7 pectolytic bacteria per gram have been reported in soil immediately adjacent to plant roots. Species of *Bacillus, Clostridium,* and *Pseudomonas* are frequently among the dominant pectin hydrolyzers under grass (14). Acidity affects the composition of the flora; thus, the population of pectolytic streptomycetes is favored by high pH while the fungi become more significant with a fall in pH. In forest litter and compost heaps, fungi and *Pseudomonas* spp. are particularly vigorous (27).

The biological retting of fiber plants such as flax, hemp, and jute relies on microbial enzymes to digest the pectic substances of the middle lamella. The resultant solubilization of the polysaccharides leads to a loosening of the cellulose fibers from the residual tissues. Among the organisms that cause natural retting are *Bacillus* and *Clostridium* spp.

Pathogenicity and the decay of vegetables and fruits are often associated with the hydrolysis of pectic materials. Some pathogens solubilize the middle lamella by means of their pectic enzymes and thereby separate individual plant cells from one another. The loosened cells then either autolyze or are killed by the pathogen or by secondary invaders. Generally, any factor which reduces the enzymatic activity of the pathogen decreases the disintegration of the host's tissues. Despite the clear association between pectic attack and pathogenicity, the possession of these enzymes, particularly by organisms tested only in culture media, cannot be taken as conclusive evidence for the production of pathological symptoms because many pectolytic organisms never cause disease. The failure of pectolytic microorganisms to attack higher plants may result from their inability to use tissue components as nutrients or, if invasion and growth is successful, the tissue environment may be deleterious to pectic enzyme production.

Pectic enzymes appear to be related to wilt diseases caused by certain soil-borne fungi. In these wilts, particularly among those caused by *Fusarium* and *Verticillium* spp., the fungus enters the host by way of the roots and grows up through the vascular system. Culture filtrates of the tomato wilt fungus, *Fusarium oxysporum* f. *lycopersici*, induce the wilting and vascular discoloration typical of diseased tomatoes. The filtrates contain pectic enzymes which, upon purification, still produce typical disease symptoms when placed in contact with tomato cuttings, i.e., wilting, vascular discoloration, vessel plugging, and decreased transpiration. A mechanism for fusarium wilts has been formulated which proposes that the fungus produces pectin-digesting enzymes in the vascular system, and the enzymes catalyze the decomposition of the pectic materials in the xylem cell walls. In the process, pectin fragments are released into the vessels, there to react with calcium or similar cations to form pectin gels. Such viscous gels effect a mechanical blockage to the movement of water in the conducting vessels, and the wilt ensues (11). The hypothesis of an enzymatic mechanism for wilting has not gone unchallenged, and other hypotheses have been suggested.

Three enzymes or classes of enzymes are concerned in the degradation of pectic substances: (a) protopectinase, which decomposes protopectin with the formation of soluble pectin; (b) pectin methylesterase (PME), which hydrolyzes the methyl ester linkage of pectin to yield pectic acid and methanol—

$$\text{pectin} \xrightarrow{\text{PME}} \text{pectic acid} + \text{methanol} \qquad \text{(II)}$$

(c) polygalacturonase (PG), which destroys the linkages between galacturonic acid units of either pectin or pectic acid with the release of smaller chains and ultimately free galacturonic acid. The interrelationships between the various reactions are summarized in figure 1. The existence of a separate catalyst having the properties ascribed to protopectinase is still in doubt. Further, a number of polygalacturonase types are known.

Polygalacturonase and pectin methylesterase are formed and released into the surroundings as extracellular enzymes. These catalysts do not seem to be affected by the presence of clays, which frequently lower the activity of extracellular enzymes (17). PME and PG are apparently adaptive in most microorganisms, synthesized only in the presence of the specific polygalacturonic acid substrates. In several species, however, pectic enzymes may be constitutive, i.e., produced by microorganisms during growth on compounds unrelated to the specific substrate for the enzyme. In the hydrolysis of pectic acid by PG, only small amounts of free galacturonic acid accumulate during the early stages of decomposition; di-, tri-, tetra-, and penta-

Figure 1. Substrate specificities of pectic enzymes.

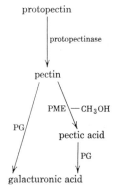

galacturonic acids are produced by the enzyme. In the later stages of the hydrolysis, the longer molecules disappear under the catalytic influence of PG, and the concentration of free galacturonic acid rises (7, 16).

Inulin

Inulin is a polysaccharide composed of fructose units, that is, a fructosan. The inulin molecule has approximately 25 to 28 fructose residues in the carbohydrate chain bound in 1,2-linkage. The substance occurs in a number of plants as the storage carbohydrate, replacing starch in this regard, and it has been reported in tubers, roots, stems, and leaves.

There is also a polysaccharide made up of fructose units in which the sugar units are bound together through the number 2 carbon of one fructose and the number 6 carbon of the next sugar in the chain. This is a 2,6-fructosan.

Many microorganisms utilize inulin. Bacteria of the genera *Pseudomonas, Flavobacterium, Beneckea, Micrococcus, Cytophaga,* and *Clostridium,* many streptomycetes, and a heterogeneous group of fungi use the fructose polysaccharide as carbon source for growth. The enzyme converting inulin to smaller fructose units is called inulinase. Little attention has been given to the transformation despite the large population active on the carbohydrate. But it has been shown that inulinase, an extracellular catalyst, is highly active in several fungi, and up to 80 per cent of the substrate is hydrolyzed in 14 to 24 hours (2). On the basis of the rapid turnover exhibited in vitro, it is likely that fructosans are readily transformed in soil.

Certain microorganisms possess two fructosanases—inulinase, which by the nature of its substrate is a 1,2-fructosanase, and a 2,6-fructosanase. These enzymes are both extracellular. Some fungi, e.g., *Penicillium funiculosum,* produce both the 1,2- and the 2,6-

fructosanases while others produce only one or the other of the polysaccharide-splitting enzymes. The enzymes are generally not formed when the organisms are grown on simple sugars but are excreted in appreciable amounts in the presence of the fructosan. The mechanism of action, however, is somewhat different for the two catalysts. The 2,6-fructosanase of a *Streptomyces* sp. leads to the accumulation of levanbiose, a sugar containing two fructose units. The hydrolysis of fructosan by the 1,2-fructosanase (inulinase) of *Aspergillus fumigatus*, on the other hand, results in the accumulation of slightly longer chains of fructose units. In contrast, the fructosanases of *Fusarium moniliforme* and *P. funiculosum* transform the fructosan entirely to fructose with no accumulation of significant quantities of intermediary compounds (15). Apparently, there are several end-products of fructosanase action—short fructose polymers, levanbiose, or free fructose. Nevertheless, the ultimate fate of the large molecule is an enzymatic degradation to units small enough to enter the cell. The simple fragments but not the original polysaccharide are oxidized within the microorganism to provide energy for proliferation. Extracellular catalysts of the fructosanase type thus bridge the gap between unavailable and available carbonaceous nutrients.

Gums and Related Polysaccharides

Gums are exuded by the bark, leaves, and roots of higher plants. The property classing a material as a gum is the capacity to swell in water and to form viscous solutions. Chemically, the plant gums are related to the hemicelluloses but differ in that, following mild acid treatment to liberate the simple sugars, a residue remains which is resistant to hydrolysis. Two of the more completely characterized gums are gum arabic and mesquite gum. The former contains arabinose, rhamnose, galactose, and glucuronic acid in its structure while mesquite gum is composed of arabinose, galactose, and methyluronic acid in a ratio of 4:2:1. Gum arabic is obtained from the bark of *Acacia* spp., mesquite gum from the exudate of the bark of mesquite, *Prosopis juliflora*.

Gums are probably of no great consequence to the bulk of materials entering the soil, but they are important in carbon transformations of soil organic matter because many microorganisms synthesize gums or related substances during growth. Not all of the bacterial gums are included in the class of plant constituents delineated by the definition above, but the microbial products are typically slimy or viscous in nature, and their structure is generally that of a polysaccharide. For example, the extracellular gum produced by several *Rhizobium* spp. is a polysaccharide composed of glucose, pentose, and glucuronic acids while many species of *Bacillus* form viscous materials about their cells which are polymers of fructose or glucose. Other bacteria produce gums or slimes which yield arabinose and galactose upon acid hydrolysis.

The decomposition and utilization of gums by microorganisms in a variety of environmental circumstances have been the subject of some inquiry. Aerobic and anaerobic mesophiles as well as thermophiles utilize plant gums, and the microbiological degradation of gum arabic, gum tragacanth, and mesquite gum has been demonstrated (10, 19). In addition to isolates of *Pseudomonas, Cytophaga,* and *Achromobacter,* spore-forming bacteria and Basidiomycetes can digest one or several plant gums. It is apparent, however, that the few organisms cited are not indicative of the paucity of microbial types but rather are a consequence of inadequate study of the transformation. For example, all 114 *Bacillus* strains tested by Blackwood (4) exhibited enzymatic activity upon barley gum although the rate of breakdown varied markedly from strain to strain.

In contrast to the meager information on plant gums, considerable attention has been given to the chemistry and decomposition of the gums synthesized by bacteria pathogenic to man, particularly that of *Diplococcus pneumoniae.* The capsular polysaccharide gum of the pneumonia bacterium is digested by a gram negative, spore-forming bacillus. From the culture of the bacillus, an enzyme preparation can be obtained capable of converting the capsular polysaccharide of type III *D. pneumoniae* to simple sugars. This enzyme exhibits a considerable degree of specificity as it hydrolyzes the polysaccharide of type III but not those of type I and type II *D. pneumoniae* nor several other capsular carbohydrates. Other soil bacteria decompose the polysaccharides of type I and type II pneumococci, however. The responsible strains have been placed in the genera *Bacillus, Flavobacterium,* and *Saccharobacterium* (3, 22).

Chitin

Chitin is the most common polysaccharide in nature whose basic unit is an amino sugar. This polysaccharide is a structural constituent giving mechanical strength to organisms containing it. Chitin is insoluble in water, organic solvents, concentrated alkali, or dilute mineral acids, but it can be solubilized and degraded either enzymatically or by treatment with concentrated mineral acids. In structure, chitin consists of a long chain of N-acetylglucosamine units in linear arrangement. The empirical formula is $(C_6H_9O_4 \cdot NHCOCH_3)_n$, and the pure compound contains 6.9 per cent nitrogen.

Chitin is undoubtedly an important substance in the carbon cycle in soil not only because of its availability to microbiological attack but also as a result of its continuous microbial biosynthesis. Soil chitin originates in the remains of insects that spend part or all of their life undergound, but it also arises from fungus tissue in which it is a common constituent. Consequently, even in the absence of added chitin, the aminopolysaccharide is formed in soil by the biosynthetic action of the fungus population. Here, then, is a native component of the soil's organic fraction, one whose supply is replenished as a result of microbial cell synthesis. The supply is thus independent of insect remains.

Chitin is produced by members of both the plant and animal kingdoms. In the cell walls of most fungi, considerable amounts of the polysaccharide are deposited. The carbohydrate is also part of the cellular structure of many basidiomycetes and of some yeasts, but it is not found in the cell walls of bacteria, actinomycetes, or in several groups of Phycomycetes and Ascomycetes. The chitin component of the fungus hyphal wall can make up a large proportion of the total cellular material, but growth conditions, age, temperature, and pH alter the concentration. Filamentous fungi commonly contain 2.6 to 26.2 per cent chitin on a dry weight basis (5). Chitin is found in the skeletons of a number of invertebrate animals, and a substantial quantity of the polysaccharide becomes incorporated into soil in the form of insect remains.

The application of chitin to soil stimulates the microflora, and this chemically stable compound is mineralized in relatively short periods. Pure chitin has a narrow C:N ratio so that the nitrogen supply exceeds the microbiological requirement. Consequently, mineral nitrogen will accumulate provided that the population is active. In periods of less than 2 months, 30 to 60 per cent of the chitin nitrogen is mineralized in aerobic environments, but the chitin is decomposed more slowly than proteins or nucleic acids (6, 25).

Arable soils contain large numbers of chitinoclastic organisms. Up to 10^6 microorganisms per gram of soil utilize the polysaccharide. In contrast to the relatively small proportion of actinomycetes in the total microflora, approximately 90 to 99 per cent of the chitinoclastic population are actinomycetes (table 2). Only a fraction of the chitin digesters in unamended soil are bacteria, and less than 1 per cent are fungi. The actinomycetes thus are the dominant segment of the aerobic chitinoclastic flora of untreated soils. The ability of several per cent of the autochthonous microorganisms to utilize chitin indicates that the substrate may be always available as a carbon source. However, since chitin digesters are not specific for any one carbohydrate, they may be merely autochthonous organisms using a variety of food sources, one of which could be the polysaccharide of N-acetylglucosamine. But, the abundance of chitin in fungal mycelium strongly suggests that it is one of the nutrients sustaining the autochthonous population.

In soils amended with chitin, more than 90 per cent of the chitin-decomposing organisms are likewise actinomycetes provided that aera-

TABLE 2

Relative Abundance of Chitinoclastic Actinomycetes in Several Soils of Holland (25)

Soil	Population/g $\times 10^3$		Per Cent of Actinomycetes in	
	Total	Chitino-clastic	Total Flora	Chitin-Digesting Flora
Sandy soil, pH 4.7	2,460	400	12	97
Sandy soil, limed, pH 6.8	7,650	920	17	96
Sandy soil, manured, pH 6.4	16,800	2,540	16	90
Clay soil, manured, pH 7.5	25,900	2,710	9	99

tion is ample. Counts of chitin digesters in such samples may be as high as 700 million per gram. *Streptomyces* and lesser numbers of *Nocardia* spp. constitute the bulk of the population. In contrast to the population of well-aerated environments, bacteria dominate the decomposition in poorly-drained habitats (25).

Growth of chitinoclastic microorganisms in chitin-containing agar media is often characterized by a zone of clearing around the colonies. The halo results from the destruction of the insoluble substrate. Many soil isolates utilize chitin as a carbon source, others as a nitrogen source, while not a few satisfy both their carbon and nitrogen needs from the compound.

Chitin decomposition is a characteristic common to species of *Streptomyces*, but the capacity to synthesize the needed enzyme is likewise found in *Nocardia* and *Micromonospora* strains. Among the bacteria, individual strains of *Achromobacter, Bacillus, Beneckea, Chromobacterium, Cytophaga, Flavobacterium, Micrococcus,* and *Pseudomonas* may participate in the transformation. Of these, *Beneckea* has as a generic trait the ability to digest chitin. In addition to the aforementioned bacteria, certain non-spore-formers possibly related to coryneform bacteria metabolize chitin (25). Among the fungi, chitin hydrolysis has been reported for *Fusarium, Mucor, Mortierella, Trichoderma, Aspergillus, Gliocladium, Penicillium, Thamnidium, Absidia,* and several basidiomycetes. Although the fungi are apparently not prominent in the transformation in nature, the possession of the requisite enzyme system seems to be characteristic of many of the soil isolates since, in one investigation, 42 of 100 cultures tested were active in laboratory media (23). Anaerobic bacteria have not been extensively studied, but chitin can be broken down in the absence of O_2. The group acting anaerobically includes some of the sulfate-reducing bacteria (1).

During the breakdown of chitin, several substances are liberated. Careful characterization of the products of *Pseudomonas chitinovorans* and *Cytophaga johnsonae* has revealed the presence of N-acetylglucosamine, glucosamine, acetic acid, and ammonia (25). These compounds are further metabolized, and most of the substrate-carbon is recovered as CO_2 and cell protoplasm. The rate-limiting reaction in the transformation is usually the initial hydrolysis of the insoluble substrate so that intermediates rarely accumulate in appreciable quantities.

The chitin molecule is comparatively large, and is at the same time highly insoluble. To make a substrate of this nature available, an organism must excrete an extracellular enzyme to solubilize and shorten the molecule so that the products can enter the cell to be oxidized therein. The formation of the extracellular chitinase is a characteristic typifying the responsible actinomycetes, bacteria, and fungi. In most species, chitinase is adaptive; some *Streptomyces*, however, form the enzyme in the absence of the specific substrate (12).

On the basis of the four characterized products cited above, a mechanism for the degradation can be postulated. The long polymer is probably hydrolyzed to yield ultimately the repeating unit of the aminopolysaccharide, N-acetylglucosamine. This is then converted to acetic acid and glucosamine, and the ammonia is liberated from the latter compound or one of its subsequent derivatives. One need only to include in the sequence the disaccharide form of the repeating unit, diacetylchitobiose, which is formed by chitinase preparations (21). Chitinase, therefore, probably degrades chitin to the disaccharide stage and then another enzyme, a chitobiase, cleaves the

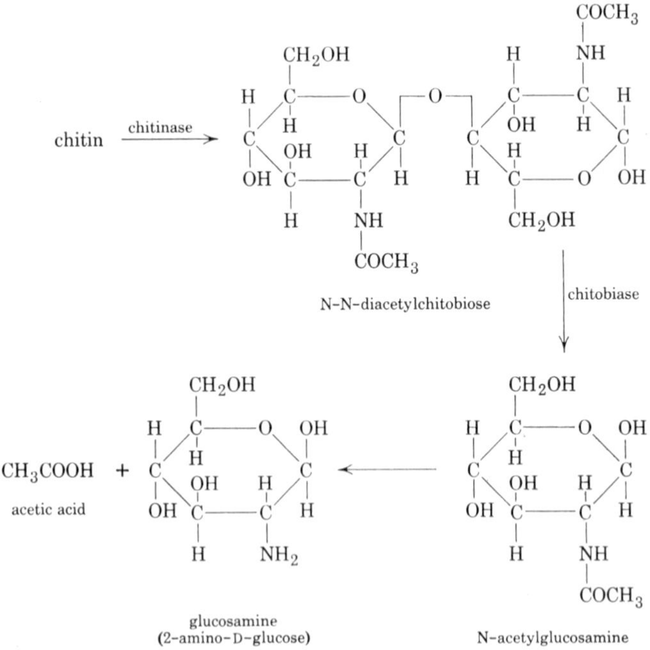

Figure 2. Pathway of chitin breakdown.

disaccharide into two acetylglucosamine fragments (figure 2). A mechanism for chitinase which results in the formation of the disaccharide is similar to amylase and cellulase whose actions lead to the accumulation of maltose and cellobiose, both disaccharides of the repeating sugar unit. Once at the glucosamine level or the equivalent glucose sugar, the product is readily attacked and serves within the cell to supply carbon and energy.

With chitin as with the other polysaccharides subjected to microbiological decomposition, the critical sequence is the initial conversion of the long, complex molecule to its simple sugar derivatives. This portion of the transformation is characteristically catalyzed by extracellular enzymes which, though providing no energy for biosynthetic reactions, convert the complex polysaccharides into simple derivatives that penetrate into the microorganism, there to be metabolized. Therefore, the physiological characteristic distinguishing the polysaccharide-attacking species is their capacity to produce the necessary extracellular enzymes.

REFERENCES

Reviews

Deuel, H., and E. Stutz. 1958. Pectic substances and pectic enzymes. *Adv. Enzymol.*, 20:341–382.

Peat, S. 1951. The biological transformations of starch. *Adv. Enzymol.*, 11: 339–375.

Whelan, W. J. 1953. The enzymic breakdown of starch. In R. T. Williams, ed., *Biological transformations of starch and cellulose.* Cambridge Univ. Press, Cambridge, pp. 17–26.

Wood, R. K. S. 1955. Pectic enzymes secreted by pathogens and their role in plant infection. In J. W. Howie and A. J. O'Hea, eds., *Mechanisms of microbial pathogenicity.* Cambridge Univ. Press, Cambridge, pp. 263–293.

Literature cited

1. Aleshina, W. J. 1938. *Mikrobiologiya,* 7:850–859.
2. Asai, T. 1937. *J. Agric. Chem. Soc. Japan,* 13:1165–1176.
3. Avery, O. T., and R. Dubos. 1930. *Science,* 72:151–152.
4. Blackwood, A. C. 1953. *Canad. J. Botany,* 31:28–32.
5. Blumenthal, H. J., and S. Roseman. 1957. *J. Bacteriol.,* 74:222–224.
6. Bremner, J. M., and K. Shaw. 1954. *J. Agric. Sci.,* 44:152–159.
7. Demain, A. L., and H. J. Phaff. 1954. *Nature,* 174:515.
8. Diehm, R. A. 1930. *Proc. Comm. III, 2nd Intl. Cong. Soil Sci.,* Leningrad, pp. 151–157.
9. Drobnik, J. 1955. *Folia Biol.,* 1:29–40.

10. Fuller, W. H., and A. G. Norman. 1943. *J. Bacteriol.*, 46:273–280.
11. Gothoskar, S. S., R. P. Scheffer, J. C. Walker, and M. A. Stahmann. 1953. *Phytopathol.*, 43:535–536.
12. Jeuniaux, C. 1955. *Compt. Rend. Soc. Biol.*, 149:1307–1308.
13. King, H. D., and R. H. Wallace. 1956. *Canad. J. Microbiol.*, 2:473–481.
14. Lambina, V. A. 1957. *Mikrobiologiya*, 26:66–74.
15. Loewenberg, J. R., and E. T. Reese. 1957. *Canad. J. Microbiol.*, 3:643–650.
16. Luh, B. S., and H. J. Phaff. 1954. *Arch. Biochem. Biophys.*, 51:102–113.
17. Lynch, D. L., and L. J. Cotnoir. 1956. *Soil Sci. Soc. Am., Proc.*, 20:367–370.
18. Mollenhof, H. H., F. B. Smith, and P. E. Brown. 1936. *Proc. Iowa Acad. Sci.*, 43:117–121.
19. Norman, A. G. 1934. *Ann. Applied Biol.*, 21:454–475.
20. Prevot, A. R., and J. Pochon. 1951. *Ann. Inst. Pasteur*, 80:672–674.
21. Reynolds, D. M. 1954. *J. Gen. Microbiol.*, 11:150–159.
22. Sickles, G. M., and M. Shaw. 1934. *J. Bacteriol.*, 28:415–431.
23. Skinner, C. E., and F. Dravis. 1937. *Ecology*, 18:391–397.
24. Stark, E., and P. A. Tetrault. 1951. *Canad. J. Botany*, 29:104–112.
25. Veldkamp, H. 1955. *Meded. Landbouw. Wageningen*, 55:127–174.
26. Wieringa, K. T. 1947. *Proc. 4th Intl. Cong. Microbiol.*, Copenhagen, pp. 482–483.
27. Wieringa, K. T. 1955. *Z. Pflanzernahr. Dung.*, 69:150–155.

14

Transformation of Hydrocarbons and Pesticides

Among the innumerable reactions of the carbon cycle resulting in a mineralization of organic carbon is found a series of transformations that leads to the degradation of hydrocarbons. Numerous hydrocarbons or their derivatives are added to or synthesized within the soil, and their mineralization and formation is of significance in the general cycle of carbon. Many herbicides, insecticides, and fungicides are halogen-substituted hydrocarbons, and the decomposition of these synthetic compounds in soil has a bearing upon the duration of pesticidal action. Therefore, the microbiological utilization of hydrocarbons and related compounds is both agronomically and biologically important.

Formation of Methane

In the aerobic decomposition of organic matter, the main gas evolved is CO_2. At low O_2 tensions, appreciable CH_4 is released from the decaying cellulose, hemicelluloses, proteins, organic acids, and alcohols. When CH_4 production is most vigorous, its volume may almost equal the quantity of CO_2 liberated. Yet, the capacity to form CH_4 is uncommon in the biological realm, but the few active species are widely distributed in environments containing little O_2.

In wet paddy soils, considerable CH_4 is formed during the anaerobic decomposition of carbonaceous substrates. Although H_2 is also a common end-product of anaerobic metabolism, little is lost to the

227

atmosphere from flooded fields since it is probably used by the CH_4-producing bacteria as a source of energy for growth. Flooded soils planted to rice frequently evolve less CH_4 than corresponding uncropped sites, but the incorporation of carbon as green manures greatly increases CH_4 production (9). Methane formation is also influenced markedly by acidity. The maximum rate occurs in environments of near neutral pH, and there is little activity below pH 6.0. Analogous effects of acidity have been reported in studies with pure cultures of the responsible microorganisms.

The biosynthesis of CH_4 is limited to a rather specialized physiological group of bacteria living in waterlogged soils, marshes, swamps, manure piles, the intestines of higher animals, and in marine and fresh water sediments. All of these bacteria are strict anaerobes, and they will not proliferate in the presence of O_2. It is difficult to obtain pure cultures of the responsible bacteria, and many early investigations were carried out with impure or enrichment cultures. Mixed populations contain many organisms which are themselves unable to produce the gas.

The CH_4-forming bacteria have many physiological properties in common, but they are heterogeneous in cellular morphology. Some are rods, some cocci, while others occur in clusters of cocci known as sarcinae. Certain of the species, moreover, form endospores. Barker has proposed that all of the CH_4-forming bacteria, despite their morphological dissimilarities, are related biochemically and should be grouped into a single family, Methanobacteriaceae. The family is divided into four genera on the basis of cytological differences.

I. Rod-shaped bacteria
   A. Non-sporulating. *Methanobacterium*
   B. Sporulating. *Methanobacillus*
II. Spherical cells
   A. Sarcinae. *Methanosarcina*
   B. Not in sarcinal groups. *Methanococcus*

Anaerobes which evolve CH_4 are unable to utilize the conventional carbohydrates and amino acids available to most heterotrophs. Glucose and other sugars are not fermented by pure cultures, and polysaccharides are likewise resistant to attack. The only organic substrates metabolized by the bacteria are short-chain fatty acids such as formic, acetic, propionic, *n*-butyric, *n*-valeric, and *n*-caproic acids and simple alcohols such as methanol, ethanol, *n*- and isopropanol, *n*- and isobutanol, and *n*-pentanol. Several of the sub-

TABLE 1

Substrate Specificity of Methane-Forming Bacteria

Organism	Substrates
Methanobacterium formicicum	H_2, CO, formic acid
Methanobacterium propionicum	Propionic acid
Methanobacterium sohngenii	Acetic and butyric acids
Methanobacillus omelianskii	H_2, primary and secondary alcohols
Methanosarcina barkeri	H_2, CO, acetic acid, methanol
Methanosarcina methanica	Acetic and butyric acids
Methanococcus mazei	Acetic and butyric acids
Methanococcus vannielii	H_2, formic acid

strates utilized are listed in table 1. In nature, however, a mixed flora is the rule, and many other compounds serve in the CH_4 fermentations of natural populations. However, the conversion of sugars, proteins, cellulose, and hemicelluloses to CH_4 requires two or more microbial groups, one acting on the complex nutrients and the methane bacteria fermenting the organic acids and alcohols produced by the primary microflora.

A variety of reactions can lead to the evolution of CH_4 in O_2-depleted environments. The processes have been characterized in mixed populations and frequently in pure cultures. Typical are the following:

$$CO_2 + 4H_2 \rightarrow CH_4 + 2H_2O \qquad (I)$$

$$4HCOOH \rightarrow CH_4 + 3CO_2 + 2H_2O \qquad (II)$$

$$CH_3COOH \rightarrow CH_4 + CO_2 \qquad (III)$$

$$2CH_3CH_2OH \rightarrow 3CH_4 + CO_2 \qquad (IV)$$

It should be noted that the major products of the degradation of simple molecules are CO_2 and CH_4, but the ratio of the two gases varies with the substrate in question.

The most common mechanism for CH_4 formation is the reduction of CO_2; i.e., the simple organic molecule is fermented and CO_2 is utilized as the electron (or hydrogen) acceptor. If CO_2 is not supplied to the microbial fermentation, it is produced in the decomposition of the organic substrate and subsequently reduced. In the case of acetic acid, this occurs as follows:

$$CH_3COOH + 2H_2O \rightarrow 2CO_2 + 8(H)$$

$$8(H) + CO_2 \rightarrow CH_4 + 2H_2O$$

$$Net: \quad CH_3COOH \rightarrow CH_4 + CO_2$$

The CO_2 reduction pathway has been established for the fermentation of a variety of carbonaceous compounds, and a generalized equation for the process can be formulated.

$$4H_2R + CO_2 \rightarrow 4R + CH_4 + 2H_2O \qquad (V)$$

The CH_4 here arises by reduction of CO_2 at the expense of the hydrogen donor, H_2R, which is thereby converted to product R. Typical of this type of change are many of the reactions brought about by *Methanobacillus omelianskii*. This organism utilizes simple alcohols (H_2R) such as ethanol, *n*-propanol, and *n*-butanol, metabolizing them as described in equation V to give as products (R) acetic, propionic, or *n*-butyric acids. In the fermentation of ethanol, 93 to 96 per cent of the substrate is oxidized to acetate, and 0.5 mole CO_2 disappears and 0.5 mole CH_4 appears for each ethanol oxidized (1).

$$2CH_3CH_2OH + CO_2 \rightarrow 2CH_3COOH + CH_4 \qquad (VI)$$

Should the CO_2 supplied be isotopic, then the CH_4 recovered will contain the isotope. On the other hand, should the carbon of the organic molecule be tagged, then the organic product but not the CH_4 will bear the isotopic label.

The substance represented as H_2R is frequently organic, but it need not be. As early as 1920, Harrison proposed that H_2 evolution is inconsequential in paddy fields solely because the gas reacts with CO_2 to yield CH_4. A number of bacteria have subsequently been isolated which, in pure culture, are capable of using molecular H_2 for the reduction of CO_2 in a manner identical with the type reaction given by equation V.

$$4H_2 + CO_2 \rightarrow CH_4 + 2H_2O \qquad (VII)$$

An interesting transformation is carried out by *Methanosarcina barkeri*, the conversion of carbon monoxide to CH_4. The process involves not one but two steps, the second identical with the reaction described above (11).

$$4CO + 4H_2O \rightarrow 4CO_2 + 4H_2$$

$$CO_2 + 4H_2 \rightarrow CH_4 + 2H_2O$$

Net: $4CO + 2H_2O \rightarrow 3CO_2 + CH_4$ (VIII)

Therefore, even this CH_4 fermentation proceeds by way of the CO_2 reduction pathway.

A limited number of substrates are fermented by a second mechanism. One *Methanosarcina* sp. decomposes methanol and acetate, the CH_4 arising from the methyl groups of the alcohol or the acetate. This has been confirmed by the use of isotopic C^{14}.

$$C^{14}H_3COOH \rightarrow C^{14}H_4 + CO_2$$ (IX)

This pathway for acetate fermentation is essentially a simple decarboxylation (16). Not only does the methyl-carbon of acetate go into CH_4, but the hydrogens attached to the carbon atom are transferred with it.

It is difficult to show the microbiological production of gaseous hydrocarbons other than CH_4 by conventional chemical techniques, but mass spectrometric analysis has revealed the evolution of traces of ethane, ethylene, propane, and propylene during the rotting of cellulose-manure mixtures. Enrichment cultures developing anaerobically produce ethane, ethylene, and sometimes acetylene, propylene, and propane, and certain fungi in pure culture synthesize traces of the gaseous hydrocarbons ethylene, propylene, ethane, propane, and acetylene (4). Undoubtedly, other organisms can do likewise, and the microorganisms should prove especially interesting from a comparative viewpoint. With the exception of CH_4, however, gaseous hydrocarbons have no known significance in soil.

Oxidation of Aliphatic Hydrocarbons

The microflora responds to the addition to soil of paraffin, petroleum, petroleum products, and other aliphatic hydrocarbons, and the resultant population causes the added substrate to disappear. These transformations are of great significance in the terrestrial cycle of carbon because waxes and other constituents of plant tissue contain aliphatic hydrocarbons. It has been estimated that approximately 0.02 per cent of higher plants may be considered as hydrocarbon or hydrocarbon-like in structure. Another source of supply is the soil microflora itself which can synthesize a variety of highly complex, hydrocarbon-like molecules. Likewise, hydrocarbon oxidizers probably metabolize the oils used as carriers for insecticide sprays, which, even when applied to the foliage, ultimately reach the soil. In addition, the soil under asphalt-paved highways possesses a large bacterial flora capable of utilizing the asphalt.

The short persistence of hydrocarbons of many types is indicative of a vigorous population, and counts in excess of 10^5 per gram have been recorded when paraffin is used as the growth substrate. Among the substances used by the flora are paraffin, kerosene, gasoline, mineral and lubricating oils, asphalts, tars, and natural and synthetic rubbers. Methane, ethane, propane, butane, pentane, hexane, and many other aliphatic hydrocarbons of the type structure C_nH_{2n+2} are decomposed as well (figure 1). Both saturated and unsaturated molecules are attacked. Long-chain hydrocarbons are generally more available than the simple, short-chain substances; that is, increasing molecular weight favors decomposition. The unsaturated forms are more easily degraded than the saturated molecules, and

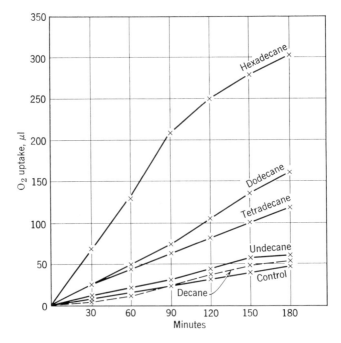

Figure 1. Oxidation of hydrocarbons by *Nocardia opaca* (19).

the branched compounds exhibit a greater susceptibility to the action of microbial enzymes than straight-chain hydrocarbons (21).

Environmental conditions govern the rate of transformation. The oxidation is sensitive to temperature, but the decomposition occurs from as low as 0°C to about 55°C. Where thermophiles are present, the rate of reaction at elevated temperatures is quite rapid. The oxidation at about 0°C is, of course, extremely slow. Many of the strains are sensitive to acidity and frequently show little growth below pH 6. The availability of other carbonaceous substrates affects hydrocarbon destruction, a depression in rate being common in the presence of a readily metabolized substrate. The depression probably results from a preferential utilization of the second carbon source. Hydrocarbon decomposition will proceed in the absence of free O_2 provided that an alternate electron acceptor like sulfate is supplied. Although sulfate-reducing bacteria actively degrade straight-chain hydrocarbons in the absence of O_2, few denitrifying bacteria seem capable of utilizing such substrates for the reduction of nitrate (7). However, as anaerobiasis favors the reduction of both sulfate and nitrate, little hydrocarbon loss can be expected in O_2-depleted environments.

Many bacteria metabolize aliphatic hydrocarbons of long or short chain length, but there are characteristically one or more of the simpler gaseous compounds, particularly CH_4, which cannot be oxidized by these microorganisms. For example, of two *Mycobacterium* strains described by Bokova (2), one utilized compounds varying in chain length from ethane (C_2H_6) to the high-molecular-weight paraffin hydrocarbons, the other from propane (C_3H_8) to the paraffins. Neither could oxidize CH_4. The metabolism of ethane can be accomplished by species of *Mycobacterium, Nocardia, Streptomyces, Pseudomonas, Flavobacterium,* cocci, and several filamentous fungi. Especially common in the utilization of the simple compounds are the mycobacteria. High-molecular-weight hydrocarbons are consumed by a variety of microorganisms including the acid-fast mycobacteria, *Nocardia, Pseudomonas, Streptomyces, Desulfovibrio, Corynebacterium,* several cocci, and many fungi.

Oxidation of Methane

Methane is biologically unique among the gaseous hydrocarbons in two ways. First, it is the only one produced in large amounts through microbial action. Second, it is metabolized by microorganisms which are largely inactive on the larger hydrocarbon molecules. Moreover, the status of CH_4 as a carbonaceous substrate not having the carbon-carbon linkage typical of biologically synthesized organic molecules provides an interesting problem in the delineation of heterotrophy and chemoautotrophy.

Paddy soils frequently contain a surface film which brings about the oxidation of CH_4. To isolate the biological agents of the oxidation from the film, advantage is taken of their capacity to develop in inorganic media incubated in an atmosphere of CH_4 and O_2. The microorganism obtained is a short, motile, rod-shaped bacterium possessing a single flagellum.

Methane oxidizers occur in well-drained soils, paddy fields, stream beds, pond mud, sewage, and barnyard manure. The bacteria are not uncommon in soil, particularly in surroundings containing both CH_4 and O_2. The organisms probably subsist on the CH_4 released from the lower regions of the soil in anaerobic decomposition, and they seem to be more abundant in lower layers than near the surface. In fact, their prevalence in the subsoil of areas containing deposits of petroleum or natural gas has led to the suggestion that they be used as geological tools in prospecting for natural gas (12).

In the process of CH_4 oxidation, O_2 is consumed and CO_2 produced. For each mole of CH_4 that disappears, two moles of O_2 theoretically are required.

$$CH_4 + 2O_2 \rightarrow CO_2 + 2H_2O \qquad (X)$$

Since CH_4 is also a carbonaceous nutrient for the organism, some of the gas will go into the formation of cell substance. The experimental values therefore do not necessarily agree with the theoretical equation because of carbon assimilation. The more efficient the bacterium is in assimilation, i.e., efficient in utilizing the energy released by oxidation for cell synthesis, the greater will be the disparity from the theoretical ratio of $1CH_4:2O_2$ (13).

There are clear differences among the CH_4-oxidizing bacteria with regard to the substrates they metabolize. Some strains use CH_4 or methanol as carbon sources, but they cannot develop upon more complex hydrocarbons, alcohols, or carbohydrates. Yet, other isolates metabolize a number of simple hydrocarbons such as ethane, propane, ethylene, and hexane. The lack of uniformity in compounds susceptible to attack implies a heterogeneity in the active population although frequently the genus name *Methanomonas* has been applied to the entire group. The demonstration that two *Mycobacterium* spp. develop upon either methane or propane (14) supports the hypothesis that other bacterial groups are concerned in the transformation.

The establishment of a separate genus, *Methanomonas,* is based upon a single physiological property, the capacity to oxidize CH_4. It would seem that this is a rather tenuous criterion for classification because several organisms differing in morphology and physiology carry out the same biochemical step. Moreover, the belief that the CH_4 oxidizers are chemoautotrophs, using CH_4 for energy and CO_2 for carbon, is no longer tenable because experiments with radioactive carbon have shown that at least part of the cell carbon is derived from CH_4. As the classical CH_4-oxidizing bacterium is a short, gram negative rod with a single polar flagellum, Leadbetter and Foster (13) have proposed the abolition of the genus name *Methanomonas* and the redesignation of the group as a single species, *Pseudomonas methanica.*

Cell suspensions of CH_4 oxidizers metabolize methanol, formaldehyde, and formic acid in addition to the gaseous hydrocarbon. Incubation of the bacteria with CH_4 in the presence of the inhibitor iodoacetate results in an accumulation of methanol. If sodium sulfite is present during the oxidation, the formation of formaldehyde can be demonstrated. Further, cells incubated with either CH_4 or formaldehyde liberate formic acid (3, 6). The results of such studies on the oxidation and accumulation of these one-carbon compounds indicate that the pathway of CH_4 oxidation proceeds as shown in equation XI.

$$CH_4 \rightarrow CH_3OH \rightarrow HCHO \rightarrow HCOOH \rightarrow CO_2 \qquad (XI)$$

Decomposition of Aromatic Compounds

Aromatic compounds, although rarely dominating the organic substrates reaching the soil, represent an important group of substances subjected to attack by the microflora. The lignin decomposed in vast amounts has a structure based upon an aromatic nucleus as do a number of humus constituents. Several of the amino acids found in proteins and many of the herbicides used for weed control are essentially modified aromatic hydrocarbons. Moreover, as many of the aromatic substances are phytotoxic, their destruction is essential in order to prevent the creation of unfavorable conditions for crop production.

Many members of the soil microflora destroy aromatic hydrocarbons and their derivatives. Specific microorganisms decompose molecules such as phenol, naphthalene, and anthracene containing one, two, and three benzene rings, respectively. Apparently, bacteria are the dominant microbial group concerned in the mineralization of compounds of this type, largely species of *Pseudomonas, Mycobacterium, Achromobacter,* and *Bacillus,* but *Nocardia* spp. frequently appear prominently. Under some conditions, the fungi and streptomycetes may participate in the breakdown of aromatic hydrocarbons. The filamentous microorganisms may also be important in the decomposition of certain aromatic humus constituents.

Bacteria concerned in the aerobic decomposition are widespread, and almost every soil contains organisms growing upon a variety of these compounds. Not only are the microorganisms widely distributed but the diversity of organic substances utilized by them is immense. Every naturally occurring aromatic hydrocarbon and many of those created by the chemist in the laboratory are metabolized. The species dominating the transformations are not substrate-specific in the sense of the cellulose bacteria for they utilize simple sugars or organic acids as well as hydrocarbons. Indeed, growth on hydrocarbons or hydrocarbon derivatives is typically slower than the development upon more conventional nutrient sources.

A consideration of the many compounds and numerous metabolic pathways is beyond the scope of the present discussion. A typical reaction sequence involving several aromatic molecules is shown in figure 2. Characteristic of these processes is the oxidation of side chains, where present, and the cleavage of one cyclic unit at a time. Thus, anthracene is converted to an intermediate with only two benzene rings, and the latter is further oxidized to a benzene derivative like salicylic acid. Ultimately, the benzene derivative is cleaved to a non-cyclic molecule related to its aromatic precursor. The pathway of degradation of most aromatic structures passes through this stage, and catechol and one or two related substances are the last cyclic compounds preceding ring cleavage. The final steps are likewise similar in that succinic and acetic acids are produced from the six

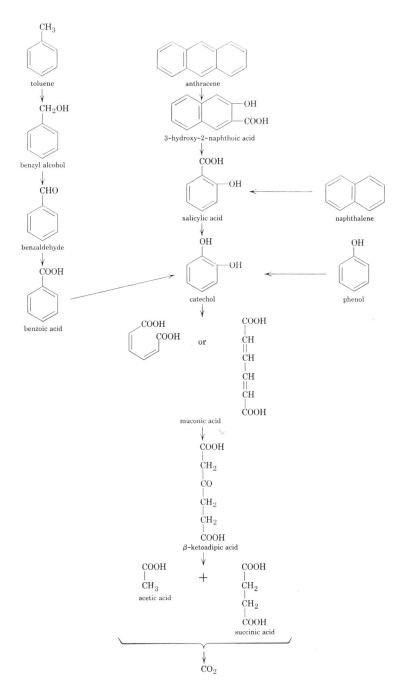

Figure 2. The pathway of decomposition of several aromatic compounds.

237

carbons originally in the benzene ring, and these two organic acids in turn are oxidized to CO_2 and water.

Microbiological Decomposition of Pesticides

In recent years, one of the dramatic changes in American agriculture has resulted from the introduction of pesticides. *Pesticides* are substances designed to control or eradicate a specific pest of economic crops. Herbicides, insecticides, fungicides, and nematocides are the broad groups of chemicals included by the general term pesticides. Of the four, herbicides alone have been investigated intensively from the viewpoint of ascertaining microbiological influences on persistence and decomposition of pesticides in soil.

With few exceptions, herbicides are organic molecules which, by virtue of their organic character, may serve as substrates for a small or large segment of the microflora. If suitable as a carbonaceous nutrient for microorganisms, the herbicide will disappear from the soil in a relatively short period of time. Biological degradation is frequently desirable as repeated applications of non-decomposable compounds could ultimately lead to their accumulation in concentrations detrimental to plant growth. The observations that sensitive crops can be planted several weeks or months after a field has been treated with herbicidal chemicals bear witness to the great activity of the microflora in metabolizing new and unique compounds synthesized by the organic chemist.

The number of substances examined as potential herbicides is enormous. Phenoxyalkyl carboxylic acids, substituted ureas, nitrophenols, chlorinated acetic and propionic acids, phenylcarbamates, thiolcarbamates, and others have all found application for the control of specific weeds in turf management and in crop production. The diversity of materials precludes general statements with regard to the availability, persistence, or microbiology of herbicides. Each substance or, at best, group of substances must be examined individually.

Two herbicides will be considered to illustrate some of the problems in the microbiology of pesticides. The examples selected, 2,4-dichlorophenoxyacetic acid and 2,4,5-trichlorophenoxyacetic acid, represent a class of weed-killing agents known as phenoxyalkyl carboxylic acids. For the sake of simplicity, the two are abbreviated 2,4-D and 2,4,5-T.

CH$_2$COOH   CH$_2$COOH

O   O

2,4-D   2,4,5-T

When 2,4-D is applied to the soil, a segment of the microbial population develops which can cause the oxidation of the herbicide. That the disappearance is largely biological is apparent from the prolonged persistence of the herbicide in sterile soil. The time required for detoxification of 2,4-D in normal, unsterilized soil varies greatly in different localities because the physical and chemical environment for the detoxifying population is rarely the same. For the complete destruction of 2,4-D applied at recommended field rates, several pounds per acre, a period of 2 to 8 or more weeks is required. The major factors which govern the rate of microbial destruction of the pesticide are temperature, soil texture, moisture, and pH. As a rule, any management practice which favors microbial proliferation leads to a more rapid metabolism of 2,4-D. Thus, improving the moisture status, raising the temperature, and liming shorten the period of effectiveness of 2,4-D and many other herbicides (10, 15).

Several bacteria metabolizing 2,4-D have been isolated in pure culture. Neither fungi nor actinomycetes seem active in the transformation of the compound. Strains of *Achromobacter, Arthrobacter, Corynebacterium, Flavobacterium,* and *Mycoplana* grow in 2,4-D agar and cause the breakdown of the dichlorophenoxyacetic acid. Examination of the structure of the molecule reveals that removal of the side chain, dehalogenation, and cleavage of the aromatic ring are required for complete mineralization. Studies with an *Achromobacter* sp. have shown that cells grown on 2,4-D contain enzymes catalyzing the oxidation of several chlorophenols and chlorocatechol (17, 18). These facts suggest that the pathway of breakdown may proceed by an initial removal of the acetic acid side chain followed by a transformation of phenol as indicated in figure 2.

The herbicide 2,4,5-T is structurally similar to 2,4-D. The sole difference is the presence of a third chlorine atom on the benzene ring. Yet, the slight modification has a dramatic effect on the biological availability and, hence, persistence of the compound (figure

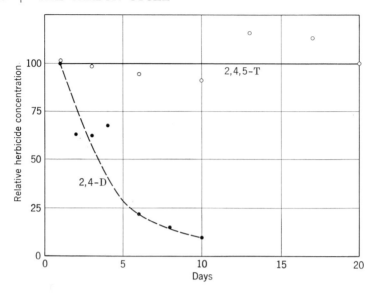

Figure 3. Microbial decomposition of 2,4-D and 2,4,5-T in soil suspensions (20).

3). Soils treated with 2,4,5-T still contain the pesticide long after all vestiges of toxicity due to equivalent quantities of 2,4-D have disappeared. Even under optimum conditions, 2,4,5-T remains in non-sterile soil for periods of six months to a year or more (5). In agreement with results showing the prolonged duration of phyto-toxicity, an organism utilizing 2,4,5-T for growth has yet to be iso-lated. Simple structural alterations in the pesticide molecule, there-fore, can have important agricultural consequences because of the ability or inability of the microscopic inhabitants to degrade the applied herbicide. Effects of molecular structure upon biological de-composition have been found with a number of other pesticides.

Many individual chemicals and groups of compounds have been examined in the search for new and better herbicides, and a number of these materials have entered agricultural practice. Only in a few instances, however, has the period of persistence been estab-lished; moreover, the detoxification has not always been verified as being microbiological. Chemical and photochemical reactions, vola-tilization, and leaching likewise lead to loss of activity of pesticidal compounds applied to soil. A partial list of the herbicides decom-posed microbiologically is presented in table 2. The tabulated data on persistence serve only an illustrative purpose since the duration of phytotoxicity varies with the habitat and with meteorological conditions.

One of the major causes of the differences noted in the period required for microbiological detoxification is the composition of the environment surrounding the active population. The major factors governing microbial destruction of herbicides in soil appear to be temperature, moisture, pH, depth, and organic matter level. As a rule, environmental modifications resulting in enhanced microbial development and metabolism increase the rate of herbicide degradation. Thus, a rise in temperature or the liming of acid soils tends to shorten the period of persistence. As expected, the rate of decomposition generally is more rapid near the surface than at some depth, and it is likewise more rapid in neutral than in acid conditions.

TABLE 2

Decomposition and Period of Persistence of Several Herbicides

Name of Compound	Abbreviation	Persistence in Soil	Active Organisms
3-(p-chlorophenyl)-1,1-dimethylurea	Monuron	4–12 mo	*Pseudomonas*
4-chlorophenoxyacetic acid	4-CPA		*Achromobacter* *Flavobacterium*
2,4-dichlorophenoxyacetic acid	2,4-D	2–8 wk	*Achromobacter* *Corynebacterium* *Flavobacterium*
2,4,5-trichlorophenoxyacetic acid	2,4,5-T	5–11 mo	
2-methyl-4-chlorophenoxyacetic acid	MCPA	3–12 wk	*Achromobacter* *Mycoplana*
2,2-dichloropropionic acid	Dalapon	2–4 wk	*Agrobacterium* *Pseudomonas*
Dinitro-o-sec-butylphenol	DNBP	2–6 mo	*Corynebacterium* *Pseudomonas*
4,6-dinitro-o-cresol	DNOC		*Corynebacterium*
Isopropyl N-phenylcarbamate	IPC	2–4 wk	
Isopropyl N-(3-chlorophenyl)carbamate	CIPC	2–8 wk	
Trichloroacetic acid	TCA	2–9 wk	*Pseudomonas*
2,3,6-trichlorobenzoic acid	2,3,6-TBA	>2 yr	

Parallel to the decomposition of these compounds is the formation of new substances, some of which in turn may have biological effects. There is, for certain herbicides, evidence for the microbiological formation of growth-stimulating factors which influence either plant development or the subterranean microflora. In other instances, phytotoxic intermediates may be formed during the decomposition of the herbicides. One compound, 2-(2,4-dichlorophenoxy)ethyl sulfate, is itself inactive but is readily converted in soil to herbicidal derivatives, namely 2,4-D and related substances. Responsible for this conversion are members of the subterranean population, *Bacillus cereus* var. *mycoides,* for example, functioning in the transformation in vitro. The synthesis by the microflora of both inhibitory and stimulatory intermediates indicates the practical importance of biochemical research on the products formed during the destruction of pesticides.

There is as yet little information on microbial destruction of fungicides and insecticides. The fungicide known as semesan, technically 2-chloro-4-(hydroxymercuri)phenol, is biologically detoxified, but many fungicides are apparently inactivated by other means. Some of the insecticides exhibit a very long persistence, benzene hexachloride and chlordane persisting for more than 10 years, so that it is unlikely that biological agencies are of consequence in their destruction. Nevertheless, considerable further investigation is required in order to ascertain the microbiological influences upon the fully accepted as well as the newly introduced pesticides.

Effects of Pesticides on the Microflora

Pesticides are antibiological agents designed to control one or several types of agricultural pests. As inhibitors for biological systems of one sort, the pesticides may exert simultaneously a deleterious influence upon the saprophytic soil population, the result of which may be detrimental to plant growth. A compound applied to legume seeds to prevent fungal attack could at the same time prevent the root nodule bacteria from initiating the important symbiotic N_2-fixing association. A second compound could affect organic matter decomposition and delay the decay of carbonaceous residues. Clearly, pesticides which are not rapidly decomposed may accumulate to an extent that the rates of microbiological processes important to soil fertility are altered.

Each new compound introduced into agriculture—herbicide, insecticide, fungicide, or nematocide—must be carefully examined to determine whether it does have such an influence and, if so, the extent of the damage. Moreover, it is imperative to test a number of the biological processes in soil, not just one, to be certain that the injury or lack thereof is fully documented. The results of many investigations have demonstrated that herbicides applied at the recommended field rates generally have no harmful effects upon the microscopic population or upon its biochemical activities. Only at concentrations many-fold higher than those recommended are these chemicals toxic; often the first sign of inhibition does not appear until herbicide levels of one hundred times the accepted rates are added to soil. Occasionally, a partial inhibition is noted with certain herbicides, but this is invariably temporary and the inhibition is soon relieved. The reason for the lack of significant toxicity is the low chemical concentrations needed for weed control, i.e., usually less than 10 lb per acre, which is equivalent to only a few parts per million of soil.

Similar results are obtained with most of the insecticides, and little or no inhibition is found as a result of using DDT, benzene hexachloride, chlordane, aldrin, dieldrin, parathion, and toxaphene. Among the more sensitive processes to such compounds are nitrification and legume nodulation; where damage is noted, it is usually upon one or both of these two. However, it is unlikely that the inhibitions would materially affect crop production, particularly when weighed against the benefits accruing from proper usage of the pesticides.

Fumigants and fungicides, however, do affect markedly the saprophytic population as well as the pathogens they are designed to control. The degree of inhibition and the duration of the effect vary with the chemical, the soil, and environmental conditions. Ultimately, the population will become re-established, but the return to normalcy may require only a few days or, occasionally, more than a year. With certain chemicals and certain crops, the elimination of one or another segment of the microflora may be reflected in a modification in plant growth, but permanent influences on the biological characteristics of soil are unlikely. Clearly, however, the extent and duration of fungicidal effects on the non-pathogenic microflora must be carefully ascertained lest some microbiological group needed for nutrient transformations be eliminated and the crop yield reduced.

Detailed discussions of the effects of pesticides upon the microflora will be found in several of the reviews cited below.

REFERENCES

Reviews

Barker, H. A. 1956. *Bacterial fermentations.* John Wiley and Sons, New York.
Eno, C. F. 1958. Insecticides and the soil. *J. Agric. Food Chem.,* 6:348–351.
Martin, J. P., and P. F. Pratt. 1958. Fumigants, fungicides, and the soil. *J. Agric. Food Chem.,* 6:345–348.
Newman, A. S., and C. R. Downing. 1958. Herbicides and the soil. *J. Agric. Food Chem.,* 6:352–353.
ZoBell, C. E. 1950. Assimilation of hydrocarbons by microorganisms. *Adv. Enzymol.,* 10:443–486.
ZoBell, C. E. 1946. Action of microorganisms on hydrocarbons. *Bacteriol. Rev.,* 10:1–49.

Literature cited

1. Barker, H. A. 1941. *J. Biol. Chem.,* 137:153–167.
2. Bokova, E. N. 1954. *Mikrobiologiya,* 23:15–21.
3. Brown, L. R., and R. J. Strawinski. 1958. *Bacteriol. Proc.,* 1958:122–123.
4. Davis, J. B., and R. M. Squires. 1954. *Science,* 119:381–382.
5. DeRose, H. R., and A. S. Newman. 1947. *Soil Sci. Soc. Am., Proc.,* 12:222–226.
6. Dworkin, M., and J. W. Foster. 1956. *J. Bacteriol.,* 72:646–659.
7. Hansen, R. W., and R. F. Kallio. 1957. *Science,* 125:1198–1199.
8. Harrison, W. H. 1920. *Mem., Dept. Agric. India, Chem. Ser.,* 5:181–194.
9. Harrison, W. H., and P. A. S. Aiyer. 1913. *Mem., Dept. Agric. India, Chem. Ser.,* 3:65–106.
10. Hernandez, T. P., and G. F. Warren. 1950. *Proc. Am. Soc. Hort. Sci.,* 56:287–293.
11. Kluyver, A. J., and C. G. T. P. Schnellen. 1947. *Arch. Biochem.,* 14:57–70.
12. Kuznetsov, S. I., and Z. P. Telegina. 1957. *Mikrobiologiya,* 26:513–518.
13. Leadbetter, E. R., and J. W. Foster. 1958. *Arch. Mikrobiol.,* 30:91–118.
14. Nechaeva, N. B. 1949. *Mikrobiologiya,* 18:310–317.
15. Newman, A. S., and A. G. Norman. 1947. *J. Bacteriol.,* 54:37–38.
16. Stadtman, T. C., and H. A. Barker. 1951. *J. Bacteriol.,* 61:81–86.
17. Steenson, T. I., and N. Walker. 1956. *Plant and Soil,* 8:17–32.
18. Steenson, T. I., and N. Walker. 1957. *J. Gen. Microbiol.,* 16:146–155.
19. Webley, D. M., and P. C. De Kock. 1952. *Biochem. J.,* 51:371–375.
20. Whiteside, J. S., and M. Alexander. 1960. *Weeds,* 8:204–213.
21. ZoBell, C. E. 1948. *J. Gen. Microbiol.,* 2:VIII–X.

THE NITROGEN CYCLE

INTRODUCTION

The biological availability of nitrogen, phosphorus, and potassium is of considerable economic importance because they are the major plant nutrients derived from the soil. Of the three, nitrogen stands out as the most susceptible to microbial transformations. This element is a key building block of the protein molecule upon which all life is based, and it is thus an indispensable component of the protoplasm of plants, animals, and microorganisms. Because of the critical position of the nitrogen supply in crop production and soil fertility, a deficiency markedly reduces yield as well as quality of crops; and because this is one of the few soil nutrients that is lost by volatilization as well as by leaching, it requires continual conservation and maintenance.

Nitrogen undergoes a number of transformations which involve organic, inorganic, and volatile compounds. These transformations occur simultaneously, but individual steps often accomplish opposite goals. The reactions may be viewed in terms of a cycle in which the element is shuttled back and forth at the discretion of the microflora. A small part of the large reservoir of N_2 in the atmosphere is converted to organic compounds by certain free-living microorganisms or by a microbial-plant association that makes the element directly available to the plant. The nitrogen present in the protein or nucleic acids of plant tissues is used by animals. In the animal body, the nitrogen is converted to other simple and complex compounds. When the animals and plants are subjected to microbiologi-

245

cal decay, the organic nitrogen is released as ammonium, which in turn is utilized by the vegetation or is oxidized to nitrate. The latter ion may be lost by leaching, it may serve as a plant nutrient or, alternatively, it may be reduced to ammonium or to gaseous N_2 which escapes to the atmosphere, thereby completing the cycle. The present discussion is concerned with the nitrogen cycle of terrestrial habitats, but the same general sequence occurs in aquatic environments.

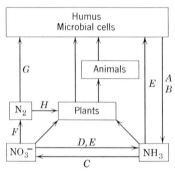

A. Ammonification   E. Immobilization
B. Mineralization   F. Denitrification
C. Nitrification   G. N_2 fixation. Non-symbiotic
D. Nitrate reduction   H. N_2 fixation. Symbiotic

The portions of the nitrogen cycle governed by microbial metabolism are composed of several individual transformations. In *nitrogen mineralization*, part of the large reservoir of organic complexes in the soil is decomposed and converted to the inorganic ions used by plants, ammonium and nitrate. Microbial mineralization results in the degradation of proteins, polypeptides, nucleoproteins, nucleic acids, and aromatic compounds. In contrast to the conversion of the complex to the simple substances is *nitrogen immobilization* or assimilation. Microbiological immobilization leads to the biosynthesis of the complex molecules of microbial protoplasm from ammonium and nitrate. The mineralization of organic nitrogen and the microfloral assimilation of inorganic ions proceed simultaneously.

Nitrogen, once in the nitrate form, may be lost from the soil in several ways. Because of its solubility in the soil solution, nitrate readily moves downward out of the zone of root penetration. Nitrate and ammonium will also be removed to satisfy the nutrient demand of the plant cover. The greatest biological leak in the otherwise closed cycle is through *denitrification*, whereby nitrogen is removed entirely from the realm of ready accessibility because the end-product of denitrification, N_2, is unavailable to most macro- and micro-organisms.

Any leaks in the cycle deplete the soil's nitrogen reserve and eventually could have drastic effects on man's agricultural economy. But since the leakage to the atmosphere is omnipresent, there must exist a reverse process to maintain the balance; otherwise the world's nitrogen reservoir would be diminishing continuously. Although inert as far as plants, animals, and most microorganisms are concerned, N_2 is acted upon by certain microorganisms, sometimes in symbiosis with a higher plant, which can use it as a nitrogen source for growth. This process, *nitrogen fixation*, results in the accumulation of new organic compounds in the cells of the responsible organisms. The N_2 thus fixed re-enters general circulation when the newly formed tissues are in turn mineralized.

By means of these reactions, the subterranean microflora regulates the supply and governs the availability and chemical nature of the nitrogen in soil.

15

Mineralization and Immobilization of Nitrogen

The soil nutrient which plants require in greatest quantity is nitrogen, the element that serves as the keystone of the proteinaceous matter of living tissue. Yet, despite its critical role in plant nutrition, nitrogen is assimilated almost entirely in the inorganic state, as nitrate or ammonium. On the other hand, the bulk of the nitrogenous materials found in soil or added in the form of crop residues is organic and, hence, largely unavailable. The release of the bound element and the mobilization of the vast reservoir of organically combined nitrogen is essential to the recycling of the nutrient and therefore to soil fertility.

The conversion of organic nitrogen to the more mobile, inorganic state is known as *nitrogen mineralization,* a process analogous to the liberation of CO_2 from carbonaceous materials in that both transformations result in the release of the elements in inorganic forms. The two processes are also similar in that they are the sole means of regenerating the nutrient in a form usable for the development of green plants. As a consequence of mineralization, ammonium and nitrate accumulate and organic nitrogen disappears. These products delineate two distinct microbiological processes, *ammonification,* in which ammonium is formed from organic compounds, and *nitrification,* the oxidation of ammonium to nitrate. Ammonium is typically associated with a waste-product overflow in microbial metabolism, the accumulated ammonium representing the quantity of substrate nitrogen in excess of the microbial demand. Nitrification, however, is usually associated with the energy-yielding reactions in the metabolism of autotrophic bacteria.

Mineralization of the nitrogen in humus, proteins, nucleic acids, or related materials is determined by measurement of the formation of inorganic (mineral) nitrogen. Early microbiologists chose to limit their analyses to ammonium, the first inorganic product, but the results were soon found to be misleading. Nitrate production has also been used as a criterion of mineralization. The latter approach is not as objectionable as the former, but it is not too difficult to select localities where ammonium production is rapid and nitrate is not formed at all. Clearly, the most suitable procedure is the assay of all inorganic products—ammonium, nitrite, and nitrate. More sophisticated techniques requiring the stable isotope, N^{15}, have been developed. Isotopic procedures for the measurement of mineralization rates are indispensable in environments in which the conversion of inorganic nitrogen to microbial proteins is proceeding rapidly.

Nitrogen Mineralization

Almost all of the nitrogen found in surface soil horizons is in organic combination. Nevertheless, the chemical composition of this portion of the soil organic fraction is inadequately understood. Detected in extracts or hydrolyzates are essentially all of the known amino acids in combined form, minute amounts of free amino acids (2 to 400 parts per billion), amino sugars such as glucosamine and galactosamine, and several of the purine and pyrimidine bases derived from nucleic acids. Bound amino acids generally constitute from 20 to 50 per cent of the total humus nitrogen while from 5 to 10 per cent is amino sugar–nitrogen. Nucleic acid derivatives make up only a small portion of the total, probably no more than one-tenth. The chemical nature of the remainder is unknown.

The nitrogenous compounds present in the soil organic fraction are readily metabolized by microorganisms in culture solution, but they persist for long periods in nature. The resistance to attack is appreciable so that only a small proportion of the nitrogen reservoir of the soil is mineralized in each growing season. The anomalous resistance to biological destruction has aroused considerable interest, and several hypotheses have been advanced to account for the slow mineralization in soil when compared with the rapid breakdown in culture systems. One hypothesis states that the proteins form complexes with non-nitrogenous constituents of humus, lignin-protein complexes for example, which render the proteins less susceptible to digestion. A second hypothesis proposes that clay minerals spare proteins by entrapping them within the lattice of the clay crystal. Extracellular proteolytic enzymes, themselves proteins, are adsorbed by clays, and they may thereby be rendered less active. The lignin-protein complex explanation of the observed resistance of soil nitrogen has received some experimental support. Thus, the mixing together of a pure protein with lignin results in a retardation in the rate of nitrogen mineralization (6). The protection of the substrate from proteolysis is more complete for lignin-protein complexes than for clay-protein complexes. The demonstration of a protective action in vitro, however, does not necessarily signify that the same holds true in nature.

The net change in the amount of inorganic nitrogen, N_i, is expressed by the relationship

$$\Delta N_i = \text{organic nitrogen mineralized} - (N_a + N_c + N_l + N_d) \quad (I)$$

where N_a, N_c, N_l, and N_d represent the nitrogen assimilated by the microflora, removed by the crop, lost by leaching, and volatilized by denitrification, respectively. The rate at which organic nitrogen is converted to ammonium and nitrate is termed the mineralization rate, and the velocity of such release in environments receiving nitrogen-rich crop residues ranges from less than 1.0 to 20 ppm nitrogen per day, i.e., up to 40 lb of nitrogen per acre under optimal conditions. The rate represents the gross liberation of N_i and is not the amount typically seen in practice. The net quantity of inorganic nitrogen produced for a constant quantity of metabolized substrate is governed by leaching, denitrification, and particularly microbial assimilation. Consequently, though the production of N_i may be great, no increase or sometimes a decrease may be observed in measurements of the ammonium or nitrate content of soil.

The mineralization of organic nitrogen and organic carbon are related to one another. In unamended soil, the two elements are mineralized at parallel rates, and the ratio of CO_2-C to N_i produced is essentially constant at approximately 7 to 15:1. Soils active in the one transformation are generally active in the second. The ratio of C mineralized:N mineralized decreases somewhat as the rate of N_i production increases so that a microflora vigorously forming nitrate tends to release carbon and nitrogen in a ratio of ca. 7:1 while those least active exhibit ratios near 15:1 (28). The equilibrium may be upset by the introduction of external substrates; for example, protein-poor residues favor CO_2 evolution whereas protein-rich materials favor N_i release.

Little is known of the immediate source of the ammonium formed by decomposition of the many nitrogenous complexes added to or found within the soil. Precursors of the inorganic nitrogen may well be certain amino acids and amides in humus since the level of non-basic amino-nitrogen and often amide-nitrogen falls during mineralization (20). With plant materials, on the other hand, the water-soluble nitrogen is often the fraction most readily converted to ammonium, and the rapidity of ammonium release from crop residues is therefore often closely related to the quantity of water-soluble nitrogen.

Microbiology

Innumerable investigations have dealt with the ability of micro-organisms to utilize nitrogen-containing organic molecules. With few exceptions, ammonium is a major product of the reaction. Population estimates made on diverse soils reveal that approximately 10^5 to 10^7 organisms per gram are ammonifiers, but such determinations have little importance by themselves because estimates of the population size are governed by the nitrogen compound provided as substrate in the culture medium. A simple amino acid has a vast group of microorganisms acting upon it while the nitrogen of chitin is freed by only certain select genera. Proteins serve as carbon or nitrogen sources for a large segment of the microflora, and populations of casein and albumin decomposers of from 10^5 to more than 10^6 have been observed in the A horizon. The data of table 1 demonstrate the capacity of some of the predominant bacteria to utilize gelatin. It is apparently not uncommon for more than one-sixth of the bacteria detected on dilution plates to liquefy the protein, gelatin.

In nature, the breakdown of proteins and other nitrogenous substances is the result of the metabolism of a multitude of microbial strains each of which occupies some large or small niche in the pathway of degradation. A diverse flora liberates ammonium from organic nitrogen compounds; indeed, almost all bacteria, fungi, and actinomycetes attack some complex form of the element, but the rate of decomposition and the compounds thus utilized vary with the spe-

TABLE 1

Utilization of Gelatin by the Bacterial Flora of Canadian Soils (23)

	% of Group Which	
Bacterial Group	Grow on Gelatin	Liquefy Gelatin
Short rods		
gram positive	57	25
gram negative	57	14
gram variable	34	0
Arthrobacter spp.	100	100
Coccoid rods, gram positive	39	17
Cocci	42	33
Long rods, non-sporulating	86	14
Bacillus spp.	67	44

cies and genus. Because the ultimate liberation of ammonium from organic matter is an action associated with many physiologically dissimilar microorganisms, nitrogen is mineralized in the most extreme conditions. The amount of ammonium which accumulates, however, varies with the organism, the substrate, the soil type, and environmental conditions.

Microorganisms synthesize extracellular, proteolytic enzymes for the decomposition of proteins. The initial stages of the transformation are mediated by catalysts functioning outside of the cell, where they cleave the large protein molecule to simpler units. The proteolytic population consists of aerobic bacteria, fungi, and actinomycetes as well as certain facultative and strict anaerobes. Several intermediary products are formed in aerobic proteolysis; these quickly disappear so that the major end-products of protein breakdown are CO_2, ammonium, sulfate, and water. Anaerobically, foul-smelling compounds are released in the degradation of protein-rich materials, a conversion known as *putrefaction*. The final products of the anaerobic transformation are ammonium, amines, CO_2, organic acids, indole, skatole, mercaptans, and hydrogen sulfide.

Pure proteins are decomposed readily by species of *Pseudomonas, Bacillus, Clostridium, Serratia,* and *Micrococcus*. The first two genera are particularly numerous in soil receiving purified proteins. Proteolysis is a common criterion in bacteriological classification, and the digestion of casein and the liquefaction of gelatin are important taxonomic characters. In spite of the emphasis given to the study of casein- and gelatin-hydrolyzing bacteria, many of the strains are not important in the decomposition of the more common proteins found in nature. The proteins in plant tissues need not be acted upon by the same bacteria that rapidly hydrolyze the pure substances in vitro.

Many fungi readily decompose proteins, amino acids, and other nitrogenous compounds with the liberation of considerable quantities of ammonium. Soil isolates use these materials as carbon and nitrogen sources and, with the sulfur-containing amino acids, for sulfur as well. Fungi frequently release less ammonium than bacteria since the fungi assimilate more of the nitrogen for the purpose of cell synthesis. Without question, the fungi occupy a dominant position in proteolysis in certain soils, particularly in acid localities. Extracellular proteolytic enzymes are likewise produced by numerous actinomycetes, and the attack by actinomycetes upon vegetable proteins, serum proteins, casein, egg albumen, and gelatin in culture has been fully documented. The protein-metabolizing enzymes of certain actinomycetes are released only by old cells that have begun to autolyze, and these may in reality be intracellular catalysts liberated upon lysis of the hyphae (3). However, the slow growth habits of the actinomycetes make their role in soil proteolysis difficult to assess.

The microbiology of protein breakdown in soil is inadequately understood. It is probable that bacteria dominate in neutral or alkaline environments, but fungi and possibly actinomycetes contribute to the transformation. The key group in acid habitats is, with little question, the fungi. Anaerobic bacteria dominate the flora when O_2 is lacking. Following the initial degradation of the protein, microorganisms appear which are incapable of attacking proteins but which can utilize the metabolic wastes of the proteolytic species.

Environmental Influences

The biochemical heterogeneity of the microflora bringing about nitrogen mineralization is a critical factor in determining the influence of environmental factors upon the transformation. Because aerobic and anaerobic, acid-sensitive and acid-resistant, and spore-forming and non-spore-forming microorganisms function in the degradation of nitrogenous materials, at least some segment of the population is active regardless of the peculiarities of the habitat so long as microbial proliferation is possible. Consequently, mineralization is never eliminated in arable land, but the rate is markedly affected by the environment. Physical and chemical characteristics of the habitat such as moisture, pH, aeration, temperature, and the inorganic nutrient supply will govern the velocity of mineralization. The protective benefits to nitrogen compounds of clay and possibly lignin are likewise of importance.

The rate of production of inorganic nitrogen, usually measured as nitrate, is closely correlated with the total nitrogen content of the soil (1). Sites rich in nitrogen liberate more of the inorganic ions than deficient areas in a given time interval. It is possible to approximate the amount of the element liberated during a growing season under optimal climatic conditions because of the correlation between N_i production and total nitrogen. In the northeastern United States, for example, crops that make their maximum development in the summer have made available to them each year 2 to 4 per cent of the total humus nitrogen while crops growing in the cooler part of the year have 2 per cent or less made available during the period of peak growth. Therefore, in the case of corn growing on a soil with 0.17 per cent nitrogen, approximately 68 to 136 lb would be released from humus.

$$(2 \text{ to } 4\%) \ (0.17\% \times 2{,}000{,}000 \text{ lb soil per acre}) = 68 \text{ to } 136 \text{ lb}$$

In poorly drained land, the unsuitable water relationships depress microbial metabolism, thereby lowering the mineralization percentage. As a general rule, 1 to 4 per cent may be taken to indicate the quantity of soil organic nitrogen released to the crop during the growing season in temperate latitudes.

The ammonifying population includes aerobes and anaerobes, and organic nitrogen is mineralized, consequently, at moderate or at excessively high moisture levels. Ammonium is slowly formed at water levels slightly below the permanent wilting percentage, but improving the moisture status stimulates mineralization (22). The optimum for ammonification generally falls between 50 and 75 per cent of the water-holding capacity of the soil (figure 1). Ammonification is not eliminated by soil submergence, and the process is rapid in wet paddy fields, where the O_2 level is quite low. Fol-

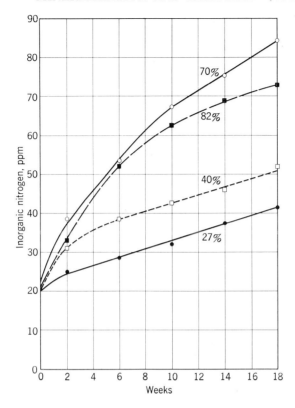

Figure 1. Changes in mineral nitrogen content of a loam soil incubated at 27, 40, 70, and 82 per cent of the water-holding capacity (25).

lowing flooding, the quantity of ammonium increases as complex organic molecules are degraded, but the ammonium level attains a maximum after which no appreciable change is noted (12). Despite the beneficial influence of aeration, ammonium is produced under complete anaerobiasis; the final inorganic product, however, is affected by the presence of O_2 as ammonium is converted to nitrate only in well-aerated habitats.

Mineralization is influenced by the pH of the environment. All other factors being equal, the production of inorganic nitrogen—ammonium plus nitrate—is greater in neutral than in acid soils. Acidification tends to depress but does not eliminate mineralization. The liming of acid soils is stimulatory as the pH is brought closer to the optimum for the active microflora. Organic nitrogen accumulates in acid soils, presumably because of the slow mineralization, so that a rapid release is noted when such soils are limed.

Temperature likewise affects the mineralization sequence as each biochemical step is catalyzed by a temperature-sensitive enzyme produced by microorganisms whose growth is in turn conditioned by temperature. Thus, at 2°C, the microflora slowly mineralizes the organic complexes, but there is no increase in ammonium or nitrate when soil is frozen. Elevation of the temperature from the freezing point to the optimum enhances the mobilization of nitrogen in proportion to the greater warmth. In contrast to most microbiological transformations, the optimum temperature for ammonification is not in the mesophilic range but rather it is above 40°C, usually between 40 and 60°C. Ammonium accumulates in composts and manure piles maintained at 65°C, demonstrating thereby the activity of thermophiles.

Nucleic Acid Metabolism

Nucleic acids are second only to proteins in importance as nitrogenous substrates for the microbial flora. These nitrogen-rich substances are found in plant and animal tissues and are also concentrated within microbial protoplasm; consequently, the fate of nucleic acids has a considerable bearing upon the mineralization sequence. An important feature in nucleic acid decomposition is their adsorption by clays as adsorption probably retards the degradation of the molecule (9).

Plant and animal tissues contain two types of nucleic acids, ribonucleic acid (RNA) and deoxyribonucleic acid (DNA). Structurally, each is a polynucleotide, that is, a polymer of the structural unit known as a mononucleotide. Mononucleotides consist of a purine or pyrimidine base, a sugar, and phosphate. The sugar in RNA is ribose and in DNA it is deoxyribose. Adenine and guanine are the purines that are found in both RNA and DNA molecules. Of the pyrimidines, cytosine is found in RNA and DNA, uracil only in the former, and thymine in the latter type of nucleic acid.

In the decomposition of nucleic acids, the long molecules are initially converted into smaller fragments and ultimately to the individual mononucleotides. The attack is mediated by the enzymes ribonuclease and deoxyribonuclease which act on RNA and DNA,

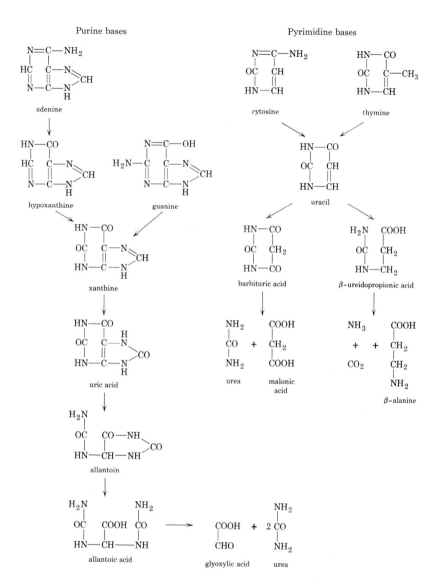

Figure 2. Biochemistry of purine and pyrimidine decomposition.

respectively, and produce from them the mononucleotides. These extracellular enzymes are synthesized by certain species of *Aspergillus, Penicillium, Streptomyces, Clostridium, Bacillus,* and *Achromobacter,* each of which is thereby enabled to use nucleic acids as nutrients in culture. The next step in the decay is the removal of the phosphate from the simple nucleotide to yield a substance composed of a purine or pyrimidine base still linked to the sugar. The final stage in the degradation is the separation of the purine or pyrimidine base from the sugar.

$$(\text{base-sugar-P})_n \rightarrow \text{base-sugar-P} \rightarrow \text{base-sugar} \rightarrow$$
nucleic acid   mononucleotide

$$\text{sugar} + \text{purine and pyrimidine bases} \quad (\text{II})$$

In the subsequent metabolism of the sugar, CO_2 is evolved and, depending upon the availability of O_2, organic acids may be produced. The nitrogenous bases are decomposed as shown in figure 2. Bacteria of the genera *Pseudomonas, Micrococcus, Corynebacterium,* and *Clostridium* degrade the purine and pyrimidine compounds shown in the figure, but it is unlikely that bacteria are the sole responsible agents in soil.

Decomposition of Urea and Cyanamide

Urea is a product of the destruction of the nitrogenous bases contained in the nucleic acids (figure 2). Urea is likewise an important agricultural fertilizer, but it may also enter the soil in the excretory products of higher animals. The position of urea as an intermediate in microbial metabolism, as an animal excretory product, and as a nitrogenous fertilizer makes it a key compound in the nitrogen cycle.

Urea applied to soil is very readily hydrolyzed, and as much as 200 to 400 ppm urea-nitrogen may be transformed to ammonium at 10°C in periods of less than one week (4). The conversion is even more rapid at higher temperatures. The pH of soils receiving urea rises as ammonium is produced, and the conversion may proceed so rapidly that free ammonia is lost to the atmosphere. The volatilization is appreciable only where the buffering capacity is low, a situation common in manure piles or where the urea is applied on the soil surface. Following the initial increase, the pH falls as the ammonium is oxidized to nitric acid. Urea hydrolysis is favored by warm temperatures and is quite rapid at 37°C, but the transformation proceeds at a good rate at 2°C. The conversion of urea to ammonium in soil far exceeds the rate of nitrate appearance so that ammonium continues to accumulate as long as urea is present.

Many microorganisms possess the enzyme urease, the catalyst responsible for hydrolyzing urea. Ammonium carbamate is an intermediate in the hydrolysis.

$$CO(NH_2)_2 + H_2O \xrightarrow{\text{urease}} H_2NCOONH_4 \rightarrow 2NH_3 + CO_2 \quad \text{(III)}$$

The number of active organisms measured by plating varies from several thousand in the highly acid peats to greater than a million per gram in the most suitable locales. Bacteria, fungi, and actinomycetes synthesize urease and therefore can use urea as a nitrogen source for growth. Most frequently studied are species of *Bacillus, Micrococcus, Sarcina, Pseudomonas, Achromobacter, Corynebacterium, Clostridium,* and a diverse collection of filamentous fungi and actinomycetes. The observation that urea disappears slowly under anaerobiasis is in agreement with the difficulty in obtaining obligate anaerobes which hydrolyze urea. The bacteria that are active in the absence of air are the facultative anaerobes (27).

A small group of true bacteria have been termed *urea bacteria* not because they are necessarily the dominant organisms in the hydrolysis but because of their tolerance to high urea levels and their nutritional affinity for the compound. Two types of urea bacteria can be differentiated, cocci and spore-forming rods. Both develop well in alkaline solution and release enormous quantities of ammonia. The spore-forming rods are members of the genus *Bacillus* and are best represented by *Bacillus pasteurii* and *Bacillus freudenreichii.* The cocci are classified as either *Micrococcus ureae* or *Sarcina ureae.* By comparing counts performed with and without pasteurization at 80°C, it is possible to show that a large proportion of this group of urea decomposers exists in the spore form in soil.

Urea bacteria are isolated easily from manure or soil by enrichment in solutions containing high concentrations of urea. In pure culture, the organisms show a characteristic sensitivity to acidity, and growth proceeds only in neutral or alkaline media. The sensitivity to the hydrogen ion is apparent in field investigations as well since the urea bacteria are absent or sparse in areas of pH 4.0 to 5.5. Urea breakdown in acid environments, therefore, probably can be attributed to the non-specific flora (7, 8).

Calcium cyanamide is an important nitrogenous fertilizer that is itself not utilized by crops, but it is converted rapidly in soil to assimilable products. The decomposition of calcium cyanamide proceeds in three steps, an initial hydrolysis to cyanamide, a subsequent conversion of cyanamide to urea, and a microbial hydrolysis of urea by means of urease.

$$CaCN_2 + 2H_2O \rightarrow H_2CN_2 + Ca(OH)_2 \qquad (IV)$$
$$H_2CN_2 + H_2O \rightarrow CO(NH_2)_2 \qquad (V)$$
$$CO(NH_2)_2 + H_2O \rightarrow 2NH_3 + CO_2 \qquad (VI)$$

The first two steps are in part non-biological, but the urea transformation is entirely enzymatic. A number of microorganisms, *Aspergillus niger* for example, use cyanamide as a nitrogen source and produce urea from it. Ammonium formation from calcium cyanamide is influenced appreciably by soil texture, pH, and organic matter content. At high concentrations, calcium cyanamide is converted to dicyandiamide which not only is mineralized slowly but is itself a potent inhibitor of nitrification (16, 24).

Nitrogen Immobilization

To maintain the organic matter and nutrient level in agricultural land, it is customary farm practice to plow under undecayed or sometimes partially rotted crop residues or manure. Almost invariably this leads to a decrease in the inorganic nitrogen content of the soil, a depletion which may extend for some time. An analogous nitrogen change occurs following the incorporation of pure carbohydrates. In the decay of succulent green manures, however, the level of inorganic nitrogen rises. The N_i disappearance following the addition of nitrogen-poor crop residues, a process known as *nitrogen immobilization*, results in a marked depression of nitrogen uptake by the plant (figure 3) and a consequent decrease in crop yield.

Immobilization results from the microbial *assimilation* of inorganic nutrients. As new cells or hyphae are formed, not only must carbon, hydrogen, and oxygen be combined into protoplasmic complexes but so must nitrogen, phosphorus, potassium, sulfur, magnesium, and iron. Each one of these elements is thus immobilized. The microbiological removal of available ions is of agronomic importance only for the plant's macronutrients, of which nitrogen is the most prominent. In the case of nitrogen, immobilization is a conse-

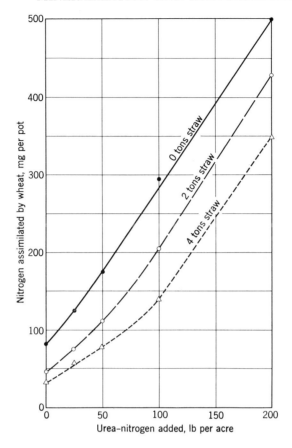

Figure 3. Effect of urea and straw applied to soil on the nitrogen uptake by wheat (17).

quence of the incorporation of ammonium and nitrate into proteins, nucleic acids, and other organic complexes contained within microbial cells. Immobilization is, therefore, the converse of mineralization; the latter returns microbial and plant nutrient elements to the inorganic state whereas the former combines inorganic ions into organic compounds.

Microorganisms cannot multiply nor can organic matter be decomposed unless nitrogen is assimilated into microbial protoplasm, and assimilation will take place as long as there is microbial activity. Even when a pure protein is added to soil, not all its nitrogen is mineralized; some always goes into the biosynthesis of the cells of the microscopic inhabitants. Whenever mineralization occurs, immobilization runs counter to it; thus, a determination of the quantity of inorganic nitrogen produced or lost during incubation does not measure one or the other process but rather the net release or tie-up. The gross figure is greatly underestimated.

In the decomposition of proteins in culture, a portion of the nitrogen liberated is reassimilated by the new cells generated. The net quantity of ammonium produced is therefore the amount of protein-nitrogen mineralized less the amount of nitrogen utilized in the synthesis of cellular constituents, assuming no accumulation of intermediates. The inclusion in culture media of a fermentable carbohydrate together with the organic nitrogen compounds further reduces the amount of ammonium that accumulates. The apparent retarding influence of carbohydrates on the production of ammonium from proteins and amino acids may be attributed to an assimilation of ammonium by the additional organisms appearing in the decomposition of the carbohydrate or to a microbial preference for the carbohydrate to the protein. In soil, only the former explanation applies as the mixed flora utilizes both substrates.

Ammonium salts are the most readily assimilated nitrogen sources for most bacteria, actinomycetes, and fungi. Chemically fixed or non-extractable ammonium in soil is largely unavailable, however, and only the extractable cation is used to a significant extent. Complex organic nitrogen preparations or individual amino acids are frequently incorporated in laboratory media because they provide growth factors, but the nitrogen is usually obtained from these molecules only following ammonification. Many filamentous fungi and gram negative bacteria develop readily with either ammonium or nitrate salts in the absence of amino acids. Certain organisms cannot use nitrate, and a rare few fail to utilize ammonium as sole source of the element. Strains that use nitrate, however, invariably use ammonium so that assimilation of the former indicates a higher order of physiological development. In laboratory media containing both ions, the ammonium tends to disappear first, and the nitrate may sometimes remain until almost all the ammonium is gone. In like fashion, ammonium is preferentially utilized to nitrate in the decomposition of organic matter. Not only is there a selective uptake so that extractable ammonium is utilized almost to the exclusion of nitrate in soil, but the decomposition of carbonaceous materials is more rapid when nitrogen is supplied in the reduced condition (11).

A large part of the nitrogen of proteins or protein-rich compounds added to soil is recovered in the mineral form. The added protein serves as both a carbon and a nitrogen source for the microflora, and much of the organic nitrogen is liberated as ammonium because the demand for the former element far exceeds the need for the latter. Frequently as much as three-fourths of the nitrogen of pure proteins is recovered as inorganic nitrogen in short incubation periods. Should the protein be mixed with a carbohydrate, however, the population developing upon the greater supply of carbon will be larger, and more nitrogen will be required for the new flora. Consequently, the supply of nitrogen in the protein will not outweigh the demand to as great an extent, and less ammonium will be released. From this point of view, accumulated ammonium reflects but a waste product of metabolism, the cation remaining behind only when not needed for microbial proliferation.

A quantification of the aforementioned observations permits characterization of the interactions between the microbial nutrient demand and the supply. Calculations of this nature are of no mere academic interest as they are used for predictive purposes in nitrogen fertilizer recommendations. Data on the chemistry and physiology of microorganisms or empirical field results can be used to develop the critical relationships. Consider the decay of a typical organic material. In the process of rotting, the carbon is liberated as CO_2, the organic nitrogen as ammonium. The decomposition results in a simultaneous synthesis of additional microbial protoplasm, a process requiring the assimilation of carbon and nitrogen from either the substrate or the environment. To estimate the nitrogen needed to satisfy the demands for cell synthesis, data on the extent of carbon assimilation and the C:N ratio of the cells formed are required. As a rule, for mixed populations, 5 to 10 per cent of the substrate-carbon is assimilated by bacteria, 30 to 40 per cent by fungi, and 15 to 30 per cent by actinomycetes. The carbon content of microbial protoplasm is typically 45 to 50 per cent of the dry weight, but the percentage of nitrogen varies with the age of the culture and the environment. As first approximations, C:N ratios of 5:1, 10:1, and 5:1 may be proposed for the cellular components of bacteria, fungi, and actinomycetes, respectively (26). By combining the figures for carbon assimilation and protoplasmic constitution, it can be calculated that for the decomposition of 100 units of substrate-carbon it is necessary to provide 1 to 2, 3 to 4, and 3 to 6 units of nitrogen for bacteria, fungi, and actinomycetes, respectively. Taking the example of a plant product having approximately 40 per cent carbon, for each 100 parts of organic matter undergoing decay, 0.4 to 0.8, 1.2 to 1.6, and 1.2 to 2.4 parts of nitrogen are needed by the bacterial, fungal, and actinomycete flora.

Straw containing 0.5 per cent nitrogen and 40 per cent carbon, when subjected to attack by fungi, has only 0.5 units of nitrogen to satisfy the active biological agents that require 1.2 to 1.6 units so that a deficit of 0.7 to 1.1 units of nitrogen appears in the environment. Consequently, any ammonium or nitrate present or formed will be immobilized immediately. The extent of immobilization is less for a bacterial flora, greater for actinomycetes. This argument, based entirely on considerations of microbial nutrition, maintains that the microflora assimilates essentially all the nitrogen contained in residues poor in protein. In protein-rich residues, the excess is liberated into the environment as ammonium, which may be subsequently oxidized to nitrate. For example, in the fungal decomposition of 100 lb of alfalfa containing 3.0 per cent nitrogen and 40 per cent carbon, there is a surplus, and 1.4 to 1.8 lb of nitrogen are mineralized. Similar calculations can be applied to the immobilization of any element provided the appropriate values are known.

Extension of these theoretical considerations to agricultural practice is not difficult. Illustrative of many studies are the data cited in table 2, which were obtained from soil treated with dried blood or roots of various plants. The nitrate present after a 3-month incubation period can be taken as indicative of a net mineralization or immobilization. The experiment suggests that neither a net loss nor a net gain of inorganic nitrogen occurs in soils receiving organic materials containing approximately 1.7 per cent nitrogen while nitrate accumulates in soil treated with materials richer in nitrogen. In practice, organic substrates containing more than 1.8 per cent nitrogen, upon decomposition, immediately increase the N_i level. Here, the mineralization rate, m, exceeds i, the immobilization rate. A temporary removal of N_i follows the application of materials with 1.2 to 1.8 per cent nitrogen, but the initial period is followed by a stage in which m exceeds i so that ammonium and/or nitrate accumulates. Crop residues with less than 1.2 per cent nitrogen deplete the inorganic nitrogen reserve within about 1 week, and the deficiency is not alleviated in periods of several months or longer. In the last instance, crops will suffer from nitrogen starvation unless proper fertilization practices are followed.

TABLE 2

Nitrate Level in Soils Incubated with Materials of Varying Nitrogen Contents (14)

Organic Amendment	Nitrogen Content of Substrate *	After 3 Months	
		Nitrate-N in Soil	N Change
	%	mg	mg
Untreated soil	—	946.6	—
Dried blood	10.71	1751.1	+804.5
Clover roots	1.71	924.4	−22.2
Corn roots	0.79	510.6	−436.0
Timothy roots	0.62	398.4	−548.2
Oat roots	0.45	207.3	−739.3

* All materials applied at rates to give 600 mg N.

The critical nitrogen levels are frequently expressed in terms of C:N ratios. In natural materials with approximately 40 per cent carbon, the critical levels corresponding to 1.2 to 1.8 per cent are C:N ratios of ca. 20 to 30:1. Wider ratios favor immobilization, narrower ratios mineralization. It must be borne in mind, however, that decomposition results in CO_2 release, the volatilization decreasing the C:N ratio of protein-deficient residues. Ultimately, when the ratio falls below the critical range, m will exceed i, and nitrogen will appear in inorganic form. The economics of crop production often do not allow for the long wait required for the slow change, and it is a common practice to fertilize in order to bring the C:N ratio of plowed-under residues to ca. 30 to 35:1 or to a final nitrogen content of 1.2 to 1.5 per cent on a dry weight basis. This fertilizer is for the microflora, not for the crop.

A convenient means of expressing the deficit following the application of materials with wide C:N ratios is by the *nitrogen factor.* This factor is defined as the number of units of inorganic nitrogen immobilized for each 100 units of material undergoing decomposition or, operationally, the amount of nitrogen that must be added in order to prevent a net immobilization from the environment (21). To determine the nitrogen factor, excess ammonium is added to the crop residue, and the increase in organic nitrogen is determined at intervals during the decay. Values for the nitrogen factor vary from as little as 0.10 or less to as high as 1.3. For mature crop remains, values for the factor usually fall between 0.5 and 1.0 when the nitrogen is applied at the beginning of the decomposition. But, if the carbonaceous matter is allowed to rot for some time prior to fertilizer application, the nitrogen factor is less because the C:N ratio of the resultant material has been narrowed.

The nitrogen factor is an equilibrium value representing the opposing forces of mineralization and immobilization. Both mineralization and immobilization take place regardless of the percentage of nitrogen in the organic matter. In order to estimate the rate of one of two opposing transformations, isotopic tracers are used. For example, when N^{15}-labeled ammonium is applied to soil, the N^{15} tracer moves into the organic reservoir with immobilization while, in mineralization, the non-tracer N^{14} from the organic fraction dilutes the N^{15} in the inorganic pool. Isotopic experiments show that both transformations are proceeding regardless of environmental conditions. Should the immobilization rate, i, exceed the mineralization rate, m, N_i will not accumulate, and any initially present will disappear. Where i is less than m, N_i accumulates and becomes available for plant utilization.

Comparison of the simultaneous mineralization and immobilization is of considerable importance, for the results indicate the course of the nitrogen transformations at a given time. Typically, following the addition of materials with wide C:N ratios, e.g., 70:1, i exceeds m, so that the net effect is one of mineral nitrogen disappearance. With carbonaceous substrates of narrow C:N ratios, e.g. 15:1, m exceeds i, so the inorganic nitrogen content increases. In fallow land, m exceeds i whereas the reverse is generally true in cropped soil. On the other hand, both m and i are increased by cropping (2).

The rate and extent of microbial nitrogen assimilation are intimately linked with the type of carbonaceous substances undergoing decay. In general, a stimulation of biological activity is accompanied by an enhanced immobilization as protoplasmic turnover is increased. The rate of immobilization is therefore related to the availability of the organic molecule, very rapid with readily oxidized carbohydrates, moderate with less suitable materials, and particularly slow with resistant tissue components such as lignin or well-rotted manure. Thus, for a constant percentage of nitrogen or C:N ratio, the disappearance of inorganic nitrogen is associated with the rate of organic matter breakdown. Further, the nitrogen requirement for the decomposition of lignified or resistant tissues is generally quantitatively less than for the more succulent plants because little microbial protoplasm is synthesized. Immobilization is also correlated with pH and soluble soil phosphate, results that are not unexpected because of the qualitative and quantitative effects of pH and phosphorus on the size and biochemical capacities of the microflora (29).

The immobilization of inorganic nitrogen has important agronomic ramifications. Plants are poor competitors with the microflora when the inorganic nitrogen level is inadequate for maximum development of both macro- and microorganisms. Immobilization accompanying soil amendment with nitrogen-poor crop residues is undesirable during the growing season since a critical nutrient is rendered unavailable. On the other hand, the same reaction may be beneficial in the autumn of the year because nitrate and ammonium are tied up and are not lost by leaching during the winter season. The following spring, the nitrogen bound into microbial protoplasm is mineralized, at least in part, to ammonium and nitrate which can then be utilized by plants. The season of year thereby determines whether immobilization is beneficial or detrimental.

Biochemistry of Protein Decomposition

The protein molecule is composed of a long chain of amino acids, all of which have the general type structure $H_2NCHRCOOH$ where R may be a hydrogen atom, a single methyl group, a short carbon chain, or a cyclic structure. Some twenty different amino acids are found in the protein molecule, linked together by peptide bonds (CO—NH). Peptides are composed of short chains of amino acids. The molecule of the protein and peptide has the type structure shown below.

$$\ldots NHCCONHCCONHCCO\ldots$$

with H above each C, and R, R′, R″ below.

Enzymes that attack and hydrolyze the peptide bonds of proteins and peptides are known as *proteases*. These are considered to be of two general types, exopeptidases, which hydrolyze peptide bonds in the vicinity of the end of the amino acid chain, and endopeptidases, which hydrolyze bonds at a distance from the terminal end of the chain. The latter are sometimes termed proteinases because they hydrolyze both proteins and peptides whereas the former cleave only simple peptides and have no influence on proteins.

In the decomposition of proteins and peptides, free amino and free carboxyl groups are released.

$$\ldots \underset{R}{\overset{H}{NHCC}}ON\underset{R'}{\overset{H}{HCC}}ON\underset{R''}{\overset{H}{HCCO}}\ldots \xrightarrow[\text{enzyme}]{H_2O}$$

$$\ldots \underset{R}{\overset{H}{NHCCOOH}} + H_2N\underset{R'}{\overset{H}{CCO}}N\underset{R''}{\overset{H}{HCCO}}\ldots \quad (VII)$$

In the process, the proteolytic enzymes cleave the protein molecule to peptones (long amino acid chains), peptides, and finally to the free amino acids that are the end-products of protease action. The reaction is a hydrolysis as the enzyme ruptures the peptide bond by the addition of water. Many microorganisms utilize peptones, peptides, and amino acids in contrast to the few genera degrading native proteins.

Because it is too large to enter into the microbial cell, the protein molecule must first be cleaved to smaller units which can be assimilated. Within the confines of the cell, the simple derivatives can serve as sources of energy, carbon, and nitrogen. To convert the protein to assimilable forms, the microorganism must excrete an extracellular endopeptidase. Demonstration of extracellular proteases in vitro is accomplished by removing the cells from the culture medium and testing the filtrate for activity. It is likely that there are several different endopeptidases produced by microorganisms, but the problem has received little attention. The proteases of fungi are generally tolerant to acidity, and they commonly function from pH 4 to 8. Most bacterial proteases are quite sensitive to reaction, acting optimally in the vicinity of pH 7 to 8. Following the enzymatic degradation of the large protein molecule, the simple derivatives enter the cell for further metabolism. For the release of energy for growth, the substrate must be transformed within the cell itself.

The amino acids liberated by proteases serve as carbon and nitrogen sources for innumerable heterotrophs, each of which may be able to utilize one or several of these compounds. The nitrogen of most amino acids is removed as ammonia prior to significant decomposition of the carbon-containing portion of the molecule, and the microorganism gets its nitrogen by assimilation of the ammonia. The common mechanisms for the initial degradation of amino acids are *deamination,* the removal of ammonia, and *decarboxylation,* in which the carboxyl is removed.

a. Deamination by direct removal of ammonia:

$$RCH_2CHNH_2COOH \rightarrow RCH=CHCOOH + NH_3 \quad (VIII)$$

b. Oxidative deamination:

$$RCHNH_2COOH + \tfrac{1}{2}O_2 \rightarrow RCOCOOH + NH_3 \quad (IX)$$

c. Reductive deamination:

$$RCHNH_2COOH + 2H \rightarrow RCH_2COOH + NH_3 \quad (X)$$

d. Decarboxylation:

$$RCHNH_2COOH \rightarrow RCH_2NH_2 + CO_2 \quad (XI)$$

The amino acids produced from the proteins are mineralized at different rates. Some amino acids are resistant and others highly susceptible to decomposition. Ammonia is formed readily from arginine and tryptophan, for example, while lysine, threonine, and methionine have a more extended persistence in soil (10, 19). After deamination, the carbon residue is attacked aerobically or anaerobically to yield CO_2 and various organic products.

The inanimate portion of soil has a profound effect upon proteolysis. Because the initial degradation of the protein molecule requires the elaboration of extracellular enzymes, substances which adsorb or otherwise inactivate the biological catalysts influence the decomposition. Clay is prominent in such adsorption phenomena, and some clay minerals remove a number of enzymes from solution and thereby diminish biochemical activity. Little adsorption by kaolinite occurs above the isoelectric point while the removal is magnified at pH values below the isoelectric point of the enzyme. The former effect arises from the fact that the enzyme has a negative charge above its isoelectric point and is repelled by the negatively charged kaolinite (13, 15).

Clays may also decrease the rate of protein decomposition by adsorption of the proteinaceous substrate (figure 4). Thus, substances like gelatin are quite resistant to attack when adsorbed in a monolayer on the crystal lattice of montmorillonite whereas resistance to hydrolysis is diminished when the protein is present on the clay in two or more layers (18). The clay mineral attapulgite has a simi-

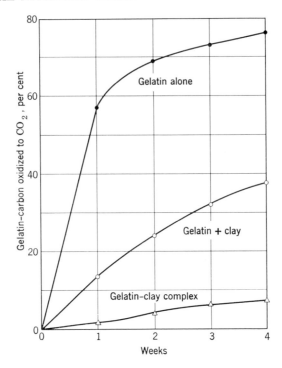

Figure 4. Effect of montmorillonite on gelatin decomposition in sand culture (18).

lar protective role while illite has little influence. There is also an intriguing reverse effect. When a denatured protein is adsorbed by kaolinite, the rate of its hydrolysis by a proteolytic *Pseudomonas* sp. and a *Flavobacterium* sp. is greater in the presence of the colloidal material than in its absence. The greater transformation of the adsorbed compound likely results from the clay mineral functioning as a surface for the concentration of adsorbed substrate and enzyme (5).

REFERENCES

Reviews

Broadbent, F. E. 1955. Basic problems in organic matter transformations. *Soil Sci.*, 79:107–114.

Fry, B. A. 1955. *The nitrogen metabolism of micro-organisms.* Methuen and Co., London.

Green, N. M., and H. Neurath. 1954. Proteolytic enzymes. In H. Neurath and K. Bailey, eds., *The proteins*. Academic Press, New York, Vol. 2, pp. 1057–1198.

Harmsen, G. W., and D. A. van Schreven. 1955. Mineralization of organic nitrogen in soil. *Adv. Agron.*, 7:299–398.

Literature cited

1. Allison, F. E., and L. D. Sterling. 1949. *Soil Sci.*, 67:239–252.
2. Bartholomew, W. V., and F. E. Clark. 1950. *Trans. 4th. Intl. Cong. Soil Sci.*, Amsterdam, 2:112–113.
3. Bechtereva, M. N., N. A. Kosheleva, and V. E. Khrisanovskaya. 1958. *Mikrobiologiya*, 27:32–38.
4. Broadbent, F. E., G. N. Hill, and K. B. Tyler. 1958. *Soil Sci. Soc. Am., Proc.*, 22:303–307.
5. Estermann, E. F., and A. D. McLaren. 1959. *J. Soil Sci.*, 10:64–78.
6. Estermann, E. F., G. H. Peterson, and A. D. McLaren. 1959. *Soil Sci. Soc. Am., Proc.*, 23:31–36.
7. Gibson, T. 1935. *Arch. Mikrobiol.*, 6:73–78.
8. Gibson, T. 1935. *Zent. Bakteriol.*, II, 92:414–424.
9. Goring, C. A. I., and W. V. Bartholomew. 1952. *Soil Sci.*, 74:149–164.
10. Greenwood, D. J., and H. Lees. 1956. *Plant and Soil*, 7:253–268.
11. Jansson, S. L., M. J. Hallam, and W. V. Bartholomew. 1955. *Plant and Soil*, 6:382–390.
12. Lopez, A. B., and N. L. Galvez. 1958. *Philippine Agric.*, 42:281–291.
13. Lynch, D. L., and L. J. Cotnoir. 1956. *Soil Sci. Soc. Am., Proc.*, 20:367–370.
14. Lyon, T. L., J. A. Bizzell, and B. D. Wilson. 1923. *J. Am. Soc. Agron.*, 15:457–467.
15. McLaren, A. D. 1954. *J. Phys. Chem.*, 58:129–137.
16. Nommik, H. 1958. *Acta Agric. Scand.*, 8:404–440.
17. Pinck, L. A., F. E. Allison, and V. L. Gaddy. 1946. *J. Am. Soc. Agron.*, 38:410–420.
18. Pinck, L. A., R. S. Dyal, and F. E. Allison. 1954. *Soil Sci.*, 78:109–118.
19. Putnam, H. D., and E. L. Schmidt. 1959. *Soil Sci.*, 87:22–27.
20. Rendig, V. V. 1951. *Soil Sci.*, 71:253–267.
21. Richards, E. H., and A. G. Norman. 1931. *Biochem. J.*, 25:1769–1778.
22. Robinson, J. B. D. 1957. *J. Agric. Sci.*, 49:100–105.
23. Taylor, C. B., and A. G. Lochhead. 1938. *Canad. J. Research*, C, 16:162–173.
24. Temme, J. 1948. *Plant and Soil*, 1:145–166.
25. van Schreven, D. A. 1958. *Van Zee Tot Land*, 26:26–52.
26. Waksman, S. A. 1924. *J. Agric. Sci.*, 14:555–562.
27. Weyland, H. 1957. *Zent. Bakteriol.*, II, 110:471–489.
28. Winsor, G. W., and A. G. Pollard. 1956. *J. Sci. Food Agric.*, 7:618–624.
29. Winsor, G. W., and A. G. Pollard. 1956. *J. Sci. Food Agric.*, 7:613–617.

16

Nitrification

The termination of the reactions involved in organic nitrogen mineralization occurs at the point where ammonium is formed. This, the most reduced form of inorganic nitrogen, serves as the starting point for a process known as *nitrification*, the biological formation of nitrate or nitrite from compounds containing reduced nitrogen. Organic nitrogen compounds cannot be directly converted to nitrate, and ammonium generally must first be liberated as a consequence of the mineralization processes.

The importance of the nitrifying microorganisms rests upon their capacity to produce the nitrate which is the major nitrogen source assimilated by higher plants. Nitrate is produced not only in soil but also in marine environments, manure piles, and during sewage processing, where it is the product of the final stage in rendering organic nitrogen non-offensive.

During the Napoleonic era, nitrate salts were in great demand in France for gunpowder manufacture, and with the natural source cut off by war, the nitrates were prepared in niter heaps that consisted of piles of soil mixed with manure and lime. The explanations for the phenomenon of nitrate synthesis advanced during the early nineteenth century were of a chemical nature, the product reputedly being formed by reaction of atmospheric O_2 and ammonium, with the soil considered as chemical catalyst. In contrast to this theory, Pasteur postulated that the formation of nitrate was microbiological and analogous to the conversion of alcohol to vinegar. The first experimental evidence that nitrification is biological is attributed to Schloesing and Muntz (29), who added sewage effluent to a long tube filled with sterile sand and $CaCO_3$. For 20 days the ammonium concentration in the liquid remained unaltered, but then ammonium was destroyed and nitrate appeared. Heating the column or the addition of an antiseptic eliminated the transformation, but it could be reinitiated by the application of a small quantity of garden soil. It remained for S. Winogradsky (33) to isolate the responsible agents.

Under certain conditions, two separate and distinct steps are distinguishable in nitrification. Since nitrite frequently appears during ammonium oxidation, it seemed apparent to early microbiologists that the transformation involved an initial oxidation to nitrite and a subsequent conversion of the latter to nitrate. The validity of this theory was established when two groups of bacteria were isolated and described, each catalyzing a separate portion of the reaction sequence. Because nitrite is rarely found in nature even in habitats where nitrification is proceeding rapidly, the nitrate formers must generally occur in the same environments as the ammonium oxidizers. Information on the responsible species, however, has been collected with difficulty because of their slow growth habits and their frequent overgrowth by rapidly proliferating contaminants.

Environmental Influences

Physical and chemical factors affect the rate of ammonium oxidation. This fact is simply demonstrated as nitrification rates in sterile soils receiving the same inoculum differ according to soil type. The remarkable degree of sensitivity of the process to external influences is attributed in part to the great physiological similarity of the responsible species; as a result, modification of the environment often has a profound significance in governing the production of the end-product. When the habitat becomes unfavorable, in acid or anaerobic conditions for example, little or no nitrate is detected, but ammonium accumulates because ammonification is less sensitive to environmental change.

Chief among the ecological influences is acidity. Several careful investigations have demonstrated a significant correlation between nitrate production and pH. In acid environments, nitrification proceeds slowly even in the presence of an adequate supply of substrate, and the responsible species are rare or totally absent at great acidities. An exact limiting pH cannot be ascertained since a variety of physicochemical factors in soil will alter any specific boundaries. Typically, the rate falls off markedly below pH 6.0 and becomes negligible below 5.0, yet nitrate may occasionally be present in fields down to 4.0 and sometimes lower. Some soils nitrify at 4.5, others do not; the difference is possibly attributable to acid-adapted strains or to chemical differences in the two habitats. The acidity affects not only the transformation itself but also the microbial numbers, neutral to alkaline soils having the largest populations (32). The pH values for growth of these bacteria depend to some extent upon the locality from which they originated. Strains derived from acid soils are more tolerant of high hydrogen ion concentration than those from areas of alkaline pH, certain isolates of the former category having an optimum near 6.5 while 7.8 is preferred by strains of the latter group (14).

Because of the microbial sensitivity to hydrogen ions, nitrification in acid soils is markedly enhanced by liming. At reactions near the optimum, the lime addition has little to no effect. Indeed, in extremely acid environments devoid of nitrate, liming may lead to ammonium oxidation in sites where the transformation had not previously occurred. Often the failure to nitrify is entirely a consequence of acidity, and the condition may therefore be readily alleviated by liming.

Oxygen is an obligate requirement for all species concerned, making adequate aeration essential. Where the O_2 supply is inadequate for microorganisms, there will be little ammonium oxidation, and the reaction ceases in the total absence of O_2. Because of this nutritional characteristic, soil structure will affect the accumulation of nitrate through its influence on aeration. In controlled experiments, artificial aeration stimulates the bacteria to greater activity and nitrate accumulates more rapidly, while a reduction in the partial pressure of O_2 below that found in air reduces nitrification (4).

Because moisture affects the aeration regime of soil, the water status of the microbial habitat has a marked influence upon nitrate production. At one extreme, waterlogging limits the diffusion of O_2, and nitrification is suppressed. At the opposite pole, in arid conditions, bacterial proliferation is not retarded by the supply of gaseous nutrients but rather by the insufficiency of water, and irrigation increases both the nitrifying population and nitrate biosynthesis. The optimum moisture level varies considerably with different soils, but nitrates generally appear most readily at one-half to two-thirds the moisture-holding capacity.

The interaction of moisture, temperature, cropping, and mineral nutrients largely makes up the seasonal effect. The dominant influence will be determined by the specific environment and cannot be predicted accurately. Further, the season of year at which nitrate is most abundant does not necessarily coincide with the time of maximal microbial activity because plant uptake, microbial immobilization, and leaching all reduce the nitrate level. In temperate zones, nitrate formation is generally most rapid in spring and autumn and slowest during the summer and winter months, but annual fluctuations of moisture and temperature can alter the seasonal effects appreciably.

Nitrification is markedly affected by temperature, and many investigations have confirmed the fact that below 5°C and above 40°C the rate is very slow. There is evidence of a slow nitrate formation almost down to the freezing point, a fact of significance to nitrogen losses in cooler climates where leaching or denitrification of the end-product may occur during autumn and winter; this loss can lead to a lack of response in the spring to fall-applied nitrogenous fertilizers unless the element is tied up in some way. Increasing the temperature from the lower extremes produces a more rapid ammonium oxidation until the optimum range is attained. This range varies, presumably because of physiological differences in the dominant bacterial strains, but the optimum usually lies between 30 and 35°C.

The type of crop may have a bearing upon the size and activities of the nitrifying microflora. With many crops, no preferential influences can be ascertained, but sometimes a single plant species is without effect upon nitrification in one soil type while increasing it in another. As early as 1913, Lyon and Bizzell demonstrated that soil under alfalfa formed nitrate more vigorously than samples taken under timothy. Explanations for these observations are lacking, but an alteration in physical structure or chemical characteristics of the soil in proximity to the roots may contribute to the phenomenon.

Production of Nitrate from Various Substrates

The soil perfusion apparatus (22) such as that shown in figure 1 is a convenient means for the study of nitrification. In normal operation of the apparatus, a metabolite is continuously percolated through a soil column, the repeated perfusion permitting direct study of the kinetics of the transformation and the effects of environmental change. The original metabolite-containing solution, after complet-

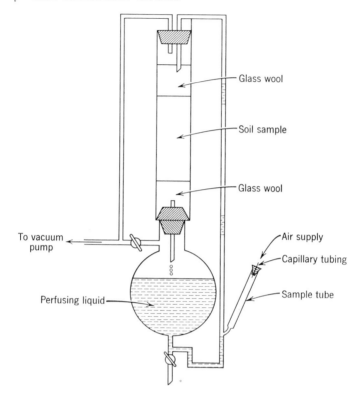

Figure 1. The soil perfusion apparatus.

ing its passage through the column, is recirculated so that the system is complete, a single respiring population being investigated as a biological unit. Designed originally for nitrification investigations, it has subsequently been adapted to studies of other organic and inorganic conversions.

By means of the perfusion technique, the rate of ammonium oxidation or nitrate synthesis may be conveniently estimated. When expressed as a function of time, a plot of the transformation yields a sigmoid curve similar to that obtained when increases in bacterial numbers are depicted on a linear scale. In the initial perfusion, the system becomes enriched with the nitrifying bacteria, and the rate of ammonium oxidation upon reperfusion is linear. Such an enriched sample will, when treated with fresh ammonium, consume almost the theoretical quantity of O_2 for the complete conversion to nitrate.

Alternatively, when a soil that had been initially perfused with ammonium is reperfused with nitrite, the oxidation commences immediately, demonstrating that both an ammonium- and a nitrite-oxidizing flora developed during the conversion of ammonium to nitrate.

The sigmoid relationship in linear expressions shows, when presented logarithmically, the exponential plot characteristic of bacterial growth (31). This is demonstrated by the results in figure 2; such exponential changes indicate that the reaction in soil is bacterial as the fungi and actinomycetes do not exhibit logarithmic increases in biochemical activity. The reaction rate cannot be determined precisely

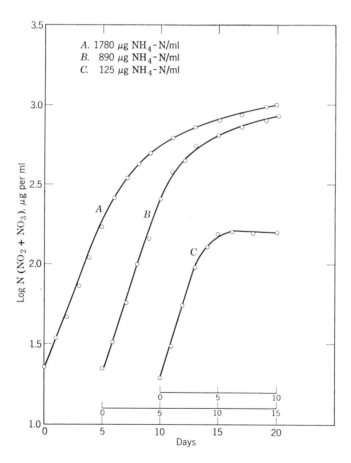

Figure 2. Logarithmic plot of the nitrification rate at three ammonium concentrations (31).

by ammonium disappearance because of chemical adsorption of the cation by the soil's cation exchange complex, but it can be measured by the accumulation of the products of the transformation, nitrite and nitrate. Consequently, a logarithmic plot of the appearance of nitrite-nitrogen plus nitrate-nitrogen under controlled conditions yields a straight line from the slope of which an apparent generation time for the nitrifying bacteria can be obtained.

Adsorption of ammonium by the clay fraction has a profound influence upon its microbiological availability, and the tenacity of the adsorption and the rate of release directly affect ammonium metabolism. Such adsorbed cations are oxidized by the chemo-autotrophs although the nature of the clay and the amount of ammonium affect the percentage of the adsorbed chemical that is nitrified. The availability of the chemically fixed ion is low with usually less than 25 per cent nitrified in periods of 2 to 5 months (27).

The rate of nitrate production varies with the material undergoing transformation. In environments having a near neutral reaction, nitrates appear more rapidly from ammonium salts than from organic nitrogen compounds whereas nitrates are formed faster from organic materials in certain acid soils. The unexpected difference results from the increase in alkalinity during ammonification that makes the environment more favorable for the nitrifiers. The oxidation of anhydrous NH_3 or NH_4OH in acid soils is likewise more rapid than the nitrification of ammonium salts, and here too the rates parallel the differences in alkalinity following treatment. When urea is hydrolyzed by urease-producing microorganisms, the resulting ammonia increases the pH so that the formation of nitrate in acid soils is also greater for urea than for $(NH_4)_2SO_4$ (12). No such effect of nitrogen carrier would be expected in soils whose reaction is closer to the optimal range for the nitrate-producing bacteria.

The natural intermediate, nitrite, is readily metabolized in slightly acid, neutral, and in calcareous soils. The oxidation under most circumstances is quantitative, and the theoretical formation of nitrate is observed. As with ammonium, nitrite additions lead to an enrichment of the microflora active on the anion. If enriched soil is placed in a respirometer and treated with a fresh increment of nitrite, one-half mole of O_2 is consumed for each mole of nitrite supplied.

$$NaNO_2 + \tfrac{1}{2}O_2 \rightarrow NaNO_3 \qquad (I)$$

However, not all of the nitrite-nitrogen added to acid soils is recovered as nitrate-nitrogen. The observed losses are chemical rather than biological as they occur in acid soils or buffer solutions that have been sterilized, but they are only of consequence at reactions below pH 5.0 to 5.5. In actual practice, when ammonium oxidation takes place at a pH lower than 5.0 to 5.5 or where the acidity produced in nitrification increases the hydrogen ions to an equivalent extent, the formation of nitrite can lead to a significant chemical volatilization of nitrogen.

Nitrification in Various Environments

During the growing season, agricultural crops assimilate large quantities of nitrate so that the production of this plant nutrient in soil is of considerable importance. Certain chemical properties of the microbiological habitat serve to alter the magnitude of the transformation. Acidity has been the most fully investigated. There is also evidence that nitrification is proportional to the cation exchange capacity (23), and Allison and Sterling (3) have demonstrated a correlation between total nitrogen content and the liberation of nitrate from the soil organic fraction, the magnitude of release varying directly with the humus nitrogen present. In alkali soils of high salt content, nitrate production is commonly retarded as the tolerance of the nitrifiers to salinity is not great.

Some soils, particularly highly acid fields that are freshly limed, respond to the addition of biochemically active nitrifying inocula. Frequently, the use of fungicides largely or completely eliminates the nitrifying species so that ammonium will persist and may become potentially phytotoxic. Once the pesticide has been dissipated, the treated soil often responds to inoculation although natural contamination would ultimately overcome the deficiency.

The nitrifying activity of these organisms is of importance to mineral solubility. As ammonium salts are oxidized, nitric acid is formed, and the pH falls. This tends to increase the availability to plants of certain ions which are normally obtained only with difficulty, and nitrification has thus been implicated in changes in concentration of soluble potassium, phosphate, magnesium, and calcium. The nitric acid may thus serve to solubilize unavailable mineral elements. There is also evidence that $CaCO_3$ is acted upon by the products of the nitrifying microflora with a resultant leaching out of the calcium (20).

The Nitrifying Bacteria

Considerable uncertainty still exists as to the status of many of the organisms reported to be capable of catalyzing ammonium or nitrite oxidation. This results from the difficulties in obtaining isolates whose purity is beyond reasonable doubt. Contaminants in autotrophic cultures often remain undetected because many of the offending strains are morphologically identical to the predominant organisms and because neither the autotrophs nor many of the contaminating heterotrophs develop appreciably on conventional laboratory media.

The pioneering work of S. Winogradsky established that nitrification is associated with the metabolism of certain chemoautotrophic bacteria. Two groups were distinguished, one deriving its energy for cell synthesis by the oxidation of ammonium, the other by the oxidation of nitrite. In *Bergey's manual of determinative bacteriology* (7), all the nitrifying autotrophs are classified in the family Nitrobacteriaceae of the order Pseudomonadales. Members of the family form no endospores and vary in shape to include rods, ellipsoids, cocci, and spirilla. Not all species possess flagella but, where present, the flagella are usually polar. Despite the lack of morphological homogeneity, physiological similarity stands out, especially with respect to the energy-yielding reactions; the energy for growth is derived solely from the metabolism of ammonium or nitrite. Seven genera are recognized in the family:

I. Oxidize ammonium to nitrite
   A. Zoogloea not formed
      1. Cells ellipsoidal. *Nitrosomonas*
      2. Cells spherical. *Nitrosococcus*
      3. Cells spiral. *Nitrosospira*
   B. Zoogloea formed
      1. Zoogloea surrounded by common membrane forming a cyst. *Nitrosocystis*
      2. Cells occur in masses in slime layer without a common membrane. *Nitrosogloea*

II. Oxidize nitrite to nitrate
   A. Zoogloea not formed. *Nitrobacter*
   B. Zoogloea formed. *Nitrocystis*

Of the seven, only *Nitrosomonas* and *Nitrobacter* are encountered frequently, and these two are undoubtedly the major nitrifying chemoautotrophs. The cells of the former are ellipsoidal in shape and may be either motile or non-motile. Two species are recognized, *Nitrosomonas europaea* (figure 3) and *Nitrosomonas monocella.* Bomeke (6) proposed a third representative, *N. oligocarbogenes,* that differs from *N. europaea* by its larger size, lower efficiency, and greater sensitivity to high temperature. Two species of *Nitrobacter* are recognized, *N. winogradskyi* and *N. agilis.*

Nitrosococcus species are not frequently encountered in nitrifying enrichments and have been rarely reported. The cells are large, gram positive, non-motile spheres, 1.5 to 1.7 μ in diameter, forming no zoogloea. Three genera are distinguished by their ability to form a zoogloea, *Nitrosocystis* and *Nitrosogloea* among the nitrite producers and *Nitrocystis,* a nitrate former. The validity of these three genera has been the subject of considerable doubt as they resemble certain stages in the life cycle of the myxobacterium *Sorangium.* Present

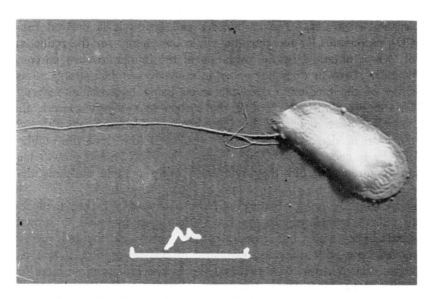

Figure 3. Electron photomicrograph of *Nitrosomonas europaea.*

evidence suggests that the original cultures of *Nitrosocystis, Nitrosogloea,* and *Nitrocystis* consisted of typical nitrifiers contaminated with the fruiting bodies of heterotrophic slime bacteria (15). The same does not hold for *Nitrosocystis javanensis,* a bacterium characterized as producing hard colonies on silica gel (34). This microorganism was distinguished from *Nitrosomonas* spp., which allegedly develop only soft colonies, but it has since been shown that pure cultures of *Nitrosomonas* can exhibit both hard and soft colonies on silica gel (21) so that the differentiation is no longer tenable. The remaining ammonium-oxidizing autotroph, *Nitrosospira,* is rarely found and does not seem to be common in nature.

The established chemoautotrophic nitrifying genera are, therefore, fewer in number than might be expected in view of the significance of nitrate production for plant growth. *Nitrosomonas* and *Nitrobacter* are prevalent in nature while *Nitrosococcus* and *Nitrosospira* are less common. The validity of the remaining three groups is questionable because the original strains probably consisted of mixtures of organisms.

The nitrifying autotrophs are all obligate in their reliance upon inorganic materials for energy; not only is organic carbon not utilizable by these bacteria but their oxidative capacity is limited solely to nitrogen compounds, and no energy is obtained from other inorganic substrates. The carbon for cell synthesis is derived from CO_2, carbonates, or bicarbonates while the energy for the reduction of CO_2 is obtained by the oxidation of the inorganic nitrogen compounds. Growth does not occur in conventional laboratory media, many of the medium ingredients even being bactericidal. Except for the peculiarities regarding the carbon and energy sources, the mineral requirements resemble those known for heterotrophs although the nutrient demand in laboratory studies is low since the number of cells is never great. These bacteria have no known growth factor requirements, but they synthesize every organic molecule that participates in the vital functions of biological systems.

One of the unique features of *Nitrosomonas* spp. is their tendency to adhere tenaciously to the $CaCO_3$ particles included in growth media to serve as a buffer and a carbon source, and the cells are removed only with difficulty. Because of this adsorption, it was assumed that *Nitrosomonas* required the presence of solid surfaces for proliferation. A method of culturing *N. europaea* in the absence of insoluble medium constituents has been described, however, thereby dispelling the concept that the bacteria require adsorption for growth to take place (10). Under such conditions in culture solutions, a generation time of 11 hours is observed, slow by comparison with heterotrophs but rapid for nitrifiers. From a logarithmic plot of nitrite and nitrate-nitrogen against time, an apparent generation time for ammonium oxidizers in soil was calculated to be approximately 30 hours (31). These data show that the frequent statements regarding the beneficial effect of soil or soil extract are incorrect providing the cultures are grown under optimal conditions. There is also no stimulation of nitrite production by *N. europaea* by either B vitamins or amino acids (16) so that the sole nutritional requisites are an inorganic energy source and a number of inorganic salts. Modern evidence confirms the concept that members of the genera *Nitrosomonas* and *Nitrobacter* are obligate in their autotrophy with no heterotrophic stage in their life cycles. All polysaccharides, structural constituents, amino acids, and vitamins found within the organisms are synthesized from inorganic nutrients and CO_2. A remarkable nutritional simplicity is indicated, yet the metabolic complexity must be great since the bacteria are capable of synthesizing from inorganic materials all enzymes and other factors necessary for life.

Because of their capacity to utilize CO_2 as sole carbon source, the nitrifiers must bring about a reduction of CO_2 in order to convert it to the types of carbon compounds found in microbial protoplasm. For each molecule of CO_2 reduced to the level of carbon in the cell, i.e., $(CH_2O)_n$, a fixed amount of energy is required. The driving force for the reduction is the inorganic oxidation; hence, biochemical efficiency in these organisms is conveniently expressed by the ratio of inorganic nitrogen oxidized to CO_2-carbon assimilated, an N:C ratio. For the classical *N. europaea*, the ratio of ammonium-nitrogen oxidized to CO_2-carbon assimilated is approximately 35:1 (33), but in *N. monocella* and in many unclassified strains of this genus the ratio varies from approximately 14 to 70:1. In *Nitrobacter*, the ratio of nitrite-nitrogen oxidized to CO_2-carbon fixed varies from 76 to 135:1.

The reaction characterizing the chemoautotrophic bacteria of the first step in nitrification is

$$NH_4^+ + 1\tfrac{1}{2}O_2 \rightarrow NO_2^- + 2H^+ + H_2O \qquad (II)$$

The energy liberated per gram atom of nitrogen is 66 kcal. The second step (equation 1) releases 18 kcal. For both equations, the observed disappearance of substrate, the accumulation of product, and the utilization of O_2 agree with the theoretical values.

The microorganisms do not get all the energy potentially available but only a small proportion of it; the proportion is determined by their efficiency of energy utilization. For *Nitrosomonas,* the free energy efficiency ranges from 5 to 14 per cent while the efficiency of *Nitrobacter* has been calculated to be 5 to 10 per cent. The free energy efficiency may be greater in young cultures still in the logarithmic phase than in old cultures although the high efficiency may be maintained by prolonging the exponential stage of growth (10, 17). The lower N:C ratios of the ammonium than of the nitrite-oxidizers demonstrate that the former get more energy from their autotrophic reaction; i.e., less nitrogen need be turned over for each cell formed, a fact not unexpected in view of the three-fold greater energy yield.

Many microbiologists have investigated the abundance of these autotrophs in nature. The numbers of ammonium-oxidizers have been found to vary from zero up to one million or more per gram of soil. The larger counts occur only in soils of pH greater than about 6.0, yet many neutral or alkaline habitats have small populations. In most habitats, species of *Nitrosomonas* and *Nitrobacter* are found together; otherwise nitrite might accumulate to phytotoxic levels. Populations of both groups may be enlarged by use of ammonium salts, and values in excess of 10^7 per gram are not unknown. In temperate climates, nitrifiers are numerous during the warmth of the spring and rare during hot, dry summers and in winter; drying or freezing decreases their abundance but never entirely eliminates these bacteria.

In their early investigations of the nature of chemoautotrophy, microbiologists were perplexed by the total inability of these bacteria to use added carbonaceous nutrients, and it was not uncomforting to know that simple organic materials such as glucose, asparagine, or sodium butyrate completely inhibited the nitrifiers in culture media. The inhibition by certain chemicals has been confirmed in recent investigations, but careful study has revealed that many of the effects even in culture were the result of experimental errors. A diverse group of organic compounds fail to inhibit *Nitrosomonas europaea* except when present in relatively high concentrations although the levels for inhibition are still somewhat lower than for common heterotrophs. The inhibition by glucose, which was somewhat surprising in the early work, is the result of chemical changes during the sterilization of the sugar by autoclaving since even a 5 per cent solution of the sugar hardly affected the process provided sterilization was performed by means other than heating (19). There is no basis for the conclusion that ammonium oxidation in nature is inhibited by organic matter per se especially as the reaction occurs in environments with considerable soluble carbonaceous materials as in sewage and barnyard manure. The well-established role of carbohydrates in depressing the nitrate content of soil is not an influence upon the nitrate-producing bacteria but rather a consequence of the depletion of the inorganic nitrogen supply by the flora requiring inorganic nutrients for carbohydrate decomposition.

Under most conditions nitrite does not accumulate in soil, and the dominant nitrogen-containing anion is nitrate. The existence and persistence of nitrite could have a marked effect upon crop production because of its toxicity to plants and microorganisms. On the other hand, nitrite may accumulate under certain circumstances; in alkaline soils, for example, nitrate production from $(NH_4)_2SO_4$ is suppressed as the rate of ammonium application is increased. This is not an inhibition of ammonium oxidation but rather the nitrite formed is not further metabolized to nitrate so that it persists as long as ammonium is present in solution (31). Considerable field evidence indicates that nitrite accumulation is the result of two factors, alkalinity and high ammonium levels. The interaction of the variables is shown clearly in table 1. In calcareous soils, the accumulation is proportional to the rate of ammonium addition, and for constant nitrogen fertilization the effect increases with decreasing hydrogen ion concentrations. Even in the hydrolysis of proteinaceous matter or urea, the release of ammonium may lead to a significant although usually transitory suppression of nitrate formation by an analogous

TABLE 1

Effect of Lime and Nitrogen on Nitrite Accumulation (13)

Treatment	ppm Nitrite-Nitrogen			
	Soil 1	Soil 2	Soil 3	Soil 4
None	0	0	0	4
$CaCO_3$, 1%	54	59	5	5
$(NH_4)_2SO_4$, 500 ppm N	3	0	0	0
$CaCO_3 + (NH_4)_2SO_4$	255	218	260	310

mechanism. As the pH or the ammonium level falls with progress of nitrification, the suppression is relieved and nitrate production commences.

The nitrite accumulation is attributed to the marked sensitivity of the *Nitrobacter* group to ammonium salts at alkaline reaction. At pH 9.5, as little as 1.4 ppm ammonium-nitrogen suppresses the energy-yielding reaction of *Nitrobacter agilis* while having no such marked influence on the ammonium-oxidizers (2). Such observations suggest that ammonium, the natural substrate for nitrification, is a selective inhibitor in alkaline environments of the second step in nitrification by virtue of its toxicity to *Nitrobacter* spp. The active principle apparently is not the cation, ammonium, but rather the free ammonia which is favored by pH values more basic than 7.0.

Heterotrophic Nitrification

Enrichment techniques are designed to be specific for definite physiological types, and these methods are the means whereby the autotrophs are isolated. As a result, nitrification is often taken to be a purely chemoautotrophic attribute. Heterotrophs which might be able to oxidize inorganic nitrogen compounds, as they derive no energy from the process, cannot be isolated by preferential enrichment since the necessary culture solutions would require organic substrates that would favor a variety of microorganisms growing in simple organic carbon-ammonium-salts media. Nevertheless, heterotrophic nitrification is now established as a common microbial phenomenon, in vitro at least, but each suspected heterotroph must be tested separately in pure culture in order to establish its capacity to nitrify.

The first unequivocal demonstration of heterotrophic nitrification is attributed to Cutler and Mukerji (9) who isolated several bacteria producing small amounts of nitrite from ammonium salts in media low in sugar. The isolates differed from *Nitrosomonas* by their ability to grow well in peptone media and on nutrient agar. At best, only a maximum of 1.5 ppm nitrite-nitrogen was formed, but following the peak of production, the nitrite decreased and finally disappeared. None of the strains could synthesize nitrate either in sterile soil or in laboratory media. Such results on the quantities of nitrogen oxidized are in contrast to the 2000 ppm nitrogen or more transformed by *Nitrosomonas* and *Nitrobacter*.

Microorganisms capable of converting ammonium to nitrite are simple to demonstrate by the testing of random colonies from soil dilution plates. Rarely do the cultures thus obtained produce more than 1 to 2 ppm nitrite-nitrogen although values up to and sometimes greater than 5 ppm are not entirely unknown. Bacteria, actinomycetes, and fungi have been implicated in the heterotrophic process as indicated in table 2. Important in governing nitrite appearance is the C:N ratio in the medium; at wide ratios, i.e., high sugar and low ammonium, nitrite is not detected, but it does become apparent at ratios less than 10:1 (8). High levels of sugars or available carbohydrate would thus apparently suppress nitrite accumulation by heterotrophs. Nitrite production in sterile, ammonium-amended soil has also been reported for a gram negative rod, a coccus, and several streptomycetes with a maximum yield of 6.33 ppm nitrite-nitrogen (26).

The ability to produce nitrite in small quantities by oxidative pathways is relatively widespread. Among the bacteria and actinomycetes, the oxidation proceeds no further, and frequently the nitrite disappears through assimilation, especially where the nitrogen demand is great because of excessive carbon levels. Occasionally, how-

TABLE 2

Nitrite Production from Ammonium and Various Organic Compounds

Microorganism	Substrate for Nitrite Production
Pseudomonas spp.	*o*- and *p*-nitrophenol
Corynebacterium simplex	mono-, di-, and trinitrophenols
	4,6-dinitro-*o*-cresol
Nocardia spp.	*o*- and *p*-nitrobenzoate
Pseudomonas sp.	*o*- and *p*-nitrobenzoate
Aspergillus flavus	peptone and NH_4
Streptomyces spp.	NH_4
Mycobacterium rubrum	NH_4
Bacillus sp.	NH_4
Vibrio sp.	NH_4

ever, an organism is isolated which takes ammonium or amino-nitrogen all the way to nitrate; nevertheless, only a part of the initial nitrogen is converted to nitrate. This has been demonstrated with *Aspergillus flavus* (30), an organism synthesizing up to 26.0 ppm nitrate-nitrogen in culture media.

Nitrite synthesis from organic nitro compounds (table 2) is neither rare nor unexpected since the nitrogen moiety of the molecule is already in the oxidized state. Substrates thus transformed include various mono-, di-, and trinitrophenols, dinitrocresol, and nitrobenzoates. The nitro compounds are not reduced to ammonium or hydroxylamine prior to the formation of nitrite; rather the process is direct. In the transformation of nitro groups to nitrite, the percentage of nitrogen so converted is usually high, frequently more than 50 per cent, an expected result in view of the similarities of substrate and product.

Oximes of a number of organic acids are rapidly nitrified when added to soil. These compounds include oximes of pyruvic, phenylpyruvic, oxalacetic, and α-ketoglutaric acids (28). Among the organisms which in pure culture form nitrite from oximes are species of *Corynebacterium* and *Nocardia*. Strains of *Pseudomonas* likewise convert hydroxylamine to nitrite provided that the substrate is present in low concentration.

The significance of heterotrophic nitrification is difficult to assess at this time. The evidence at present does not implicate heterotrophs in most instances of nitrite or nitrate production in soil, yet they may be prominent in atypical habitats. Pure culture studies have failed to reveal any heterotroph which can nitrify as rapidly or to as great an extent as the two-genus autotrophic association, but the inefficiency of the heterotrophs may be compensated by their great numbers, and they may exert some influence on the rate of nitrate synthesis.

Biochemical Mechanism

The early investigations of Beesley (5) indicated that more ammonium-nitrogen disappeared under the influence of a mixed microflora than could be accounted for as nitrite and nitrate although a significant part of this "lost nitrogen" eventually reappeared. This evidence was taken as suggesting the appearance of intermediate compounds during nitrification. More recently, Imshenetzky, Ruban, and Buzina (18) demonstrated that more ammonium is oxidized by pure cultures of a *Nitrosomonas* sp. than nitrite formed, supporting the hypothesis that some intermediate between ammonium and nitrite is accumulating. In nature, on the other hand, all of the ammonium disappearing from neutral or slightly calcareous soils is recovered as nitrite or nitrate, and there is no significant accumulation of any other compounds. In most sudies with the perfusion apparatus as well, the recovery as nitrate of added ammonium salts is essentially quantitative.

In the nitrification step catalyzed by *Nitrosomonas* spp., the oxidation state of nitrogen is changed from the -3 of ammonia to the $+3$ of nitrous acid through the removal of six electrons. Establishing the individual steps involved and the intermediary compounds formed has been the subject of considerable interest, but it is only in recent years that some light has been shed on this difficult problem.

Non-proliferating cell suspensions of *N. europaea* convert ammonium-nitrogen quantitatively to nitrite, and the O_2 consumed and nitrite produced agree with the values predicted by equation II. Under certain circumstances, hydroxylamine (NH_2OH), which is usually highly toxic, may be oxidized as readily as ammonium itself. The O_2 uptake in the presence of hydroxylamine is 90 per cent of that predicted by equation III.

$$NH_2OH + O_2 \rightarrow HNO_2 + H_2O \qquad (III)$$

It has also been shown that extracts of these bacteria cause an enzymatic disappearance of hydroxylamine although the quantity disappearing far exceeds the nitrite synthesized (11). The formation of hydroxylamine in *Nitrosomonas* cultures metabolizing ammonium may also be demonstrated by use of the inhibitor hydrazine which suppresses the further oxidation of hydroxylamine, allowing it to accumulate. On the basis of such lines of approach, hydroxylamine is proposed to be the first intermediate in the *Nitrosomonas* reaction. The argument for this intermediate rests upon the following: (*a*) hydroxylamine is rapidly and quantitatively converted to nitrite; (*b*) it is one of the few substrates that are oxidized, showing that the bacterium has the necessary enzymes; (*c*) these enzymes are preformed in cells that have been grown upon ammonium salts, that is, such growth has built up within the cells all enzymes needed for synthesis of nitrite from hydroxylamine; and (d) the demonstration of hydroxylamine accumulation in cells by use of selective inhibitors.

A likely pathway for conversion of the substrate with an oxidation state of -3 to the *Nitrosomonas* product of oxidation state $+3$ is the consecutive removal of three pairs of electrons to give first hydroxylamine, then possibly hyponitrous acid, $H_2N_2O_2$.

$$\underset{\substack{\text{ammonia}\\-3}}{NH_3} \xrightarrow{\frac{1}{2}O_2} \underset{\substack{\text{hydroxylamine}\\-1}}{HO-NH_2} \xrightarrow{-2H} \underset{\substack{\text{hyponitrite}\\+1}}{\tfrac{1}{2}HO-N=N-OH} \xrightarrow{\frac{1}{2}O_2} \underset{\substack{\text{nitrite}\\+3}}{HO-N=O} \quad (IV)$$

Hyponitrite, however, is unstable at physiological pH, a fact that makes experimentation difficult. No evidence has yet been brought forth that these chemoautotrophs are able to form nitrite enzymatically from salts of hyponitrous acid so that its status is still unclear. It is interesting that the heterotrophic generation of nitrite from hydroxylamine by species of *Corynebacterium* and *Nocardia* is inhibited by hydrazine (24), a pattern similar to the selective inhibition of the autotrophs by this chemical. This suggests a similarity in pathways for the nitrogen in the two groups of microorganisms.

The metabolism of *Nitrobacter* spp. has only recently been the subject of intensive scrutiny. Members of the genus change the nitrogen oxidation state from $+3$ to $+5$, a yield of two electrons for each molecule transformed. Typical of cellular metabolism and energy-yielding reactions in biology is dehydrogenation, and dehydrogenation may characterize nitrate formation as well.

$$\underset{\substack{\text{nitrite}\\+3}}{HO-N=O} \xrightarrow{H_2O} \left(HO-N\begin{array}{c} OH \\ \\ OH \end{array} \right) \xrightarrow{-2H} \underset{\substack{\text{nitrate}\\+5}}{HO-N\begin{array}{c} O \\ \\ O \end{array}} \quad (V)$$

Growth and the concomitant nitrite oxidation is enhanced if the medium contains small amounts of molybdenum (35), a fact which may indicate that the nitrite-activating system contains a molybdenum-enzyme complex.

Demonstration of nitrification in *Nitrobacter agilis* extracts has provided a further tool for investigations of the mechanism of the nitrite step (1). Cell extracts with high enzymatic activity can be prepared by rupturing the bacterial cells in a sonic oscillator, and the enzyme preparations thus obtained readily convert nitrite to nitrate with no suggestion of intermediary nitrogenous compounds. The recent developments should lead to a possible reconstruction in biochemical terms of the nitrifying enzyme complex.

REFERENCES

Reviews

Delwiche, C. C. 1956. Nitrification. In W. D. McElroy and B. Glass, eds., *Inorganic nitrogen metabolism*. The Johns Hopkins Press, Baltimore, pp. 218–232.

Lees, H. 1954. The biochemistry of the nitrifying bacteria. In B. A. Fry and J. L. Peel, eds., *Autotrophic micro-organisms*. Cambridge Univ. Press, Cambridge, pp. 84–98.

Meiklejohn, J. 1954. Some aspects of the physiology of the nitrifying bacteria. In B. A. Fry and J. L. Peel, eds., *Autotrophic micro-organisms*. Cambridge Univ. Press, Cambridge, pp. 68–83.

Meiklejohn, J. 1953. The nitrifying bacteria. *J. Soil Sci.*, 4:59–68.

Quastel, J. H., and P. G. Scholefield. 1951. Biochemistry of nitrification in soil. *Bacteriol. Rev.*, 15:1–53.

Literature cited

1. Aleem, M. I. H., and M. Alexander. 1958. *J. Bacteriol.*, 76:510–514.
2. Aleem, M. I. H., and M. Alexander. 1960. *Applied Microbiol.*, 8:80–84.
3. Allison, F. E., and L. D. Sterling. 1949. *Soil Sci.*, 67:239–252.
4. Amer, F. M., and W. V. Bartholomew. 1951. *Soil Sci.*, 71:215–219.
5. Beesley, R. M. 1914. *Trans. Chem. Soc.*, 105:1014–1024.
6. Bomeke, H. 1951. *Arch. Mikrobiol.*, 15:414–427.
7. Breed, R. S., E. G. D. Murray, and N. R. Smith. 1957. *Bergey's manual of determinative bacteriology*. The Williams and Wilkins Co., Baltimore.
8. Campbell, E. G. 1932. *Science*, 75:23.
9. Cutler, D. W., and B. K. Mukerji. 1931. *Proc. Royal Soc.*, 108B:384–394.
10. Engel, M. S., and M. Alexander. 1958. *Nature*, 181:136.
11. Engel, M. S., and M. Alexander. 1959. *J. Bacteriol.*, 78:796–799.
12. Eno, C. F., and W. G. Blue. 1957. *Soil Sci. Soc. Am., Proc.*, 21:392–396.
13. Fraps, G. S., and A. J. Sterjes. 1930. *Texas Agric. Expt. Sta. Bull. 412.*
14. Gaarder, T., and O. Hagem. 1923. *Bergens Museums Aarbok*, 1:1–26.
15. Grace, J. B. 1951. *Nature*, 168:117.
16. Gundersen, K. 1955. *Physiol. Plantarum*, 8:136–141.
17. Hofman, T., and H. Lees. 1952. *Biochem. J.*, 52:140–142.
18. Imshenetzky, A. A., E. L. Ruban, and O. D. Buzina. 1955. *Mikrobiologiya*, 24:539–544.
19. Jensen, H. L. 1950. *Tidsskr. Planteavl*, 54:62–80.
20. Kauffmann, J. 1952. *Compt. Rend. Acad. Sci.*, 234:2395–2397.
21. Kingma Boltjes, T. Y. 1935. *Arch. Mikrobiol.*, 6:79–138.
22. Lees, H., and J. H. Quastel. 1946. *Biochem. J.*, 40:803–815.
23. Lees, H., and J. H. Quastel. 1946. *Biochem. J.*, 40:815–823.
24. Lees, H., J. R. Simpson, H. L. Jensen, and H. Sorensen. 1954. *Nature*, 173:358.
25. Lyon, T. L., and J. A. Bizzell. 1913. *Cent. Bakteriol.*, II, 37:161–167.
26. Nelson, D. H. 1929. *Iowa State Coll. J. Sci.*, 3:113–175.
27. Nommik, H. 1957. *Acta Agric. Scand.*, 7:395–436.

28. Quastel, J. H., P. G. Scholefield, and J. W. Stevenson. 1952. Biochem. J., 51:278–284.
29. Schloesing, T., and A. Muntz. 1877. Compt. Rend. Acad. Sci., 84:301–303; 85:1018–1020.
30. Schmidt, E. L. 1954. Science, 119:187–189.
31. Stojanovic, B. J., and M. Alexander. 1958. Soil Sci., 86:208–215.
32. Wilson, J. K. 1927. Proc. Comm. III, 1st Intl. Cong. Soil Sci., Washington, pp. 14–22.
33. Winogradsky, S. 1890. Ann. Inst. Pasteur, 4:213–231, 257–275, 760–771.
34. Winogradsky, S., and H. Winogradsky. 1933. Ann. Inst. Pasteur, 50:350–432.
35. Zavarzin, G. A. 1958. Mikrobiologiya, 27:542–546.

17

Denitrification

The various reactions of the nitrogen cycle transform one form of the element to another. Mineralization liberates the nitrogen in inorganic form, immobilization converts it back to an unavailable state, while nitrification changes the element from a reduced to an oxidized condition. Certain transformations of nitrogen lead to a net loss of the element from the soil through volatilization. For the purposes of crop production, nitrogen volatilization has a deleterious influence for it depletes part of the soil's reserve of an essential nutrient. The sequence of steps that results in gaseous loss is known as *denitrification*, the microbial reduction of nitrate and nitrite with the liberation of molecular nitrogen and, in some instances, nitrous oxide.

Denitrification is not the sole means by which microorganisms reduce nitrate and nitrite. In the utilization of the two anions as nitrogen sources for growth, microorganisms reduce them to the ammonium level. A reduction of this type serves the purpose of changing nitrogen into a form suitable for amino acid synthesis within the cell. In denitrification, on the other hand, the nitrogen is lost to the atmosphere and fails to enter the cell structure. In contrast with denitrification, which is essentially a respiratory mechanism in which nitrate replaces molecular oxygen, i.e., a *nitrate respiration*, the utilization of nitrate as a nutrient source may be termed *nitrate assimilation*. Both transformations involve reductive pathways, but the end-products of nitrate respiration are volatilized while the products of nitrate assimilation are incorporated into cell material. From an agronomic viewpoint, nitrate assimilation differs from denitrification further in that the nitrogen remains in the soil and is not put out of the realm of potential availability as a crop nutrient.

Nitrogen Losses in Soil

When nitrate and a readily available carbohydrate are added to soil, N_2 and often N_2O (nitrous oxide) are evolved by the reduction of the nitrate applied (figure 1). The evolution of nitrogenous gases is a typical result of laboratory experiments when the demand for O_2 by the microflora exceeds the supply. But the situation in agricultural practice is far more complex. The quantities of nitrate and of readily fermentable organic matter are never great, and the aeration

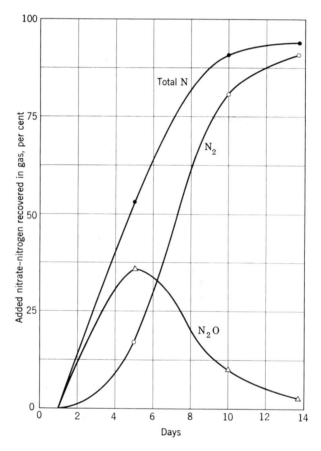

Figure 1. Liberation of N_2 and N_2O from Yolo silty clay loam treated with nitrate and alfalfa (19).

status fluctuates with the moisture regime. Further, since N_2 is omnipresent in nature, its release in the field is not simple to demonstrate quantitatively. Because the volatilization of nitrogen is a slow process and precise measurement of the gas evolution is difficult, nitrogen losses in the field usually are estimated by determining the changes in nitrogen content of soil with time. It should be borne in mind, however, that soils often contain in excess of 2000 lb of nitrogen per acre, so that measurements of losses of 20 to 40 lb per acre, an appreciable change, require very sensitive analytical techniques.

To prepare a balance sheet of soil nitrogen, it is necessary to have precise data on the quantity of nitrogen entering the soil from precipitation, seed, fertilizer, and manure as well as the quantity lost by leaching, erosion, and crop removal. If there is no net change in the soil, losses should equal gains. Should the losses exceed the gains, the nitrogen must be disappearing in some way not accounted for in the variables included in the balance sheet. Except in fields planted to legumes, a condition leading to nitrogen accretion, deficits are the rule. Several examples of the lack of nitrogen balance will suffice. In a carefully designed lysimeter experiment in Ithaca, New York, in which all sources of nitrogen were measured, Bizzell (4) observed an annual loss through unknown means of 11 lb per acre in soil under continuous timothy receiving 124 lb of nitrate-nitrogen and 38 lb per annum in a corn-oats-timothy rotation receiving 110 lb of fertilizer-nitrogen. Similar unexplained losses of 11 lb in one soil and 46 lb per acre per year in a second soil were noted in a cropped lysimeter in Geneva, New York (8).

Experiments performed in pots in the greenhouse have the advantage that drainage losses are prevented. One of the variables in the field is therefore eliminated, and the data collected are more accurate. Nevertheless, a deficit of the element remains. In uncropped pots receiving 600 ppm inorganic nitrogen, for example, from 210 to 436 ppm could not be recovered in periods of 11 months (11). Many similar investigations can be cited, all of which point to the fact that not all the nitrogen initially present in soil is recovered at the end of field, greenhouse, or laboratory experiments. Frequently, only half to three-fourths of the mineral nitrogen applied in fertilizers or formed from humus is recovered in the crop. Much of the element is removed by leaching, but an appreciable portion nevertheless disappears from the system entirely. The unaccounted-for fraction presumably is lost by biological and chemical volatilization.

Mechanisms of Nitrogen Volatilization

The foregoing discussion suggests that the liberation of gaseous nitrogen compounds may be of considerable economic importance in agriculture. The specific mechanism by which the volatilization occurs is not always readily established, but four reactions have been proposed: (a) non-biological losses of ammonia; (b) chemical decomposition of nitrite under acid conditions to yield nitrogen oxides; (c) production of N_2 by the non-enzymatic reaction of nitrous acid with ammonium or amino acids; and (d) microbial denitrification leading to the liberation of N_2 and N_2O.

The volatilization of free ammonia is appreciable under certain circumstances, and as much as one-fourth of the ammonium supplied in fertilizers or formed microbiologically may be lost in the gaseous form. In most soils, such losses are insignificant below pH 7.0, but the magnitude varies directly with increasing alkalinity, and ammonia evolution is appreciable above pH 8.0 (20). Warmer temperatures likewise favor the process, but losses are small in soils of high cation exchange capacity. During the rotting of manure or other nitrogen-rich organic matter near or at the soil surface, the pH rises during ammonification, and ammonia is released to the atmosphere. Should the increase in alkalinity associated with ammonification be sufficiently great, gaseous ammonia loss from surface-applied manure or urea will take place even at sites in which the underlying soil is highly acid.

In acid environments, nitrite decomposes spontaneously to nitric oxide, NO. For the reaction to proceed, a pH below about 5.5 is required. Nitrogen losses by this mechanism are enhanced by increasing hydrogen ion concentrations and are retarded by liming. Although nitrite decomposition is chemical, nitrite arises only by biological means either by the nitrification of ammonium or by the reduction of nitrate. Consequently, when the oxidative or reductive pathways are in operation below pH 5.5, nitrogen may be volatilized as NO through the instability of nitrite. In acid soils in which ammonium is oxidized and in which the pH is either initially below about 5.5 or falls below that value as a result of nitrification, appreciable losses occur. No volatilization is detected when ammonium is applied to areas too acid for nitrification or where the pH is high (9, 19). On the other hand, nitrification is highly sensitive to pH, and little ammonium is oxidized in acid surroundings so that nitrogen losses by the decomposition of nitrite formed from ammonium may not be too great.

Molecular nitrogen is produced chemically in the reaction of nitrous acid with amino acids or ammonium salts.

$$RNH_2 + HNO_2 \rightarrow N_2 + ROH + H_2O \tag{I}$$

The importance of this process in soil has been the subject of considerable study because the two reactants are continuously formed. Hence, the interaction potentially could take place. To test for the existence of the reaction, advantage has been taken of the fact that the two nitrogen atoms in the N_2 arise from different sources, one from nitrite and the second from ammonia or an amino compound. Thus, should N^{15}-tagged nitrite or its precursor, nitrate, be added to soil, the N^{15} content of the N_2 evolved should be half that of the nitrite or nitrate if equation I applies. The experimental data obtained using this approach have shown that, to the contrary, the N^{15} content of the gases evolved was equal to that in the added nitrate, indicating that all the N_2 comes from nitrate and none is derived from reduced nitrogen compounds. Since equation I proceeds only below pH 5.0, the reason for its apparent lack of significance in soil is that there is little nitrite formed from either ammonium or nitrate at acid pH. The little that does appear would more likely decompose to NO (2, 19).

The major mechanism of nitrogen volatilization and probably the most common means whereby N_2 and N_2O are evolved is by microbiological denitrification. The former of the two gases is commonly the dominant product, but small amounts of N_2O are found in the atmosphere. N_2O is concentrated in that portion of the atmosphere near the earth's surface, and it amounts to approximately 0.00005 per cent by volume of the lower reaches of the atmosphere (16). Because of the concentration gradient above the earth's surface, it seems likely that the atmospheric N_2O originates in the soil, a hypothesis strengthened by observations of the release of N_2O during denitrification (table 1). A third gas, NO, is evolved during denitrification, but it is observed only in acid surroundings. The relationship of pH to NO liberation suggests that the oxide is formed by the acid-dependent decomposition of the nitrite formed by the reduction of nitrate.

$$3HNO_2 \rightarrow 2NO + HNO_3 + H_2O \tag{II}$$

TABLE 1

Nitrous Oxide Evolution from Soil during Denitrification at Several Oxygen Tensions (19)

	Mole % N_2O in Denitrified Gases		
O_2 Tension	2 Days	4.5 Days	14 Days
cm Hg			
0	88	52	0
0.5	87	84	83
1.0	83	74	75
2.0	77	70	68
3.0	—	—	71
5–10	—	—	67

The NO may in turn be reduced to N_2 by the microflora, but it more likely is oxidized in air to nitrogen dioxide, NO_2.

A variety of substances appear when environments containing nitrate become deficient in O_2. Following heavy nitrate additions to flooded soil, the nitrite concentration rises; the amount is rarely great because nitrite is reduced almost as rapidly as it is formed. The ammonium concentration in flooded land treated with nitrate increases slowly, but it never becomes too high. Not all the additional ammonium need arise from nitrate as ammonification is not greatly retarded at low partial pressures of O_2. It appears, therefore, that the major products of nitrate reduction in poorly drained soils are gaseous rather than nitrite or ammonium.

Microbiology

Growth of the microorganisms concerned in denitrification is not dependent upon the reduction of nitrate. Many of the responsible bacteria are active in proteolysis, ammonification, and undoubtedly in other transformations. Consequently, the presence of a large denitrifying population does not of itself indicate that conditions are suitable for denitrification. The existence of a large population, on the other hand, does point to a large denitrifying potential. In this regard, it is important to emphasize the concept that the abundance of substrate-non-specific microorganisms should never be taken as a sign that any single one of their biochemical activities is prominent in the habitat from which the organisms were isolated. Thus, a large population of hemicellulose decomposers, ammonifiers, or antibiotic producers is *not* conclusive evidence for significant hemicellulose breakdown, ammonium release, or antibiotic synthesis. With substrate-specific organisms such as the nitrifying autotrophs, however, a dense population is good presumptive evidence for nitrifying activity. In the latter instance, growth of the bacteria is associated obligately with ammonium oxidation; the organisms in the former examples have a broad enzyme potential so that the reactions noted in culture media may be entirely unrelated to the activities in nature.

Arable fields contain an abundance of denitrifying microorganisms, and counts in excess of a million per gram are not uncommon in field soil. The population is typically larger in the immediate vicinity of plant roots. The potential for volatilization is therefore enormous, but conditions must be suitable for the organisms to change from aerobic respiration to a denitrifying type of metabolism. On the basis of the reservations outlined above, the existence of a large flora demonstrates only a potential for rapid nitrogen volatilization rather than an actual activity.

The capacity for true denitrification is limited to certain bacteria. Fungi and actinomycetes have not been implicated in N_2 production. However, any organism which during its growth causes a pH shift in the culture medium sufficient to allow for ammonia volatilization, nitrite decomposition (equation II), or for the non-enzymatic reaction of ammonium or amino groups with nitrite (equation I) will be the cause of gaseous losses, but these transformations are laboratory phenomena resulting from the marked changes in the hydrogen ion concentration of culture media. Only a small number of bacterial species can bring about denitrification as strictly defined. The active species are largely limited to the genera *Pseudomonas*, *Achromobacter*, *Bacillus*, and *Micrococcus* (table 2) although *Thiobacillus denitrificans* and an occasional *Chromobacterium*, *Mycoplana*, *Serratia*, or *Vibrio* species will catalyze the reduction. *Pseudomonas* and *Achromobacter* are the dominant genera in soil. *Bacillus* strains, though numerous, are rarely important; their abundance is usually the result of the persistence of the endospore.

TABLE 2

The Effect of pH on Bacterial Denitrification (17)

Bacterium	pH					
	4.0	5.0	6.0	7.0	8.0	9.0
	ml gas evolved/hr/g cell-nitrogen					
Micrococcus denitrificans	0	64	105	168	214	116
Achromobacter sp.	0	0	112	127	157	10
Pseudomonas denitrificans	0	15	196	138	92	0
Pseudomonas aeruginosa	0	12	218	246	251	13
Bacillus licheniformis	4	4	108	125	102	60

The denitrifying bacteria are all aerobic, but nitrate is used as the electron acceptor for growth in the absence of O_2. Thus, the active species grow aerobically without nitrate or anaerobically in its presence. Few develop in environments devoid of both O_2 and nitrate. Most substrates used for aerobic oxidation may be attacked in the absence of O_2 with equal facility in media containing nitrate. The physiological specialization for nitrate-dependent, anaerobic proliferation has been adapted for the isolation of the responsible agents. A common procedure is the use of anaerobic enrichment solutions containing large amounts of KNO_3. In such media, denitrifiers produce profuse quantities of gas and make the solution alkaline. Enrichments for thermophilic strains can be made by incubating the same medium at temperatures of 55 to 65°C. The thermophiles are almost invariably aerobic, spore-forming bacteria classified as *Bacillus* spp.

Several chemoautotrophs are capable of reducing nitrate to molecular nitrogen. *Micrococcus denitrificans*, a facultative autotroph, develops in air or anaerobically with either organic compounds or H_2 as source of energy and O_2 or nitrate as electron acceptor (18). *Thiobacillus denitrificans* is a sulfur-oxidizing chemoautotroph which differs from other thiobacilli by its ability to proliferate anaerobically providing nitrate is available. For *T. denitrificans*, the energy source in these circumstances is elemental sulfur or thiosulfate, both of which are converted to sulfate. The nitrate is converted to gaseous nitrogen.

$$5S + 6KNO_3 + 2H_2O \rightarrow 3N_2 + K_2SO_4 + 4KHSO_4 \quad (III)$$

$$5K_2S_2O_3 + 8KNO_3 + H_2O \rightarrow 4N_2 + 9K_2SO_4 + H_2SO_4 \quad (IV)$$

T. denitrificans will likewise grow well as an aerobe (3).

Many microorganisms in addition to the denitrifiers reduce nitrate. The reduction is required either in the process of protein synthesis or as a substitute for the reduction of O_2 in conventional aerobic metabolism. In the former instance, any microorganism that utilizes nitrate as a nitrogenous nutrient is able to reduce it to ammonium as it is ammonium which enters into the organic combination necessary for protein synthesis within the cell. The latter reaction, on the other hand, is found in bacteria normally considered to be aerobic but which replace the O_2 by nitrate under anaerobiasis; the products here, however, are not gaseous but rather nitrite or ammonium. It is likewise not uncommon to find nitrite in culture solutions of bacteria, fungi, and actinomycetes which reduce nitrate to ammonium. Generally, however, the nitrite produced from nitrate disappears almost as readily as it is formed, but occasional strains will accumulate nitrite.

There are thus three microbiological reactions of nitrate: (a) a complete reduction to ammonium frequently with the transitory appearance of nitrite; (b) an incomplete reduction and an accumulation of nitrite in the medium; and (c) a reduction to nitrite followed by the evolution of gaseous compounds, i.e., denitrification. Regardless of their other physiological characteristics, microorganisms that use nitrate as a nitrogen source carry out reaction a whereas cultures incapable of the complete reduction must be supplied with ammonium or other reduced nitrogen compounds for growth to proceed.

Environmental Influences

The restriction of the capacity for biological nitrogen volatilization to the bacteria and, further, to only a few genera suggests that the magnitude and rate of denitrification is markedly affected by the environment. The responsible organisms bear some physiological kinship to one another so that changes in the habitat can appreciably stimulate or largely eliminate this economically important population. Chief among the environmental influences are the nature and amount of organic matter, aeration, the moisture status, acidity, and temperature.

The rate of denitrification of the nitrate added to flooded fields is far more slow in soils low in carbon than in land rich in organic matter. In soils of the former type and to a lesser extent of the latter type, nitrogen volatilization is enhanced by the addition of carbonaceous materials. The effectiveness of organic nutrients in promoting denitrification in waterlogged soils is proportional to their availability. Readily decomposable compounds such as simple sugars or organic acids are oxidized quickly and are more stimulatory than the less readily fermentable straws or grasses, which in turn possess a greater degree of effectiveness in bringing about nitrate reduction than sawdust and lignin preparations. Well-rotted plant or animal residues, as expected, have but a minor influence, particularly when compared with the fresh materials. In contrast to the trends in waterlogged habitats, the addition of organic substances to well-drained soils diminishes the nitrogen losses, the conserving action resulting from an immobilization of inorganic nitrogen (6, 11).

Oxygen availability is another of the critical environmental determinants. Aeration affects the transformation in two apparently contrasting ways: on the one hand, denitrification proceeds only when the O_2 supply is insufficient to satisfy the microbiological demand; at the same time, O_2 is necessary for the formation of nitrite and nitrate, which are essential for denitrification. The demonstration that nitrogen is volatilized from soils maintained at normal O_2 tensions indicates that the pores and interstices in the profile are never entirely oxygenated. Anaerobic microenvironments exist at microscopic sites in well-drained soils whenever the biological O_2 demand exceeds the supply. Needless to say, decreasing the partial pressure of O_2 enhances the denitrification of added nitrate. As the soil aggregate size has a direct influence on gaseous exchange, it is not surprising that nitrogen losses decrease with increasing particle diameter because of the improved aeration. Yet, denitrification is favored by mechanical aggregates greater than 4 mm in diameter because it is more difficult for O_2 to diffuse the long distance through these large particles to the center where microbial reduction is taking place (7, 13).

The results cited above on the influence of aeration apply to soils receiving nitrate fertilizers. For gaseous loss in fields not receiving nitrate, there must be either aerobic microenvironments for the nitrifying bacteria and anaerobic sites for the denitrifiers or alternations of periods of good and bad aeration. During intermittent rainy periods, nitrate formation and nitrate reduction may both occur.

Similarly, denitrification will take place in paddy soils receiving ammonium salts, for the ammonium is oxidized in the upper zone of O_2 penetration, and the leaching downward of the resultant nitrate brings it into the underlying anaerobic zone (15). Nevertheless, the loss in flooded soils is always greater for nitrate than for ammonium.

In well-drained soils, nitrogen volatilization is related to the moisture content. Denitrification of added nitrate is appreciable at high water levels and in localities having improper drainage. No losses occur at moisture levels below 60 per cent of the water-holding capacity regardless of the carbohydrate supply, nitrate concentration, or pH. Above this figure, the rate and magnitude of denitrification is correlated directly with the moisture regime (figure 2). The effect of water is attributed to its role in governing the diffusion of O_2 to sites of microbiological activity.

Important also to the active microflora is the pH of the environment. The bacteria which bring about denitrification are sensitive to high hydrogen ion concentrations, and acid soils contain a sparse denitrifying population, probably not enough to account for economic losses. The population becomes large only above a pH of approximately 5.5. The ecological observations agree with studies of the transformation in pure culture where gas evolution by species of

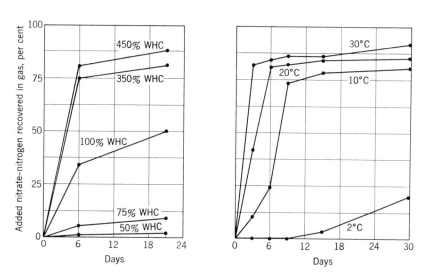

Figure 2. Effect of moisture, expressed as water-holding capacity (WHC), and temperature on the denitrification of nitrate in soil receiving glucose (6).

Pseudomonas, Achromobacter, Micrococcus, and *Bacillus* is only of consequence above pH 5.0 (table 2). Consequently, both field and laboratory investigations show that denitrification by microbial means is highly sensitive to acidity, and losses in acid soils cannot be attributed directly to biological agencies.

Acidity governs not only the rate of denitrification but also the relative abundance of the various gases. The liberation of N_2O is pronounced in environments whose pH is below about 6.0 to 6.5, and frequently N_2O makes up more than half of the nitrogenous gases evolved from acid habitats. Likewise, NO only appears in significant quantities when the pH is low. At neutral or slightly acid reaction, N_2O may be the first gaseous product, but it is reduced microbiologically so that N_2 tends to be the dominant product above pH 6. The differences in gas composition associated with pH may be largely due to the acid sensitivity of the enzyme system concerned in N_2O reduction. From the viewpoint of biochemical mechanism, the appearance of N_2O prior to N_2 is of considerable interest.

Nitrous oxide release in soil or in culture is conditioned further by the nitrate concentration. The relative proportion of the gas is greatest at high nitrate levels, that is, when the concentration of the electron acceptor (the nitrogen salt) exceeds that of the electron donor (decomposable organic matter). When additional donors are made available, the N_2O is reduced to N_2.

Denitrification is markedly affected by temperature. The transformation proceeds slowly at 2°C, but increasing the temperature enhances the rate of biological loss. The optimum for the reaction is at 25°C and above (figure 2). The transformation is still rapid at elevated temperatures and will proceed to about 60 to 65° but not at 70°C. The rapid release of N_2 in the more elevated ranges suggests an active thermophilic flora, a fact verified by the ease of obtaining enrichment cultures of thermophilic denitrifiers. The low temperature effects have considerable economic importance because the progress of nitrate reduction at 10°C or below indicates the possibility of nitrogen volatilization during the colder part of the year when plants are not assimilating the nitrate formed by nitrification.

Cropping serves to reduce losses through denitrification, and the existence of a vegetative cover may markedly affect the magnitude of volatilization (10, 11). The retardation in cropped land suggests that the vegetation is competing with the microflora for the available nitrate supply, thereby reducing the amount acted upon microbiologically. Results of this type add emphasis to the pitfalls in the indiscriminate use of bacteriological counting procedures as the denitrifying bacteria are quite numerous around plant roots despite the diminished denitrification. The physiological versatility of the responsible bacteria and the suppression of denitrification attendant upon cropping point to the hypothesis that the primary action of the denitrifying bacteria of the root zone is other than that of effecting denitrification.

In summary, denitrification requires a goodly supply of readily oxidizable organic compounds, high nitrate levels, and poor drainage, but the rate and magnitude of volatilization are also governed by acidity and temperature. The moisture status is probably the most important of these environmental variables through its effect on aeration. As a first approximation, it is proposed that biological nitrogen volatilization is most conspicuous in well-drained and actively nitrifying soils which come under partial anaerobiasis during wet periods or following the application of organic residues. The transformation may also be of economic consequence in poorly drained or flooded fields where nitrate is either added in fertilizers or generated through nitrification. Maintaining a vegetative cover to the greatest possible extent, providing for suitable drainage, and avoiding reactive nitrogen compounds may be expected to minimize volatilization.

Biochemistry of Nitrate Reduction

In the complete, aerobic oxidation of carbohydrates, the final products are CO_2 and water. With glucose, for example, the reaction is expressed as follows:

$$C_6H_{12}O_6 + 6O_2 \rightarrow 6CO_2 + 6H_2O \tag{V}$$

In the aerobic metabolism of heterotrophs, the reducing power from the carbohydrate, signified by H, is used to form water from O_2. In heterotrophic nitrate respiration, the reducing power is coupled with oxidized states of nitrogen.

$$2NO_3^- + 10H \rightarrow N_2 + 4H_2O + 2OH^- \tag{VI}$$

$$2NO_2^- + 6H \rightarrow N_2 + 2H_2O + 2OH^- \tag{VII}$$

$$N_2O + 2H \rightarrow N_2 + H_2O \tag{VIII}$$

For each two molecules of nitrate or nitrite, one molecule of N_2 is produced. In analogous fashion the thiobacillus energy-yielding reaction, which is normally linked to O_2, may be associated in *T. denitrificans* with nitrate (equations III and IV).

This explanation implies that denitrification is not anaerobic respiration in its usual, restricted sense but rather that it has a basic aerobic character with nitrate replacing the O_2, not in terms of nitrate as a "source of oxygen" but as an electron or hydrogen acceptor. In other words, the reducing power that normally is dissipated by reaction with O_2 is now dissipated at the expense of nitrate. That this is the case is supported by observations that the true denitrifying bacteria are by and large aerobes, proliferating in O_2-free circumstances only when nitrate is the alternate electron acceptor. The two acceptors, O_2 and nitrate, compete with one another for the electrons freed from the substrate, nitrate reducing O_2 uptake and O_2 depressing denitrification by pure cultures. The role of nitrate as electron acceptor for the growth of most of the responsible bacteria may also be assumed by nitrite or N_2O, both of which permit otherwise-aerobic cultures to develop anaerobically.

The suitability of nitrite for N_2 formation and its utilization in ammonium formation suggest that it is an intermediate in both denitrification and nitrate assimilation. On the basis of current knowledge, the biochemical mechanism proposed in figure 3 seems to be the likeliest pathway. In the denitrification sequence, the nitrate is reduced first to nitrite, which is transformed to some unknown nitrogenous compound. The latter is probably converted to N_2 with N_2O as intermediate, but the N_2 alternatively may be formed by a pathway not involving N_2O. Nitric oxide may be implicated as well.

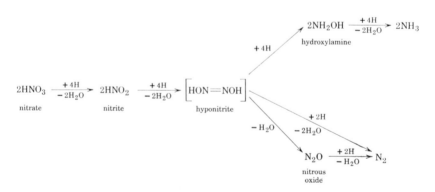

Figure 3. Biochemical pathway of nitrate reduction and denitrification.

With pure microbial cultures or in soil, there is no N_2 release from organic compounds, and denitrification specifically requires some form of oxidized nitrogen—nitrate, nitrite, or N_2O. In addition, an electron or hydrogen donor is essential. Considering nitrate as the point of initiation, the disappearance of nitrate under reducing conditions is accompanied by nitrite accumulation in soil. But within several days, neither nitrate nor nitrite can be detected as a result of their further reduction, and N_2O is found in the atmosphere above the soil. Providing the system is closed or there is limited access to air, the percentage of N_2O in the gas phase declines subsequently whereas the N_2 content increases, a consequence of the further reduction. The ammonium level increases slightly at best, and this moderate change may result, at least in part, from ammonification rather than from nitrate reduction. Consequently, most of the nitrate is converted to N_2 with no significant accumulation of ammonium (5, 13). The data obtained from experiments with soil thus lend support to the scheme postulated in figure 3.

The results of investigations of individual bacteria in vitro lend further weight to the proposed mechanism. The capacity for N_2O production is characteristic of most if not all denitrifiers. *Pseudomonas stutzeri*, for example, possesses enzymes catalyzing the formation of N_2 from nitrate, nitrite, and N_2O. Moreover, cells producing molecular nitrogen from nitrate and nitrite contain the enzyme system needed for N_2O reduction. Thus, adapting an organism to denitrification simultaneously trains it to use N_2O. This supports the position of N_2O as an intermediate. The reason for advancing the hypothesis that N_2 may be generated by a mechanism not involving N_2O is that bacteria form N_2 from nitrite in the presence of certain inhibitors but are inactive on N_2O in similar circumstances (1, 14).

The pathway shown in figure 3 assumes that the reduction of nitrate to ammonia proceeds by a sequence of two-electron changes from the $+5$ oxidation state of nitrate to the -3 of ammonia, a shift of eight electrons. The responsible enzymes are termed the nitrate, nitrite, hyponitrite, and hydroxylamine reductases. Molybdenum is required for nitrate reductase, an observation which explains the poor growth of microorganisms in molybdenum-deficient media containing nitrate as the sole source of nitrogen. The manganous ion is the cofactor for the hydroxylamine enzyme while copper and iron are functional for nitrite and hyponitrite reductases (12). The enzymes concerned in the final stages of denitrification have not been characterized.

REFERENCES

Reviews

Allison, F. E. 1955. The enigma of soil nitrogen balance sheets. *Adv. Agron.*, 7:213–250.

Delwiche, C. C. 1956. Denitrification. In W. D. McElroy and B. Glass, eds., *Inorganic nitrogen metabolism.* The Johns Hopkins Press, Baltimore, pp. 233–256.

Verhoeven, W. 1956. Some remarks on nitrate and nitrite metabolism in microorganisms. In W. D. McElroy and B. Glass, eds., *Inorganic nitrogen metabolism.* The Johns Hopkins Press, Baltimore, pp. 61–86.

Literature cited

1. Allen, M. B., and C. B. van Niel. 1952. *J. Bacteriol.*, 64:397–412.
2. Allison, F. E., J. H. Doetsch, and L. D. Sterling. 1952. *Soil Sci.*, 74:311–314.
3. Baalsrud, K., and K. S. Baalsrud. 1954. *Arch. Mikrobiol.*, 20:34–62.
4. Bizzell, J. A. 1944. *Cornell Univ. Agric. Expt. Sta. Memoir 256.*
5. Bremner, J. M., and K. Shaw. 1958. *J. Agric. Sci.*, 51:22–39.
6. Bremner, J. M., and K. Shaw. 1958. *J. Agric. Sci.*, 51:40–52.
7. Broadbent, F. E., and B. J. Stojanovic. 1952. *Soil Sci. Soc. Am., Proc.*, 16:359–363.
8. Collison, R. C., H. G. Beattie, and J. D. Harlan. 1933. *N. Y. Agric. Expt. Sta. Tech. Bull. 212.*
9. Gerretsen, F. C., and H. de Hoop. 1957. *Canad. J. Microbiol.*, 3:359–380.
10. Hauck, R. D., and S. W. Melsted. 1956. *Soil Sci. Soc. Am., Proc.*, 20:361–364.
11. Loewenstein, H., L. E. Engelbert, O. J. Attoe, and O. N. Allen. 1957. *Soil Sci. Soc. Am., Proc.*, 21:397–400.
12. Nicholas, D. J. D. 1957. *Ann. Botany*, 21:587–598.
13. Nommik, H. 1956. *Acta Agric. Scand.*, 6:195–228.
14. Sacks, L. E., and H. A. Barker. 1952. *J. Bacteriol.*, 64:247–252.
15. Shiori, M., and T. Tanada. 1954. *The chemistry of paddy soils in Japan.* Ministry Agric. and Forestry, Japan.
16. Slobod, R. L., and M. E. Krogh. 1950. *J. Am. Chem. Soc.*, 72:1175–1177.
17. Valera, C. L., 1959. Ph.D Thesis, Cornell Univ., Ithaca, N. Y.
18. Verhoeven, W., A. L. Koster, and M. C. A. van Nievelt. 1954. *Ant. van Leeuw.*, 20:273–284.
19. Wijler, J., and C. C. Delwiche. 1954. *Plant and Soil*, 5:155–169.
20. Willis, W. H., and M. B. Sturgis. 1944. *Soil Sci. Soc. Am., Proc.*, 9:106–113.

18

Nitrogen Fixation: Non-symbiotic

Nitrogen is removed from soil by leaching, denitrification, and through cropping. Intensive agriculture accentuates the drain on the limited terrestrial supply of this critical element. Recent years have witnessed a remarkable expansion of the fertilizer industry, yet only a portion of the agricultural need for nitrogen comes from chemical fertilizers. Precipitation adds several pounds each year as ammonium or nitrate, and the electrical discharges of the atmosphere return a small quantity of fixed nitrogen to the soil. Biological fixation, on the other hand, tends to right the nitrogen balance so that, despite the growth of the fertilizer industry, it is still necessary to stimulate the responsible microbial agencies to return gaseous nitrogen to the soil.

Microbiology

Biological N_2 fixation is brought about by free-living bacteria or blue-green algae, which make use of N_2 by non-symbiotic means, and by symbiotic associations composed of a microorganism and a higher plant. The agriculturally important legume-*Rhizobium* symbiosis and the association of microorganisms with certain nodulated non-legumes will be discussed in the next chapter. The establishment of an isolate as capable of using molecular N_2 is often considered an easy task, for microbial growth in a medium free of nitrogenous ingredients presumably should of itself provide proof of the ability of an organism to assimilate N_2. Often, quantitative determinations during growth

309

of a culture show slight increases in the total nitrogen content of the medium. On the basis of such criteria, claims have been made for nitrogen fixation by the following: a variety of actinomycetes; strains of the fungal genera *Aspergillus, Botrytis, Cladosporium, Mucor, Penicillium,* and *Phoma;* film-forming yeasts; and species of several bacterial genera. Wheat, corn, barley and germinating peas have been reported to utilize N_2. Growth in nitrogen-free media, however, is rarely an acceptable criterion because considerable difficulty is encountered in purifying culture solutions of the element. Further, volatile nitrogenous compounds occur in the air, particularly of laboratories, and they can be selectively absorbed by microbial cells, resulting in an apparent but fictitious N_2 fixation.

To overcome the shortcomings inherent in qualitative experiments, a number of more critical techniques have been developed. Biological N_2 fixation is frequently put on a quantitative basis by measurement of the changes in the total nitrogen content of the culture or environmental system by the Kjeldahl procedure, but this useful approach is not reliable for the detection of small nitrogen gains. Gasometric measurement of N_2 disappearance has been proposed, but the analysis is laborious. The most suitable technique for conditions in which the nitrogen gains are slight involves the use of the stable isotope, N^{15}. Should a suspect organism be capable of fixation, it will incorporate N^{15} into protoplasmic combination when exposed to N^{15}-labeled N_2. The isotopic measurement is sufficiently sensitive to detect fixation of trace quantities of the gas with remarkable accuracy.

The classical free-living microorganisms capable of utilizing N_2 are species of *Azotobacter, Clostridium,* and several blue-green algae. In recent years, the introduction of more effective screening and testing techniques has resulted in a many-fold increase in the number of active genera known. At present, strains of the following have been verified to be capable of the transformation:

a. Heterotrophic bacteria: *Achromobacter, Aerobacter, Azotobacter, Azotomonas, Bacillus polymyxa, Beijerinckia, Clostridium, Pseudomonas.*

b. Chemoautotrophic bacteria: *Methanobacillus omelianskii.*

c. Blue-green algae: *Anabaena, Anabaenopsis, Aulosira, Calothrix, Cylindrospermum, Nostoc, Tolypothrix.*

d. Photosynthetic bacteria: *Chlorobium, Chromatium, Rhodomicrobium, Rhodopseudomonas, Rhodospirillum* (table 1).

TABLE 1

Fixation of Molecular Nitrogen in Culture Media

Microorganism	Conditions	Incubation Period	Nitrogen Fixed
		days	μg N/ml
Achromobacter sp.	Aerobic	4	17
Azotobacter vinelandii	Aerobic	3	1050
Cylindrospermum cylindrica	Aerobic, light	55	52
Aerobacter aerogenes	Anaerobic	2	60
Clostridium butyricum	Anaerobic	10	136
Chlorobium sp.	Anaerobic, light	5	20
Rhodospirillum sp.	Anaerobic, light	10	76

Neither the ecological niche nor the economic or geochemical significance of many of the bacteria has been established. The most intensively investigated representatives of the group are *Azotobacter* spp., but the vast literature concerned with the genus should not necessarily be taken to indicate that they are the most important in nature. Evidence for a N_2 metabolism has also been presented for the following, but further study is warranted: the bacteria *Desulfovibrio* and *Spirillum*, certain *Nocardia* strains, and several yeasts or yeast-like organisms.

Azotobacter cells are often quite large, and the shape in some instances is distinctly reminiscent of yeast morphology. All azotobacters are strict aerobes, and they apparently possess the highest respiratory rate in either plant or animal kingdoms. These bacteria utilize few nitrogenous compounds—N_2, ammonium, nitrate, nitrite, urea, and an occasional organic nitrogen-containing molecule. Members of the genus are mesophilic, and their optimum temperature is near 30°C. When strains of *Azotobacter* utilize the gaseous form of the element, nitrogen gains range up to 1050 μg of nitrogen per milliliter of culture medium (1) while the efficiency, measured as nitrogen fixed per unit of sugar decomposed, is quite low, from 5 to 20 mg of N_2 fixed per gram of sugar oxidized. The five species of the genus, differentiated on the basis of cell shape, pigmentation, and motility, are *Azotobacter chroococcum, A. beijerinckii, A. vinelandii, A. mac-*

rocytogenes, and *A. agilis. A. chroococcum* is generally the most frequently encountered azotobacter in soils of temperate regions.

Beijerinckia spp. also are aerobic N_2 fixers, but they grow well in acid conditions and sometimes develop at a reaction as low as pH 3, whereas *Azotobacter* spp. generally fail to fix N_2 below pH 6.0. The cells of *Beijerinckia* are commonly smaller than the azotobacter cells. *Beijerinckia* spp. are apparently confined largely to tropical soils, and strains have been isolated in India, Burma, Indonesia, South America, Surinam, northern Australia, and tropical areas of Africa, their numbers ranging from a few to several thousand per gram. *Beijerinckia* is rare or entirely absent from soils of the temperate zone. There is as yet no explanation for the unique geographical distribution of the genus, and the environmental adaptation of these organisms remains as one of the few documented instances of bacterial geography. Members of the genus are adapted to another environment, that of the *phyllosphere* or leaf surface of numerous plants growing in the tropics (17).

The dominant anaerobes using N_2 are members of the genus *Clostridium.* The population of N_2-fixing clostridia in arable land may be as large as 10^5 cells per gram, but the bacteria are more dense in proximity to the plant root system. The more abundant and more completely investigated clostridia are of the *Clostridium pasteurianum–C. butyricum* type, but *C. aceticum, C. butylicum, C. felsineum, C. kluyveri, C. beijerinckii, C. lactoacetophilum, C. madisonii, C. pectinovorum, C. tetanomorphum, C. acetobutylicum,* and probably others assimilate N_2 (16). In contrast with the azotobacters, which they usually outnumber, the clostridia are found at sites of pH 5.0, and they are still capable of growth at pH 9.0. Under suitable conditions, N_2 incorporation is appreciable, and up to 180 μg of nitrogen are fixed per milliliter of culture medium. The efficiency is low, and only 6 to 8 mg of nitrogen are assimilated per gram of carbohydrate consumed.

Blue-green algae are not uncommon in well-drained fields, but their numbers are far greater in flooded soils. Many blue-green algae of soil origin grow in culture solutions devoid of fixed nitrogen compounds and effect an increase in the nitrogen content of the medium. Not all Cyanophyceae and representatives of none of the other algal classes can utilize N_2, however. Nitrogen fixation by the active strains is stimulated by increasing light intensities, but excessive light is inhibitory. The transformation is invariably slow, and gains of 30 to 115 μg of nitrogen per milliliter of solution require periods of $1\frac{1}{2}$ to 2 months for most isolates of *Aulosira, Anabaenopsis, Anabaena,*

Cylindrospermum, Nostoc, and *Tolypothrix.* The fixation, therefore, is much less rapid than in the azotobacters or clostridia. Several of the algae grow slowly in pure culture in the dark provided that sugar is present to serve as a carbon and energy source for heterotrophic metabolism, but the nitrogen gains are correspondingly small. The dark fixation of N_2 by blue-green algae is probably of no ecological significance. Blue-green algae and the legume-*Rhizobium* symbiosis have in common the capacities for photosynthesis and N_2 fixation, but the two activities occur within the same cell in the former instance whereas, in legumes, the site of photosynthesis is in the above-ground portion of the plant while N_2 enters through the roots. Both these photoautotrophic systems have a marked advantage over the heterotrophic N_2 users—their ability to develop without relying upon the limited supply of available carbohydrates in soil.

The photosynthetic N_2-fixing bacteria are divided into three families: Athiorhodaceae or non-sulfur purple bacteria; Thiorhodaceae or purple sulfur bacteria; and Chlorobacteriaceae, the green sulfur bacteria. All are affected favorably by light but are inhibited by O_2. The rate of N_2 assimilation by the photoautotrophic bacteria is quite slow, and periods of weeks are required for gains of 100 μg of nitrogen per milliliter of culture medium. The non-sulfur purple bacteria are found in flooded soils and in ditches, lake muds, or sea bottoms, but they are essentially absent from farm or forest land (13).

Certain strains of *Aerobacter aerogenes* assimilate N_2 even after many years of cultivation on complex nitrogenous media. Some isolates are active only anaerobically; others are little affected by aeration. Related to this organism is *Achromobacter*, which generally requires O_2 for active N_2 utilization, but neither of the two genera is particularly active in the transformation (14, 15). Occasional strains of *Bacillus polymyxa* and *Pseudomonas* use N_2, but the magnitude of fixation is invariably small. The ecological and agricultural importance of N_2 fixation by these four bacterial genera is entirely unknown.

Factors Affecting Nitrogen Fixation

A number of environmental factors govern the rate and magnitude of non-symbiotic N_2 fixation, and the transformation is markedly affected by the physical and chemical characteristics of the habitat. Considerable information has been obtained from investigations of pure cultures, but extension to the field is sometimes possible.

Microorganisms that assimilate N_2 have the ability to utilize ammonium and sometimes nitrate and other combined forms of nitrogen. In fact, ammonium salts are used preferentially and often at a greater rate than molecular nitrogen so that the presence of ammonium, in effect, inhibits the fixation; that is, the bacteria use the nitrogen salt rather than N_2 from the atmosphere. Ammonium or compounds converted to it, e.g., urea or nitrate, are most effective in the inhibition of fixation, but a number of amino acids have a less marked deterring influence.

Many inorganic nutrients are necessary for the development of the microorganisms, but only a select few are specifically implicated in the metabolism of N_2, that is, they are indispensable for N_2-linked proliferation. Some are required in lesser amounts for growth on ammonium salts or other fixed nitrogenous compounds. Molybdenum, calcium, and iron are critical for the fixation reaction. Molybdenum is required for the metabolism of N_2, but microorganisms will similarly not use nitrate unless molybdate is present although the molybdenum requirement for nitrate utilization is less than for N_2 fixation. Growth on ammonium salts, however, proceeds rapidly in the absence of added molybdenum. For at least some organisms, vanadium will replace molybdenum, but it is never fully as effective. In like manner, iron salts are implicated in the N_2 metabolism of *Azotobacter, Clostridium,* algae, *Aerobacter,* and *Achromobacter,* but the specific requirement for N_2 metabolism is often difficult to establish because iron is required, to a lesser extent, for growth upon fixed compounds of nitrogen. The not infrequent observations of stimulation of azotobacter by humus or soil decoctions result from the use of media deficient in iron or molybdenum, or both. A requirement for calcium has been demonstrated during N_2 assimilation by blue-green algae and some *Azotobacter* spp., but the need for calcium can sometimes be replaced by strontium.

Azotobacter is characteristically sensitive to high hydrogen ion concentrations. Ecological investigations show that, despite the wide distribution of bacteria of the genus, many soils contain none or an insignificant number (figure 1). Their absence is associated directly with pH. As a rule, environments more acid than pH 6.0 are free of the organism or contain very few azotobacter cells. Similarly, the bacteria generally will neither grow nor fix N_2 in culture media having a pH below 6.0, but an occasional variant will tolerate greater

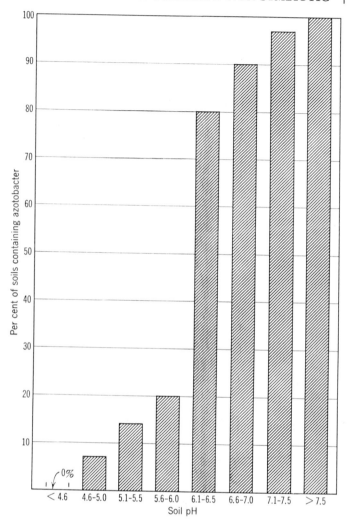

Figure 1. The effect of acidity on the distribution of azotobacter (6).

hydrogen ion concentrations. *Beijerinckia* spp. do not possess the acid sensitivity of the azotobacters, and they develop and fix N₂ from pH 3 to 9. Blue-green algae, however, develop poorly in media and are sparse in soils more acid than approximately pH 6.0 whereas the acid tolerance of *Clostridium* falls between *Azotobacter* and *Beijerinckia*. Observations of this nature indicate that nitrogen gains through *Azotobacter* or algal action cannot take place in locales more acid than pH 6.0, but another genus may be of some conceivable importance in such habitats.

There is some evidence that the occurrence of *Azotobacter* is related to the available phosphate content of soils. About 1 mg of phosphorus must be assimilated by *Azotobacter* for each 5 to 10 mg of nitrogen fixed. The distribution of blue-green algae in wet paddy fields is likewise associated with the phosphate content of the soil (12).

Nitrogen Gains in Soil

The biological return of nitrogen to soil requires the presence of a suitably large population to catalyze the transformation and environmental conditions conducive to the activities of the responsible population. The percentage of soils in any one region containing the most studied N_2 fixers, *Azotobacter* spp., varies from 0 to 80 or more, but results based upon percentage distribution merely indicate the presence or absence of an organism rather than the abundance. Azotobacter densities typically vary from nil to several thousand per gram, and it is uncommon to find counts exceeding 10^3 and indeed rare to note values in excess of 10^4 per gram. In a number of Danish localities surveyed, 46.2 per cent had nil, 26.9 per cent contained 1 to 100, 19.7 per cent showed counts of 10^2 to 10^3, 6.1 per cent had values of 10^3 to 10^4, and only 1.1 per cent possessed azotobacter counts in excess of 10^4 per gram (8). The ecology of the other N_2-fixing bacteria has received scant attention, but it is likely that, with the exception of *Clostridium* spp., their populations are small.

As a result of the scarcity of azotobacters and probably of other aerobic N_2-fixing bacteria, the question arises as to the significance of non-symbiotic N_2 fixation in agricultural practice. Many claims have been made for nitrogen gains in field plots and in lysimeters. The reports are frequently of the order of 20 to 40 lb per acre per year in temperate climates. For example, a figure of 33 lb per acre has been reported under bluegrass in Kentucky (9) and 28 lb under timothy grown in New York (10). There is no question that appreciable nitrogen increases do occur when large quantities of oxidizable carbohydrates or residues of wide C:N ratios are turned under, but the large amount of organic matter necessary for slight nitrogen gains puts practices of this type far out of the realm of good farm management.

If the azotobacter population in crop land is small, the N_2 fixed by the activities of these bacteria must be correspondingly small. Three conditions must be satisfied for azotobacter fixation to be appreciable: (a) the population must be large; (b) the rate of new cell formation needs to be rapid because N_2 incorporation is a growth-linked process; and (c) the bulk of the azotobacter nitrogen must come from the atmosphere. Assuming an acre contains 2,000,000 lb of surface soil, it can be calculated that some 10^7 azotobacter cells per gram are necessary for the fixation of 2 lb of nitrogen per acre. Should the growing season provide as many as 200 favorable days for microbial metabolism, a turnover or formation of 50,000 cells per day are required for the 2 lb nitrogen increase. Counts of this magnitude are uncommon in temperate latitudes. One may also inquire into the possibility of appreciable N_2 transformation through the metabolism of azotobacter by using the efficiency figures for the bacterium. For the assimilation of 5 to 20 mg N_2, about 1.0 g of carbohydrate is required. Thus, for the microbiological fixation of 5 to 20 lb of nitrogen per acre, 1000 lb of soil organic matter must be oxidized by azotobacter each year. Clearly, it is difficult to accept the fact that a relatively uncommon bacterium causes the breakdown of 1000 lb of humus. The chances of appreciable N_2 fixation by *Azotobacter* spp., therefore, are slight.

Despite the interest in *Azotobacter*, it is possible that one or more of the other active organisms can bring about a fixation of agronomic value. The only unequivocal means of assessing the magnitude of the transformation is by direct measurement of the increase in quantity of nitrogen in the soil itself. To overcome the many shortcomings associated with measuring small changes of nitrogen when the soil contains a large reserve of the element is a difficult task, but isotopes provide a specific procedure for detecting changes of small magnitude. In experiments designed to this end, soil aliquots are exposed to N^{15}-tagged N_2, and the soil is analyzed for its N^{15} content after suitable incubation periods. The quantity of isotope recovered in the sample is a measure of the N_2 incorporation. The results of a study using the isotopic procedure are cited in table 2. The data demonstrate (a) the absence of appreciable incorporation in soils receiving no organic matter, (b) the need for readily assimilable carbohydrates, and (c) the inhibition by acidity. Significant fixation takes place only upon the application of simple

TABLE 2

Isotopic Measurement of Non-symbiotic N₂ Fixation in Yolo Soil at 21°C (5)

Amendment	Soil pH	Nitrate in Soil	Incubation Time	Nitrogen Fixed
		lb N/A	days	lb N/A
None	7.8	31	46	0.51
Straw, 6000 lb/A	5.2–5.6	31	46	0.14
	5.8–6.3	31	46	0.04
	6.7–7.3	31	46	1.32
Alfalfa, 20,000 lb/A	7.8	45	40	0.59
Starch, 20,000 lb/A	7.8	45	40	3.5
Glucose, 20,000 lb/A	7.8	45	40	40

sugars to neutral or slightly alkaline environments so the major limiting factor in nature appears to be the deficiency of readily available energy sources.

If non-symbiotic N₂ fixation is of practical consequence in non-flooded soil, it would likely be not in cultivated land but rather in grassland, where the excretions of the extensive root network may provide an adequate supply of available carbohydrates. The evidence here too is inconclusive. Yet, the scant attention given to *Clostridium* spp. is unfortunate as their numbers run to the hundreds of thousands per gram, and the clostridia may be more important than the azotobacters. Nevertheless, it is inappropriate to attribute biochemical significance to high counts as many of the clostridia may exist as biochemically inactive spores. Further, the low efficiency and the vast quantities of carbohydrate required for anaerobic N₂ fixation make the clostridium reaction of doubtful agricultural value. The weight of evidence, therefore, supports the contention that the non-symbiotic metabolism of N₂ probably does not greatly benefit plant growth or crop production though the process probably is important in the biogeochemistry of the element by permitting the return of elemental nitrogen to terrestrial environments.

In rice fields and in other flooded areas, on the other hand, N₂ fixation may be appreciable. It is well known that rice has been cultivated for many years in certain regions with no manure or nitrogen supplementation. In wet paddy fields, an extensive blue-green algal bloom frequently develops, and it is not unlikely that the algae are enriching the environment with nitrogen. In contrast to heterotrophic bacteria, blue-green algae are not restricted in their carbon nutrition to preformed organic matter since their carbon source is CO_2. Because of their pH limitations, however, the algae incorporate N_2 most actively in soils of pH above approximately 6 (19). Despite the apparently greater importance, species of Cyanophyceae have been the subject of far less inquiry than the azotobacters. In contrast with their activities in aquatic environments, the metabolism of the blue-greens is negligible in most unflooded soils, but they may add nitrogen to denuded or barren areas in which the Cyanophyceae are often the first visible signs of life.

Bacterial Inoculation

The paucity of aerobic, free-living N_2-fixing organisms in farm land and the obvious need for nitrogen supplementation in crop production have prompted innumerable attempts to stimulate the fixation. Not infrequently, inoculant preparations of active organisms are added to soil or seed in the hope of favoring the process. Especially common is the use of azotobacter preparations for the purpose of supplementing the few such microorganisms naturally present in soil. Following the unimpressive plant responses obtained, the interest of early microbiologists waned. The failure to obtain stimulation and the decline of the large population added in the inoculant were in agreement with the ecological maxim that the distribution of microorganisms is governed by physical and chemical characteristics of the environment rather than by chance introduction.

Recent work in the Soviet Union and in other countries of eastern Europe has reopened the question of whether bacterial preparations for soil and seed inoculation might provide economic returns. At the outset, most workers outside the U.S.S.R. were in general accord as to the impracticability of inoculation with *Azotobacter* spp., but the many reports of yield increases bring the problem once again to the forefront. Among the crops claimed to benefit from azotobacter inoculation in soils of eastern Europe are corn, oats, wheat, barley, sugar beets, potatoes, cabbage, tomatoes, and carrots. Responses to such amendments occur in 50 to 70 per cent of the field crops. The yield increases are reported to be about 10 per cent, but greater stimulations are occasionally noted. To obtain the greatest response from the use of the bacterial inoculant, moisture and organic matter must be adequate, the reaction not acid, and the bacterial strain selected for maximum stimulation in the particular soil type.

Careful investigations using chemical and isotopic techniques have shown that heavy inoculation with azotobacter cultures fails to affect the incorporation of N_2 into soil. Nevertheless, it is conceivable that N_2 fixation takes place in the root zone, a region of intense microbiological activity and an area in which carbohydrates from root excretion or decomposition are abundant. Experimental evidence, however, is lacking. On the premise that benefits are accruing from bacterial treatment, explanations must be sought elsewhere than in the nitrogen transformations. One of the more plausible alternate hypotheses is that *Azotobacter* spp. produce auxins or hormones which enhance plant development, and the in vitro production of indole-3-acetic acid has indeed been verified (3, 20). The field importance of observations on auxin synthesis is unknown. A second theory states that the supplemental microorganisms exert some protective influence upon the plant in its struggle against soil-borne pathogens, but experimental support for this proposal is likewise lacking.

Considerable work in the Western Hemisphere has failed to confirm the claims of greater productivity (table 3). Careful analysis

TABLE 3

Effect of Azotobacter Inoculation on the Yield and Nitrogen Content of Greenhouse-Grown Crops (2)

Crop	Measurement	Uninoculated	Azotogen [*]	Azotobacter chroococcum
Rye	Dry wt, g	6.9	6.8	6.9
	Nitrogen, mg	274	258	266
Barley	Dry wt, g	15.1	15.1	15.0
	Nitrogen, mg	265	259	276
Kale	Dry wt, g	23.4	24.1	24.4
	Nitrogen, mg	288	314	303

[*] An azotobacter inoculant preparation.

of the Soviet experiments is difficult because of the scarcity of statistical evaluations. It is possible that the azotobacter effects are not real and may be accounted for by the normal variability of field experimentation. The greater yields are difficult to reconcile with the rapid decline of azotobacter in inoculated soil and with the absence of the specialized structure that permits the *Rhizobium*-legume symbiosis to operate so efficiently. For the present, therefore, reports of benefits arising from azotobacter inoculation must be considered as equivocal.

Biochemical Mechanism

Microorganisms that assimilate elemental nitrogen are biologically unique because they utilize a gas considered to be relatively inert. Moreover, the active species make use of N_2 when present in large or in trace amounts. The specific enzyme, *nitrogenase*, that combines with and activates the commonly non-reactive gas is often characterized on the basis of its affinity for N_2. The dissociation constant of the nitrogenase-N_2 complex, the Michaelis constant of enzymological nomenclature, is approximately 0.02 atmospheres for *Azotobacter, Rhodospirillum,* and *Nostoc,* 0.03 atmospheres for *Clostridium,* and 0.05 atmospheres for red clover. The Michaelis constant represents the partial pressure of N_2 at which the fixation is proceeding at half maximal velocity. The most rapid nitrogen incorporation takes place at somewhat higher concentrations of the gas, and the rate is appreciably slower below 0.02 to 0.05 atmospheres.

The use of accurately regulated gas mixtures for certain types of experiments resulted in an entirely unexpected discovery: H_2 prevented N_2 assimilation in both the legume-*Rhizobium* symbiotic association and in the free-living N_2-fixing microorganisms. Inhibition by H_2 is specific for the assimilation of N_2, and the utilization of combined nitrogen compounds is unaffected. The inhibition by H_2 is competitive; i.e., the effect depends upon the relative concentrations of H_2 and N_2. Thus, the influence of a fixed amount of H_2 is lessened as the N_2 concentration is increased. The phenomenon of H_2 toxicity assumes added significance because all microorganisms that assimilate N_2 likewise metabolize H_2, the former by means of nitrogenase, the latter by the enzyme *hydrogenase*. Hydrogenase is capable of activating H_2 for the reduction of a number of substances or of liberating H_2 from reduced compounds. In equation I, R represents the compound that is reduced by hydrogenase.

$$H_2 + R \; \underset{\longleftarrow}{\overset{\text{hydrogenase}}{\longrightarrow}} \; RH_2 \qquad\qquad (I)$$

The association between H_2 and N_2 is further suggested by the fact that combined nitrogen compounds such as ammonium or nitrate salts that inhibit N_2 assimilation likewise lead to a reduced hydrogenase content (7). Despite the finding of hydrogenase in N_2-fixing microorganisms, neither the role of the enzyme nor the nature of the H_2 influence has been adequately explained. The possibility that hydrogenase and nitrogenase are synonyms for the same enzyme seems unlikely because several bacteria possess hydrogenase but not nitrogenase. For the present, the role of H_2 and hydrogenase remains obscure.

Nitrous oxide is another competitive inhibitor of N_2 uptake by *Azotobacter* and *Clostridium*. Its effect is specific for N_2 as growth on ammonium is unhampered by the presence of N_2O. Yet, N_2O is slowly metabolized by *Azotobacter vinelandii,* and the nitrogen derived from the gas appears in the microbial protoplasm. Not only does N_2O affect N_2 assimilation but N_2 competitively inhibits N_2O utilization, suggesting thereby that the processes leading to the incorporation of N_2O and N_2 are in some way related.

Carbon monoxide at low partial pressures exhibits a like inhibition of the assimilation of N_2 while it is ineffective at low concentration on organisms using combined sources of nitrogen. For example, partial pressures of CO of 0.001 to 0.002 atmospheres (0.1 to 0.2 per cent) markedly suppress N_2 but not ammonium utilization by *Nostoc, Bacillus polymyxa, Azotobacter,* and *Aerobacter.* Legumes like red clover are much more sensitive, and as little as 0.01 to 0.05 per cent CO in the gas phase retards symbiotic N_2 utilization.

The pathway of nitrogen from N_2 to cellular proteins has eluded precise characterization though a small segment of the sequence has been established. Considerable emphasis has been placed upon ascertaining the key intermediate in N_2 metabolism. The key intermediate is defined as the end-product of the inorganic conversion and the point at which the nitrogen is assimilated into organic molecules. This inorganic compound is the one that combines with the carbon chain to yield the initial organic nitrogen complex. The results of recent biochemical investigations support the hypothesis that ammonia is the key intermediate. Four lines of evidence can be cited:

a. When cells actively utilizing N_2 are supplied with ammonia, the latter is assimilated immediately without the lag period required for enzymatic adaptation; i.e., the enzymes for ammonia assimilation are present in cells fixing N_2, presumably because ammonia is continually being generated from N_2.

b. Ammonia or compounds rapidly converted to it are assimilated to the exclusion of N_2.

c. The first amino acid isotopically tagged with N^{15} in short-term experiments is glutamic acid for organisms supplied with either N^{15}-labeled N_2 or with labeled ammonium salts. These results have been obtained with species of *Azotobacter, Clostridium, Nostoc, Rhodospirillum, Chromatium, Chlorobium,* and with soybean nodules. Such data suggest that the incorporation into protein of ammonia and molecular nitrogen proceeds by similar pathways.

d. The demonstration of NH_3-N^{15} formation when *Clostridium pasteurianum* or *Azotobacter* spp. are supplied with N^{15}-N_2 is particularly convincing evidence for the key role of ammonia in the process (4, 11, 21).

A postulated fixation mechanism is presented in figure 2. The carbon chain combining with ammonia is proposed to be α-keto-glutaric acid which is derived from the decomposition of carbohydrates; the product of the reaction is the amino acid, glutamic acid. Only ammonia and the succeeding products have experimental support in their behalf, and the role of all other proposed intermediates is largely speculative. Hydroxylamine may be the immediate precursor of the key substance, but there is no evidence that it can be used as a nitrogen source. *Azotobacter* strains will produce complexes of hydroxylamine when they are grown on N_2, but the same compounds are formed during growth upon ammonium salts, minimizing the significance of the finding (18). The specific and competitive inhibition of N_2 utilization by N_2O and the incorporation of the latter gas into the protoplasm of *Azotobacter vinelandii* and soybean nodules suggest that N_2O or some related molecule is formed in the metabolism of N_2. Despite the many uncertainties in investigations of the biochemistry of N_2 fixation, the mechanism is probably similar in the active microorganisms because all are affected in similar ways by several critical factors: the partial pressure of N_2; the presence of H_2, N_2O, or CO; and the absence of molybdenum. The differences between organisms with regard to N_2 fixation seem to be microbiological rather than biochemical.

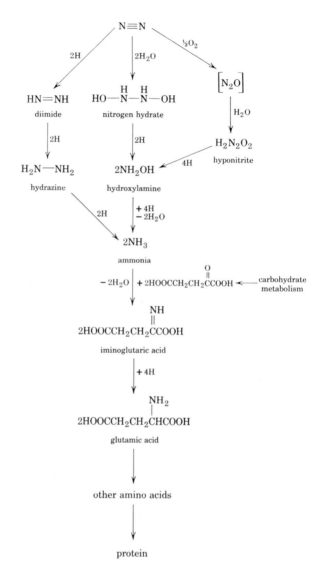

Figure 2. Postulated mechanisms of biological N_2 fixation.

REFERENCES

Reviews

Burris, R. H. 1956. Studies on the mechanism of biological nitrogen fixation. In W. D. McElroy and B. Glass, eds., *Inorganic nitrogen metabolism*. The Johns Hopkins Press, Baltimore, pp. 316–343.

Cooper, R. 1959. Bacterial fertilizers in the Soviet Union. *Soils and Fert.*, 22: 327–333.

Fogg, G. E. 1956. Nitrogen fixation by photosynthetic organisms. *Ann. Rev. Plant Physiol.*, 7:51–70.

Virtanen, A. I. 1955. Biological nitrogen fixation. *Proc. 3rd Intl. Cong. Biochem.*, Brussels, pp. 425–433.

Wilson, P. W. 1958. Asymbiotic nitrogen fixation. In W. Ruhland, ed., *Handbuch der Pflanzenphysiologie*. Springer-Verlag, Berlin. Vol. 8, pp. 9–47.

Literature cited

1. Alexander, M., and P. W. Wilson. 1954. *Applied Microbiol.*, 2:135–140.
2. Allison, F. E., V. L. Gaddy, L. A. Pinck, and W. H. Armiger. 1947. *Soil Sci.*, 64:489–497.
3. Berezova, E. F., A. N. Naumova, and E. A. Raznizina. 1938. *Compt. Rend. Acad. Sci., U.R.S.S.*, 18:357–361.
4. Carnahan, J. E., L. E. Mortenson, H. F. Mower, and J. E. Castle. 1960. *Biochim. Biophys. Acta*, 38:188–189.
5. Delwiche, C. C., and J. Wijler. 1956. *Plant and Soil*, 7:113–129.
6. Gainey, P. L. 1923. *J. Agric. Research*, 24:907–938.
7. Green, M., and P. W. Wilson. 1953. *J. Bacteriol.*, 65:511–517.
8. Jensen, H. L. 1950. *Trans. 4th Intl. Cong. Soil Sci.*, Amsterdam, 1:165–172.
9. Karraker, P. E., C. E. Bortner, and E. N. Fergus. 1950. *Ky. Agric. Expt. Sta. Bull. 557*.
10. Lyon, T. L., and J. A. Bizzell. 1933. *J. Am. Soc. Agron.*, 25:266–272.
11. Newton, J. W., P. W. Wilson, and R. H. Burris. 1953. *J. Biol. Chem.*, 204: 445–451.
12. Okuda, A., and M. Yamaguchi. 1956. *Soil and Plant Food*, 2:4–7.
13. Okuda, A., M. Yamaguchi, and S. Kamata. 1957. *Soil and Plant Food*, 2:131–133.
14. Pengra, R. M., and P. W. Wilson. 1958. *J. Bacteriol.*, 75:21–25.
15. Proctor, M. H., and P. W. Wilson. 1959. *Arch. Mikrobiol.*, 32:254–260.
16. Rosenblum, E. D., and P. W. Wilson. 1949. *J. Bacteriol.*, 57:413–414.
17. Ruinen, J. 1956. *Nature*, 177:220–221.
18. Saris, N. E., and A. I. Virtanen. 1957. *Acta Chem. Scand.*, 11:1438–1440.
19. Singh, R. N. 1942. *Indian J. Agric. Sci.*, 12:743–756.
20. Smaly, V. T., and O. I. Bershova. 1957. *Mikrobiologiya*, 26:526–532.
21. Zelitch, I., E. D. Rosenblum, R. H. Burris, and P. W. Wilson. 1951. *J. Biol. Chem.*, 191:295–298.

19

Nitrogen Fixation: Symbiotic

The continuous drain upon the nitrogen resources of the soil and the necessity for higher crop yields have led to an ever-increasing emphasis upon means of conserving the limited supply of the element. As only a fraction of the total agricultural need for nitrogen comes from synthetic and natural fertilizers, the remaining portion must be satisfied from the soil reserves and through the biological fixation of atmospheric N_2. It has been pointed out in the previous chapter that a number of free-living microorganisms can assimilate molecular nitrogen, but no higher plant or animal has the needed enzyme or enzyme system to catalyze the reaction. In certain instances, however, a symbiosis can become established in which one of the more prominent effects of the association is the acquisition of nitrogen from the atmosphere. Two members are required for the association, a plant and a microorganism. The classical example of such a symbiosis is that between leguminous plants and bacteria of the genus *Rhizobium*. The seat of the symbiosis is within the nodules that appear on the plant roots (figure 1).

Legumes, the most important plant group concerned in symbiotic N_2 fixation, are dicotyledonous plants of the family *Leguminosae*. The ten thousand or more species, of which only about two hundred are cultivated by man, are divided into three subfamilies. The largest of the three is Papilionoideae. In this subfamily are found *Trifolium, Melilotus, Medicago, Lotus, Phaseolus, Dalea, Crotalaria, Vicia, Vigna, Pisum,* and *Lathyrus.* A smaller number of genera are classified in

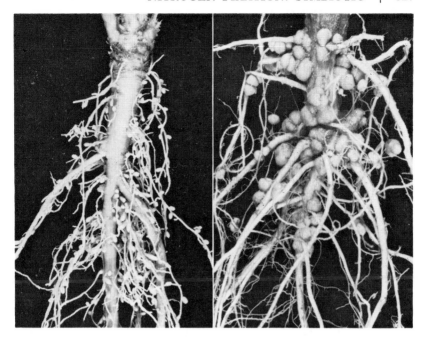

Figure 1. Well-nodulated legume roots. Left, red clover; right, soybeans. (Courtesy of J. C. Burton.)

the Caesalpinioideae while Mimosoideae is the smallest subfamily of legumes.

The Microsymbiont

Members of the genus *Rhizobium*, upon infection of the appropriate legume, can cause the formation of nodules and participate in the symbiotic acquisition of N_2. The bacteria are gram negative, non-spore-forming, aerobic rods, 0.5 to 0.9 μ wide and 1.2 to 3.0 μ long. Representatives of this genus are typically motile. Several carbohydrates are utilized, sometimes with the accumulation of acid but never of gas. *Rhizobium* is classified with *Agrobacterium* and *Chromobacterium* in the family Rhizobiaceae. The rhizobia are quite similar to *Agrobacterium radiobacter*, a bacterium which differs from the root nodule bacteria in certain minor cultural traits and in its inability to infect legume roots. The means of differentiating *Rhizobium* spp. from related bacteria is highly unsatisfactory as it relies upon the ability of the organisms to nodulate test plants. Delineation of a microbial group on the basis of a particular ecological relationship is undesirable as a bacterium living free in the soil usually is not examined for its ability to infect or nodulate given hosts. Moreover, a classification scheme of this type is inadequate because a given isolate cannot be excluded from the genus *Rhizobium* until its ability to nodulate all leguminous species has been ascertained.

Nevertheless, the agronomic significance of the rhizobia dictates that some usable diagnostic system be developed, pragmatic though it be. Clear differences between strains of the root nodule bacteria are apparent, but standard laboratory tests for their differentiation into species are rare. Speciation within the genus is based entirely, for the present at least, upon host specificity since the bacteria are limited in the plant groups they infect. The characteristic upon which the classification is based is the capacity of an isolate to invade roots of a restricted number of plant species in addition to the legume from which the microorganism was obtained. Because of the limited number of hosts, so-called *cross-inoculation* groups have been established.

A cross-inoculation group refers to a collection of leguminous species which develop nodules when exposed to bacteria obtained from the nodules of any member of that particular plant group. Consequently, a single cross-inoculation group ideally includes all host species which are infected by an individual bacterial strain. More than twenty cross-inoculation groups have been established, but only seven have achieved prominence, and no more than six have been sufficiently well delineated for the responsible bacterium to have attained species status. The accepted classification scheme based upon cross-inoculation groupings is outlined in table 1. Many legumes of agricultural importance as well as non-cultivated plants, however, are not nodulated by bacteria of the six major types. Birdsfoot trefoil (*Lotus corniculatus*), black locust (*Robinia pseudoacacia*), garbanzo (*Cicer arietinum*), hemp sesbania (*Sesbania exaltata*), and others that do not fit into the established categories require distinctly different bacterial strains. Only a small percentage of the leguminous species reported in the botanical literature are included within the six defined cross-inoculation groupings.

Several laboratory reactions are of diagnostic value. For example, *Rhizobium meliloti* acidifies litmus milk while the other five

TABLE 1

Cross-Inoculation Groups and *Rhizobium*-Legume Associations

Cross-Inoculation Group	*Rhizobium* Species	Host Genera	Legumes Included
Alfalfa group	R. *meliloti*	*Medicago*	Alfalfa
		Melilotus	Sweet clover
		Trigonella	Fenugreek
Clover group	R. *trifolii*	*Trifolium*	Clovers
Pea group	R. *leguminosarum*	*Pisum*	Pea
		Vicia	Vetch
		Lathyrus	Sweetpea
		Lens	Lentil
Bean group	R. *phaseoli*	*Phaseolus*	Beans
Lupine group	R. *lupini*	*Lupinus*	Lupines
		Ornithopus	Serradella
Soybean group	R. *japonicum*	*Glycine*	Soybean
Cowpea group	—	*Vigna*	Cowpea
		Lespedeza	Lespedeza
		Crotalaria	Crotalaria
		Pueraria	Kudzu
		Arachis	Peanut
		Phaseolus	Lima bean

species make it alkaline; on the other hand, *Rhizobium lupini* and *Rhizobium japonicum* form no serum zone in the milk whereas the remaining four produce the serum zone. Some strains acidify their culture solutions; others, particularly the soybean and cowpea bacteria, make the growth medium alkaline. *Rhizobium* isolates may also be subdivided into slowly growing and rapidly growing classes. Nevertheless, none of the laboratory procedures is as useful for taxonomic purposes as nodulation.

The six species of *Rhizobium* are not entirely distinct. For example, the soybean and cowpea bacterial groups, commonly considered to be separate, contain many similar bacterial strains, and organisms isolated from soybean nodules frequently infect cowpeas and vice versa. These results suggest that at least some of the cowpea rhizobia may be varieties of R. *japonicum*. Certain R. *lupini* strains bear a degree of similarity to the cowpea-soybean type, and a slight overlap between the clover and pea rhizobia has been reported although isolates of *Rhizobium trifolii* are relatively distinct (21). The reasons for the host specificity, where it does exist, or the lack thereof are largely unknown.

The validity of the cross-inoculation system has not gone unchallenged because many legumes are nodulated by rhizobia of other host-bacterial groups. The bacterial strains which invade legumes outside of their particular class and plants which are thus infected are examples of a phenomenon termed *symbiotic promiscuity*. Occasionally, one host is infected by microorganisms normally classified in a number of different plant-bacterium groups. The cross-inoculation classes are therefore not entirely adequate for the description of the nodulating performance of many root nodule organisms. It is interesting to note that legumes which are completely self-pollinating are invaded by few rhizobia whereas the extent of symbiotic promiscuity increases in hosts possessing a greater degree of cross pollination (30, 31). By and large, the instances of symbiosis outside of the established cross-inoculation classes are incapable of fixing N_2. Moreover, the agricultural significance of the groups still remains a key feature of the established taxonomic system, and, until a new scheme is proposed, one is forced to rely on the existing criteria which form the basis for sound legume inoculation in farm practice.

Rhizobia grow readily in culture media containing a carbon source such as mannitol or glucose, ammonium or nitrate to supply the required nitrogen, and several inorganic salts. None of the bacteria in culture solution utilize N_2; the fixation reaction is thus the result of a true symbiosis as neither symbiont can carry out the process alone. In addition to the organic carbon source, one or several B vitamins are often stimulatory or required by the microorganisms. The vitamins exerting a beneficial effect include biotin, thiamine, pantothenic acid, and riboflavin. A requirement for organic acids has also been established for *R. meliloti* (14). The need for biotin is absolute for certain strains, but it is merely stimulatory to others; some rhizobia grow well in the total absence of the vitamin.

Of particular importance to the development of the symbiotic relationship is the presence of a large population of rhizobia. Because there are no selective media for the nodule organisms, a common procedure for their enumeration is the inoculation of ten-fold dilutions from the test soil into pots of sterile soil seeded with the particular legume. After a suitable incubation period, the roots are examined, and the highest dilution giving rise to nodules is taken as an indication of the population density. In one ecological study in Iowa in which this counting method was used, the numbers of *R. meliloti* and *R. trifolii* were found to vary from as few as 10 to as many as 10^5 per gram depending upon the season of year, cropping history, and management practices. The organisms are generally more numerous in fields having a rotation containing the specific legume than in fields in which the legume is absent, and soils recently cropped to alfalfa support a larger *R. meliloti* flora than areas not planted to alfalfa for some time (29). Nevertheless, indigenous populations of some rhizobia are present in most localities; that is, the organisms are native to soils with no recent history of the macrosymbiont's presence.

The Nodulation Process

The relationship between the formation of nodules and N_2 assimilation was first demonstrated in 1888 by Hellriegel and Wilfarth, but more than half a century elapsed before studies using N^{15}-N_2 provided unequivocal proof that nodules are the seat of the fixation reaction. The localization of the N_2-metabolizing enzymes in the modified root tissue suggests that nodulation and the associated biochemical processes are of prime importance to the well-being of leguminous crops.

In the development of the nodular structure, the initial step appears to require the release into the root zone of plant excretion products stimulatory to the root nodule bacteria. The chemical nature of the excretions is still unknown, but the substances may be growth factors or energy substrates necessary for the initiation of infection. The excretions are undoubtedly the cause of the increased number of rhizobia in immediate proximity to the leguminous root; moreover, the products released by the roots appear to selectively stimulate only the bacteria of the specific cross-inoculation group (6). In most legumes, the primary invasion occurs through the root hair, which, in the presence of suitable bacteria, undergoes a deformation or curling under the influence of some microbial product, presumably indoleacetic acid. The evidence for indoleacetic acid as the stimulatory substance is far from complete, for, despite the acknowledged synthesis of the compound in vitro by *Rhizobium* spp. and the fact that the substance does cause root swellings, many other microorganisms produce indoleacetic acid and yet fail to induce nodule generation. Therefore, indoleacetic acid is possibly concerned in the process, but it is merely one of several factors.

Only a small proportion of the invaded root hairs develop nodules, usually less than 5 per cent of the infections ultimately resulting in nodules. Following the microbial penetration into the root hair, a hypha-like *infection thread* is formed. In the narrow infection tube, typically surrounded by a wall of cellulose synthesized by the host, the bacterial population is never too dense, but the microorganisms can be seen easily under the microscope. Finally, the thread branches into the central portions of the developing nodule, and the bacteria ultimately are released into their symbiont's cytoplasm, therein to multiply. Following the release, a period of rapid cell division takes place in the host's cells. The final structure consists of a central core containing the rhizobia and a surrounding cortical area in which is found the plant vascular system. A curious feature of the plant cells in the central portion of the nodule is their possession of twice the chromosome number characteristic of the host. The doubling of the chromosome number occurs in the nodules of polyploid as well as diploid legumes. The disomatic tissue probably originates from disomatic cells of the uninfected roots which, upon the approach of the invading bacteria, are stimulated to multiplication. The enzyme polygalacturonase seems to be important in root hair infection, possibly by acting on the pectin of the plant cell wall to permit bacterial penetration (8).

There are significant differences among legumes in the morphology of the nodules. Red and white clovers have club-shaped and lobed structures, the nodules of alfalfa are more branched and longer while those of cowpea, peanut, and lima bean exhibit a spherical shape. In some plants, velvet bean for example, the nodules may approach the size of a baseball whereas the nodules of other legumes are no more than several millimeters in diameter. Legumes with fibrous roots frequently have a greater abundance of nodules than plants with well-formed tap roots, and plants bearing large nodules often have only a few whereas roots with smaller structures have them in greater numbers.

Nodules are not found on all of the genera and species of Leguminosae. The apparent failure to develop the symbiosis is most evident in the subfamily Caesalpinioideae in which about half of the genera and two-thirds the species critically examined contain no nodular structures. Yet only some 1063 of a total of approximately 12,000 species of Leguminosae have been investigated to determine the presence of root nodules, and as many as 133 of the species examined have no known symbiotic association (1). The large percentage of Caesalpinioideae species that fail to develop root infections may be indicative of a degree of physiological primitiveness in which the capacity for symbiosis has never developed. However, in addition to the innate biochemical or genetic traits of the host precluding infection is the possibility that the ecological investigations have not been sufficiently intensive.

Once liberated from the infection thread into the root cytoplasm, the rhizobia assume a peculiar morphology, a cellular form that has been termed the *bacteroid* (figure 2). In morphology, the bacteroids found within the nodule are swollen and irregular, frequently appearing in star, clubbed, or branched shapes. Bacteroids vary in size and shape, and those formed by R. *leguminosarum*, for example, are distinctly different from those of R. *trifolii*. In culture media, the rhizobia can be converted to a bacteroid morphology by the addition of alkaloids or glucosides. Because N_2 fixation and bacteroids are both associated with the nodule, several attempts have been made to induce the artificial bacteroids to assimilate N_2 in the absence of the plant, but all such attempts have met with failure.

Not all rhizobia are capable of invading leguminous plants so that *infectiveness*, the ability of a strain to nodulate a given host, is of considerable economic importance. Among infective strains, moreover, the capacity of nodule bacteria to bring about N_2 fixation in conjunction with the plant varies greatly. The relative capacity of the symbiotic system, once established, to assimilate molecular nitrogen is known as its *effectiveness*. Many *Rhizobium* spp. are highly effective while others are largely or completely ineffective. A strain that does not permit fixation at a rate sufficient to meet the demands of the host is either partially effective or totally ineffective. Consequently, the mere presence of nodules is not a guarantee that a leguminous crop can benefit from gaseous nitrogen.

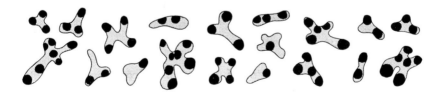

Figure 2. Bacteroids from the nodules of pea plants (28).

Ineffective root nodule bacteria produce a greater number of nodules than effective cultures, but the nodules are smaller in size and tend to be more widely distributed over the root system. On the other hand, a single microbial strain may be ineffective or partially effective on one host yet be associated with active N_2 fixation on another legume variety or species. Furthermore, bacterial strains that appear effective on certain hosts may approach parasitism on others. For example, rhizobia in an effective symbiosis with white and red clovers are sometimes parasitic upon subterranean clover (25). It is therefore not possible to conclude that a given strain is effective or ineffective in absolute terms.

The environment has a marked influence on the development of the symbiotic association. Environmental effects are exerted largely through alterations in the physiology of the host. Inadequate levels of many inorganic nutrients alter nodule development in one of several manners, but such alterations are usually reflections of abnormal plant growth. Nodulation generally takes place at all soil temperatures tolerated by the free-living plant, but nodule abundance is reduced at the cooler and warmer extremes (13). Day length and light intensity also affect the number of nodules. Those on soybeans, for example, are heavier and more abundant on plants grown in long than in short days (22). Shading tends to depress nodule weights whereas high but not excessive light intensities and high CO_2 levels increase nodule numbers. An opposite effect is noted following nitrogen additions; that is, the nodule number and weight are reduced. The influence of day length, light intensity, nitrogen, and CO_2 supply may all be interpreted in terms of the internal concentration of carbohydrates; abundant light and CO_2, which increase the plant's carbohydrate storage, favor nodule production whereas nitrogen depresses the internal carbohydrate supply and has at the same time a retarding influence on nodulation. The same facts, however, may be used to support a carbohydrate:nitrogen ratio theory for nodulation. Whether the nitrogen or carbohydrate supply is the more critical has not yet been resolved (2, 32).

Fixation of Nitrogen

The continuous cultivation of non-legumes decreases soil fertility, a condition not reversed by fertilization with phosphorus, potash, or trace minerals. Cropping to legumes results in no such depletion of the land's productivity, and succeeding non-leguminous crops frequently benefit from the legume's growth and N_2 fixation. However, the nitrogen status of soil under legumes is governed by cultural practices. When the crop is turned under, the full nitrogen gain is realized. When the legume is grazed or fed on the farm and the manure returned, the gain is not as great, yet it is appreciable. Removal of the aboveground portion of the crop, on the other hand, leads to little increase in nitrogen (table 2). In the latter practice, however, the fact that the nitrogen content of the soil does not decrease, or increases somewhat, despite the removal of large quantities of proteinaceous material is of great merit, particularly when the depleting influence of grasses or cereals and the need for expensive fertilizers are taken into consideration. Further, the results cited in table 2 demonstrate that frequently the nitrogen gain is essentially as great in grass-legume mixtures as in the pure legume stand, the al-

TABLE 2

Nitrogen Fixation and Nitrogen Gains in Soils of Ithaca, New York

Crop	Nitrogen Harvested in Crop in 4 yr	Nitrogen in Soil		Nitrogen Balance*	
		Initial	At 4 yr	4 yr	Avg/yr
	lb/A	lb/A	lb/A	lb/A	lb/A
Timothy	140	2780	2700	40	10
Brome grass	118	2840	2780	38	9.5
Timothy + N†	429	2720	2780	−131	−33
Brome + N†	478	2800	2880	−62	−16
Timothy + trefoil	695	2800	2860	735	184
Brome + Alfalfa	1044	2780	2800	1044	261
Birdsfoot trefoil	722	2820	2900	782	196
Alfalfa	1023	2840	2880	1043	261

* Net gain or loss of nitrogen taking into account the nitrogen removed by the crop, nitrogen changes in the soil, and fertilizer added.

† Received a total of 620 lb of nitrogen. All other plots received 20 lb of fertilizer nitrogen.

falfa or birdsfoot trefoil apparently assimilating the same quantity of N_2 in a pure or a mixed stand.

The fixation of N_2 by legumes that are effectively nodulated is appreciable. An idea of the magnitude of the gains under optimal conditions can be obtained from the following figures compiled from a number of field trials in the United States.

lb N_2 fixed/A/yr

Alfalfa	113–297
Red clover	75–171
Pea	72–132
Soybean	57–105
Cowpea	57–117
Vetch	79–140

Alfalfa, clovers, and the lupines are among the vigorous N_2 fixers while peanuts, beans, and peas are notably poor. Under normal farm conditions with well-nodulated roots and assuming favorable meteorological conditions, figures of 100 lb per acre per year or higher are not uncommon in temperate regions. In a well-managed pasture, the biologically catalyzed N_2 incorporation varies from 100 to 200 lb per year on each acre. Gains of this magnitude provide sufficient amounts of the element to satisfy the needs for rapid plant development. In addition, the beneficial effect of leguminous crops may persist for three or more years as measured by the improved yields of grasses or cereals in land previously growing legumes. The leguminous tree known as black locust (*Robinia pseudoacacia*) can bring about a slow but appreciable gain of nitrogen in its underlying soil. In addition, wild nodulated legumes contribute to the cycle of nitrogen on the earth's surface, but their significance is difficult to assess.

In order to obtain maximal benefits from the activities of the root nodule bacteria, one cannot usually rely upon spontaneous infection by the indigenous soil microflora. Many localities contain few fully effective rhizobia, and it is not uncommon to observe as many as 25 per cent of the bacteria in a given field to have a low degree of effectiveness, 50 per cent to have moderate ability, and only 25 per cent to be fully effective. Because of the large indigenous population of rhizobia which are not fully effective in N_2 fixation, it is not surprising that supplemental inoculation with selected bacterial strains commonly results in highly significant agronomic responses.

Several procedures have been developed to insure beneficial nodular associations. One of the most primitive is the application of soil obtained from a field previously cropped to the particular legume. Techniques of this nature are unsound because ineffective rhizobia, plant pathogens, and innumerable weed seeds may be applied together with the active microorganisms. A better method is the use of effective nodules obtained from plants of the same species. The nodules are homogenized, suspended in water, and applied to the seed at planting time. Methods involving the use of solid or liquid carriers have met with more widespread acceptance. In the original technique, the seeds were coated with a suspension of the bacteria which had been cultured in liquid media or on agar slants. In recent years, however, solid-base carriers have replaced the early inoculants. For the preparation of solid-base inoculants, a heavy suspension of rhizobia grown in liquid culture in large fermentors is mixed with a carrier of moist humus, finely ground peat, or a peat-charcoal mixture. In the farmer's hands, the seeds are wet with water and the inoculant mixed with the moist seed immediately prior to sowing. One of the recent improvements in inoculant technology is the use of adhesives such as molasses or gums to hold the inoculant to the seed.

Inoculation is recommended the first time a field is planted to a new legume species, and responses to the supplemental bacteria frequently are quite marked in these circumstances. A two-fold or greater increase in dry weight yield resulting from inoculation is not uncommon. On the other hand, where the indigenous rhizobia are numerous and effective, the response measured in terms of yield or nitrogen uptake may be slight or lacking; the absence of a stimulation is often noted in fields previously cropped to effectively and abundantly nodulated hosts of the same cross-inoculation group. But, in the absence of clear evidence to the contrary, the recommended practice is to inoculate.

Excretion of Nitrogen

Grasses or cereals grown together with legumes frequently contain more nitrogen than the corresponding grass or cereal grown alone. In a typical study, bluegrass yielded 25 lb of nitrogen per acre in a pure grass stand while, in association with clover, the yield of nitrogen in the grass was 125 lb (12). The beneficial effect of mixed cropping is often attributed to the excretion of nitrogen by legumes, the roots actively liberating the nitrogen obtained from the atmosphere. Benefits derived from mixed cropping have been observed for corn grown with soybeans or cowpeas, cereals with field peas or vetch, and pasture grasses with clover.

The first clear demonstration of the subterranean transfer of nitrogen was made by Lipman (19). He grew oats in a pot of sand placed within a second, larger container of sand that was planted to field peas. The walls of the inner container were porous in order to permit the transfer of products through the nitrogen-free rooting media. Where nutrient diffusion was possible, the oats in the inner pot grew rapidly, had a green color, and appeared sturdy. In parallel containers in which the walls of the inner pot were non-porous to prevent the movement of products, the oats were stunted and exhibited symptoms of nitrogen deficiency. The studies of A. I. Virtanen and his collaborators in Finland have firmly established the phenomenon of excretion. Virtanen encountered little difficulty in detecting nitrogen excretion, and from 10 to 80 per cent of the N_2 fixed was found to be excreted by plants grown in greenhouse conditions in Finland. Nitrogenous products were released by inoculated peas, but none were liberated by unnodulated plants growing at the expense of nitrate (31). The bulk of the nitrogen excreted by aseptically grown pea plants was in the form of amino acids, particularly glutamic acid, aspartic acid, and β-alanine.

Virtanen's work could not be reproduced elsewhere, however. Studies in the United States, Germany, Great Britain, and Australia failed to confirm the release of nitrogenous compounds from nodulated roots of peas, cowpea, alfalfa, vetch, sweet pea, soybeans and beans. The discrepancy in the results of various investigators arises from the extreme sensitivity of the excretion mechanism to the environment. Nitrogen is apparently excreted only when the rate of photosynthesis is not sufficiently rapid to provide the carbohydrates necessary to combine with the N_2 fixed in the nodule. The excess is then released by the roots. Meteorological factors that have a differential influence on the rates of photosynthesis and N_2 fixation will, therefore, influence the excretion. On the basis of this explanation, the favorable effect of temperatures of about 15°C on excretion and the inhibition at 20°C result from a differential influence of temperature on N_2 and CO_2 fixation. Light intensity likewise affects excretion, and long, cool days with moderate amounts of sunlight are beneficial (34).

The sensitivity of excretion to alterations in the environment is so marked that the significance of excretion in agriculture is still not known. This does not signify that mixed cropping is of no practical value, a conclusion contrary to much field evidence, but rather that the precise mechanism has eluded characterization. In addition to active excretion providing the additional nitrogen assimilated by a non-legume grown together with a legume, the nitrogen may arise from microbial decomposition of the sloughed-off root and nodular tissue of the legume.

N_2 Fixation by Non-leguminous Plants

Several genera of non-leguminous plants possess, at some stage in their life cycles, nodules upon their roots. Nodulated non-legumes are represented by: (a) Alnus spp., the alder tree found throughout the world; (b) Myrica gale, the bog myrtle or sweet gale; (c) Hippophae spp., distributed in large areas of Europe and Asia; (d) Elaeagnus spp., of widespread distribution in North America, Europe, and Asia; (e) Shepherdia spp., found abundantly in Canada; (f) Casuarina spp., trees and shrubs common in subtropical and tropical areas of the Americas, Asia, Australia, Indonesia, and the West Indies; (g) Coriaria spp., which occur in many environments; and (h) Ceanothus spp., shrubs in North American forests. Three of the eight genera, Hippophae, Elaeagnus, and Shepherdia, are classified in a single family, Elaeagnaceae, but the other five belong to separate families. In certain environments, species of these genera may be more abundant than the legumes so that the capacity of the nodules formed by the eight genera to assimilate N_2 has considerable ecological significance.

The role of the nodule in non-legumes is not difficult to establish. The plant's growth in nutrient solutions containing low concentrations of nitrogen is distinctly poor, and nitrogen deficiencies are evident. However, the addition to the rooting medium of a preparation of ground nodules results in the production of nodules on the test plants. The nodulated hosts then develop with no deficiency symptoms, reach a greater height, and appear more vigorous than uninoculated controls. A chemical analysis for total nitrogen or exposure of the infected hosts to N^{15}-labeled N_2 provides the final proof of the existence of N_2-metabolizing enzymes (5, 10). Some typical data for Casuarina equisetifolia are presented in table 3.

TABLE 3

**Influence of Nodulation on Growth of *Casuarina*
equisetifolia (20)**

Treatment	Nitrate in Culture	Height	Plant Weight	Nitrogen Harvested
		cm	g	g
With nodules	—	60.1	11.8	0.146
No nodules	—	40.4	1.4	0.0079
No nodules	+	49.1	6.8	0.103

Plants harvested after 142 days.

The most intensively studied of the group is the alder tree, *Alnus glutinosa*, which assimilates N_2 at a rate adequate to permit rapid development in nitrogen-deficient soils. The tree does not require nodules for growth provided that a nitrogen salt is supplied, but field-grown alders typically possess nodules that may approach the size of tennis balls, and chemical analysis of soil under alders often shows an increase in the nitrogen content. When treated with aqueous extracts of crushed nodules from field alder, greenhouse-grown plants develop nodules in 2 to 3 weeks. The optimum pH for fixation is in the vicinity of pH 5.5 to 6.0 although growth in nitrogen-free solutions is vigorous from pH 4.2 to 7.0; utilization of nitrate, however, proceeds to pH 3.3. It is estimated that an alder grove containing 4000 plants per acre of 2.5 meters high may fix approximately 200 lb of nitrogen (9, 26). Estimates for *Myrica gale* indicate a low activity in the field, about 8 lb of nitrogen per acre in each growing season (4).

In addition to plant-microorganism associations in certain of the Angiosperms, a number of Gymnosperms possess nodule-like structures that may be able to catalyze the fixation of N_2. Representatives of *Podocarpus* and *Cycas*, some of which are quite common in certain areas of the world, are included in the group of nodulated Gymnosperms. However, in no instance is there adequate evidence of N_2 utilization as measured either by development in culture solutions free of fixed nitrogen or by the more definitive criterion of uptake of isotopic N_2.

A number of tropical plants have nodule-like structures on their leaves. Such anatomical swellings have been reported for species of *Pavetta, Psychotria, Grumilea,* and *Ardisia.* The weight of evidence favors the hypothesis that the organism which induces these swellings is a bacterium, possibly a *Bacterium* sp. (36). Proof for N_2 fixation by the modified leaf tissues is lacking, and their function is probably not associated with the nitrogen nutrition of the host.

The microbiological agents responsible for nodulation of *Alnus, Myrica, Hippophae, Elaeagnus, Shepherdia, Casuarina, Coriaria,* and *Ceanothus* have not yet been isolated in pure culture despite many attempts. Moreover, no known *Rhizobium* sp. will invade and cause nodulation of any of the non-legumes. Because of the inability to obtain cultures of the responsible organisms, successful infections are brought about by removing nodules from field-grown plants, crushing the tissue, and applying the preparations to the test seedlings. Cross inoculation has been recorded for *Hippophae, Elaeagnus,* and *Shepherdia,* the three genera of Elaeagnaceae, suggesting that the infecting organisms are similar or identical. Cross-inoculation refers here to the fact that crushed nodules prepared from one genus will induce nodulation of a second. In the other five genera, however, there is no cross-inoculation, indicating thereby that the infective agents differ from one another.

The failure to isolate the causative microorganisms of nodule production in non-legumes may be attributable to an obligately symbiotic nutrition. The responsible organisms have been variously considered as bacteria, bacteria infected with bacteriophages, actinomycetes, or myxomycetes related to or identical with species of *Plasmodiophora.* Recent cytological studies of the nodules favor the last two possibilities, the organism being either an actinomycete or a slime mold, but final proof must await the isolation, cultivation, and successful reinfection by the purified strains.

Environmental Influences

The amount of N_2 acquired by legumes through the *Rhizobium* symbiosis has been the subject of considerable interest because of the agricultural significance of the process, and only the highlights can be considered here. The major environmental factors governing the fixation are the type of legume, the effectiveness of the bacteria, the inorganic or mineralizable nitrogen content of the soil, the level of available phosphorus and potassium, pH, and the presence

TABLE 4

Effect of Ammonium on Nitrogen Fixation in Gravel Culture (3)

NH₄ Addition	Sources of Plant Nitrogen		Portion of Nitrogen from Air
	Fertilizer	Air	
mg N/pot	mg	mg	%
	Soybeans		
0	0	1639	100
80	68	1692	95
320	252	2243	89
560	464	2185	82
800	648	2423	79
	Ladino Clover		
0	0	188	100
80	63	234	75
320	282	159	35
560	527	98	15
800	609	82	12

in usable form of a number of secondary nutrients. Climatic and seasonal factors have a great influence on nitrogen gains, but these will not be considered in the present discussion as such factors generally affect more the physiology of the host than the symbiotic association.

Since fixation serves as a means of obtaining the nitrogen required for growth, it is not surprising that simple, inorganic nitrogen compounds inhibit N_2 fixation (table 4). Nodule weight and numbers are diminished at relatively high nitrate or ammonium levels, but low concentrations of inorganic nitrogen salts often enhance nodulation. Measurement of the effect of fertilizers is facilitated by the use of the isotope, N^{15}. Thus, if $(N^{15}H_4)_2SO_4$ is applied to nitrogen-free solution cultures of plants acquiring N^{14}-N_2, the relative amount of N^{15} and N^{14} in the plant tissue is a measure of the quantity of nitrogen obtained from the ammonium source and the quantity from the air. By this means, it has been shown that the percentage of nitrogen derived from the atmosphere is inversely related to the nitrogen fertilization rate. It may be expected, however, that the presence of a grass will reverse the inhibition to some extent by its competition for the supply of inorganic nitrogen.

Nitrogen fixation resembles nodulation in its dependence upon the carbohydrate:nitrogen ratio within the host's tissues. A widening of the ratio stimulates the fixation of N_2, but an excessively high carbohydrate level such as that resulting from very high light intensities retards the process. The depression of fixation by low light intensities is reversed by spraying the leaves with a sucrose solution, an indication that limiting light is acting by influencing the internal carbohydrate reserve (24). The retardation of N_2 assimilation by inorganic nitrogen may be associated with the carbohydrate:nitrogen status since nitrogen additions alter the internal carbohydrate reserve.

Phosphorus and potassium through their role as essential macronutrients exert a direct influence on nitrogen gains and legume yields. Responses of the N_2-fixing and the nodulation mechanisms to phosphate and potash fertilization are associated with the vigor and well-being of the host rather than reflections of a specific stimulation to the symbiosis per se.

The growth of the legume is also governed by soil acidity, and yield, nitrogen content, and nodulation of forage legumes often respond markedly to liming. The sensitivity to pH must be considered in terms of effects upon the macrosymbiont, the microsymbiont, and upon the symbiotic interaction of the two. With most legumes and non-legumes, nodule formation takes place in a narrower range of hydrogen ion concentrations than plant growth. In many of the legumes of economic importance, the infection does not occur much below about pH 5.0 while, in pure culture, the responsible *Rhizobium* sp. exhibits a similar sensitivity to low pH. The macrosymbiont, on the other hand, will occasionally grow at pH 4.0 or below in culture solutions provided with nitrate. Soybean and its infective bacterium are notable exceptions, and nodules are formed in highly acid environments.

The inhibition in acid soil frequently is not simply an effect of the hydrogen ion concentration. Toxicity resulting from iron or aluminum is most pronounced at low pH, and one or both of these substances may be the cause of poor legume stands. There is some evidence that calcium deficiency is important in the effects of acidity upon nitrogen fixation, and insufficient calcium may decrease crop yields and diminish nodule weights. A requirement for calcium by the symbiotic system would be analogous to the need of certain *Azotobacter* spp. for the same element for growth in nitrogen-free media.

Particularly dramatic is the influence of molybdenum in acid soils. Though the total molybdenum content may be high, the availability of the element for plant nutrition is affected markedly by pH. Little is obtained from acid soils because of chemical reactions that alter the availability of the element. Organisms that obtain their nitrogen from ammonium have a very small need for molybdenum, but this is not true for N_2-utilizing agents, either non-symbiotic or symbiotic. For the incorporation of N_2 into fixed forms, molybdenum must be in abundant supply, and its low order of availability in acid environments is consequently a frequent cause of failures in legume seedling establishment or of low crop yields. The deficiency may be simply remedied, however, by the application of molybdenum salts at rates of several ounces per acre. How often the poor legume yields in acid soils result from an effect of hydrogen ions, metal toxicity, or molybdenum deficiency is not known, but some indication may be found in the remarkable stimulation by molybdenum of alfalfa, several of the clovers, and birdsfoot trefoil growing in acid soils. Molybdenum is thus necessary for symbiotic N_2 fixation, a requirement similar to that found in free-living microorganisms active in the non-symbiotic process.

Since the area immediately adjacent to the leguminous root system is the site of origin of the infecting rhizobia, it is not surprising that the associated microflora has an effect upon the development of the symbiosis. Occasional inoculation failures may result from a microbiological competition that suppresses the desired microsymbiont and prevents initiation of the infection. Alternatively, members of the microflora may exert a beneficial influence by providing growth factors, removing toxic metabolites, or by immobilizing the inorganic nitrogen and thereby enhancing nodule formation.

Rhizobium spp. are notoriously susceptible to attack and lysis by bacteriophages. Bacterial viruses specific for the clover or alfalfa bacteria are found in the roots and in the nodules of the respective macrosymbionts and also in land cropped to these legumes. They are rarely detected in areas free of clover or alfalfa plants (15, 16). Isolation of the bacteriophages is usually accomplished by incubating together an aliquot of soil with the test bacterium, then removing the bacteria by passage through a bacteriological filter. The clear filtrate containing the virus is inoculated into a fresh bacterial culture in order to confirm the lysis. Addition of the filtrate to cultures of related *Rhizobium* strains will frequently lead to lysis as well. Rarely do the viruses infect bacteria outside of the genus *Rhizobium,* and the closely related *Agrobacterium radiobacter* is usually resistant to infection by *Rhizobium* viruses.

Continuous cropping of certain legumes, particularly alfalfa and clover, occasionally results in poor plant vigor and low yields. The condition, known as alfalfa or clover sickness, has been attributed to the deleterious effects of bacteriophage upon *Rhizobium* spp. and, therefore, on the fixation of N_2. Young plants presumably are nodulated in the presence of the virus whereas, once new nodules are no longer being formed, the virus assumes dominance and N_2 assimilation is eliminated. As a consequence, use of bacteriophage-resistant strains for legume inoculation has been recommended (7). These views have not gone unchallenged. It seems unlikely that bacteriophages cause the sickness as nodules actively assimilating N_2 contain the virus and bacteriophage abundance is not correlated with the incidence of the sickness. A toxic substance excreted into the soil by the plant roots or the presence of a hitherto-undetected pathogen are more likely explanations.

Biochemistry

Many of the recent advances in the biochemistry of symbiotic N_2 fixation have been achieved with the aid of N^{15}. The lack of a suitable radioactive isotope for biological experimentation with nitrogen makes the use of the stable isotope obligatory for all tracer studies. Although the equipment needed for measurement of the concentration or atom per cent excess of N^{15} is expensive, the fact that one can ascertain with accuracy nitrogen gains of less than 0.2 per cent of that present in the initial material makes N^{15} a useful biochemical tool.

One of the dramatic outcomes of the use of N^{15}-labeled N_2 is the tracing of the compounds formed as intermediates in the conversion of the gaseous form of the element into cellular proteins. Thus, a determination of the isotopically labeled amino acids in the nodular proteins following exposure of soybeans to N^{15}-N_2 for 6 hours reveals that glutamic acid contains the highest N^{15} content (35), results analogous to those obtained with the non-symbiotic N_2-fixing microorganisms. The likeliest pathway for the formation of glutamic acid from molecular nitrogen is by the intermediary formation of ammonia. The ammonia presumably combines with α-ketoglutaric acid.

$$N_2 \rightarrow NH_3 \xrightarrow[\substack{COOH \\ | \\ CO \\ | \\ (CH_2)_2 \\ | \\ COOH}]{+2H} \begin{array}{c} COOH \\ | \\ H_2NCH \\ | \\ (CH_2)_2 \\ | \\ COOH \end{array} + H_2O \qquad (I)$$

glutamic acid

When the nodules of alder are exposed to N^{15}-N_2 under similar circumstances, the highest label is found in citrulline while glutamic acid is the second most active constituent. *Myrica gale*, on the other hand, incorporates nitrogen from N_2 most readily into the amide nitrogen of glutamine. Since the nitrogen in citrulline as well as the amide of glutamine are readily generated from ammonia, it is possible that ammonia is the inorganic precursor for the incorporation of nitrogen into organic combination in non-legumes as well as in legumes (17, 18).

Once fixed, nitrogen is transported rapidly from the nodule to the remainder of the plant. After several hours, particularly in young legumes, the tagged nitrogen is detectable in the above-ground tissue. During the latter stages of development, more than 90 per cent of the N_2 fixed is found above the soil level. The compounds involved in the translocation are as yet unknown.

The fixation of molecular nitrogen is affected greatly by the composition of the gas phase. The rate of the symbiotic incorporation varies directly with the quantity of N_2 in the atmosphere until, at concentrations greater than 15 per cent, fixation is independent of the partial pressure of N_2. Further, the responsible enzyme system in red clover functions at half maximal velocity when the gas phase contains 5 per cent N_2 (23). Optimal for N_2 fixation by red clover is a gas phase containing 10 to 40 per cent O_2, and the rate of utilization declines at O_2 levels above 40 or below 10 per cent. The O_2 requirement is the same regardless of the nitrogen source of the plant, a fact which suggests that O_2 does not affect symbiotic N_2 utilization per se (33). It is apparent from the data cited that the quantities of O_2 and N_2 present in the atmosphere are most favorable for the transformation.

Nodules of legumes actively metabolizing N_2 are distinctly red in color because of the presence of an iron-containing substance

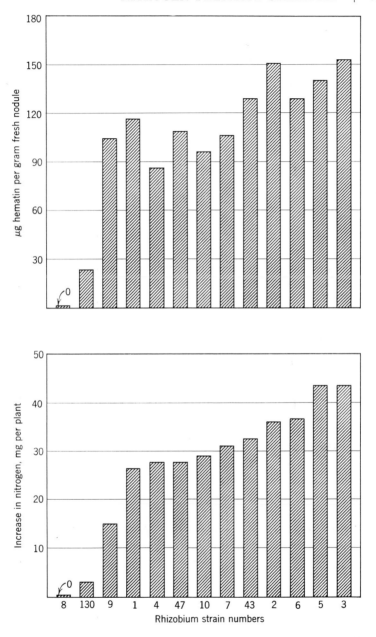

Figure 3. N₂ fixation and hematin content of pea plants inoculated with rhizobia of varying effectiveness (27).

known as *leghemoglobin*. In contrast, nodules produced by ineffective rhizobia have neither leghemoglobin nor red pigmentation. The degree of effectiveness, moreover, is correlated with the amount of leghemoglobin in the nodular tissue (figure 3). Consequently, it is possible by visual examination of the nodule contents to ascertain the relative capacity for active N_2 fixation or, by spectrophotometric determination of leghemoglobin concentration, to approximate bacterial efficiency. Because leghemoglobin is not found in rhizobium cells whether they be normal or bacteroids but only in the cytoplasm of root cells, the pigment is a plant rather than a microbial product. Yet, neither *Alnus* and *Myrica* nor the many non-symbiotic N_2 utilizers contain hemoglobin so that this material is associated exclusively with effectively nodulated legumes.

Because of its relationship to the N_2 metabolism of the Leguminosae, leghemoglobin has been the subject of considerable biochemical investigation. Its role is apparently not to stimulate *Rhizobium* spp. to utilize molecular nitrogen as all attempts to induce the bacteria to carry out the reaction in vitro in the presence of leghemoglobin have failed. There is likewise no evidence to favor the concept that the pigment, like animal hemoglobin, participates in O_2 transport. The report that N_2 oxidizes the leghemoglobin of soybean nodules is of importance, however, since it suggests a direct role for the hemoglobin in the nitrogen metabolism of the symbiotic association (11).

A considerable limitation imposed upon biochemical research has been the necessity of using the entire plant for critical investigations of the transformation. This limitation has been overcome recently by the finding that, with proper care and in short-term experiments, nodules excised from a wide variety of leguminous and non-leguminous plants still retain the capacity to incorporate N_2. This finding should provide a more direct means of investigating the biochemistry of nitrogen fixation by the symbiotic interaction of plant and microorganism.

REFERENCES

Reviews

Allen, E. K., and O. N. Allen. 1950. Biochemical and symbiotic properties of rhizobia. *Bacteriol. Rev.*, 14:273–330.

Bergersen, F. J. 1960. Biochemical pathways in legume root nodule nitrogen fixation. *Bacteriol. Rev.*, 24:246–250.

Hallsworth, E. G., ed. 1958. *Nutrition of the legumes.* Butterworth's Scientific Publications, London.

Nutman, P. S. 1956. The influence of the legumes in root-nodule symbiosis. *Biol. Rev.,* 31:109–151.

Wilson, P. W. 1957. On the sources of nitrogen of vegetation, etc. *Bacteriol. Rev.,* 21:215–226.

Wilson, P. W. 1940. *The biochemistry of symbiotic nitrogen fixation.* Univ. of Wisconsin Press, Madison.

Literature cited

1. Allen, O. N., and I. L. Baldwin. 1954. *Soil Sci.,* 78:415–427.
2. Allison, F. E., and C. A. Ludwig. 1939. *J. Am. Soc. Agron.,* 31:149–158.
3. Allos, H. F., and W. V. Bartholomew. 1959. *Soil Sci.,* 87:61–66.
4. Bond, G. 1951. *Ann. Botany,* 15:447–459.
5. Bond, G. 1957. *Ann. Botany,* 21:513–521.
6. Chailakhyan, M. Kh., and A. A. Megrabyan. 1958. *Dokl. Akad. Nauk Armyan S. S. R.,* 26:103–111.
7. Demolon, A., and A. Dunez. 1935. *Ann. Agron.,* 5:89–111.
8. Fahraeus, G., and H. Ljunggren. 1959. *Physiol. Plant.,* 12:145–154.
9. Ferguson, T. P., and G. Bond. 1953. *Ann. Botany,* 17:175–188.
10. Gardner, I. C. 1958. *Nature,* 181:717–718.
11. Hamilton, P. B., A. L. Shug, and P. W. Wilson. 1957. *Proc. Natl. Acad. Sci., U. S.,* 43:297–304.
12. Johnstone-Wallace, D. B. 1937. *Soil Sci. Soc. Am., Proc.,* 2:299–304.
13. Jones, F. R., and W. B. Tisdale. 1921. *J. Agric. Research,* 22:17–31.
14. Jordan, D. C., and C. L. San Clemente. 1955. *Canad. J. Microbiol.,* 1:668–674.
15. Katznelson, H., and J. K. Wilson. 1941. *Soil Sci.,* 51:59–63.
16. Kleczkowska, J. 1957. *Canad. J. Microbiol.,* 3:171–180.
17. Leaf, G., I. C. Gardner, and G. Bond. 1958. *J. Exptl. Botany,* 9:320–331.
18. Leaf, G., I. C. Gardner, and G. Bond. 1959. *Biochem. J.,* 72:662–667.
19. Lipman, J. G. 1910. *J. Agric. Sci.,* 3:297–300.
20. Mowry, H. 1933. *Soil Sci.,* 36:409–421.
21. Norris, D. O. 1959. *Empire J. Exptl. Agric.,* 27:87–97.
22. Sironval, C., C. Bonnier, and J. P. Verlinden. 1957. *Physiol. Plant.,* 10:697–707.
23. Umbreit, W. W., and P. W. Wilson. 1939. *Trans. 3rd Comm., Intl. Soc. Soil Sci.,* New Brunswick, A:29–31.
24. van Schreven, D. A. 1959. *Plant and Soil,* 11:93–112.
25. Vincent, J. M. 1954. *Austral. J. Agric. Research,* 5:55–60.
26. Virtanen, A. I. 1957. *Physiol. Plant.,* 10:164–169.
27. Virtanen, A. I., J. Erkama, and H. Linkola. 1947. *Acta Chem. Scand.,* 1:861–870.
28. Virtanen, A. I., J. Jorma, H. Linkola, and A. Linnasalmi. 1947. *Acta Chem. Scand.,* 1:90–111.
29. Walker, R. H., and P. E. Brown. 1935. *J. Am. Soc. Agron.,* 27:289–296.
30. Wilson, J. K. 1939. *J. Am. Soc. Agron.,* 31:159–170.
31. Wilson, J. K. 1944. *Soil Sci.,* 58:61–69.

32. Wilson, P. W., and E. B. Fred. 1939. *J. Am. Soc. Agron.*, 31:497–502.
33. Wilson, P. W., and E. B. Fred. 1937. *Proc. Natl. Acad. Sci., U. S.*, 23:503–508.
34. Wilson, P. W., and O. Wyss. 1937. *Soil Sci. Soc. Am., Proc.*, 2:289–297.
35. Zelitch, I., P. W. Wilson, and R. H. Burris. 1952. *Plant Physiol.*, 27:1–8.
36. Ziegler, H. 1958. *Ztschr. Naturforsch.*, 13b:297–301.

MINERAL TRANSFORMATIONS

20

Microbial Transformations of Phosphorus

Phosphorus is found in soil, plants, and in microorganisms in a number of organic and inorganic compounds. It is second only to nitrogen as a mineral nutrient required by both plants and microorganisms, its major physiological role being in certain essential steps in the accumulation and release of energy during cellular metabolism. Agronomically, this element may be added to soil in the form of

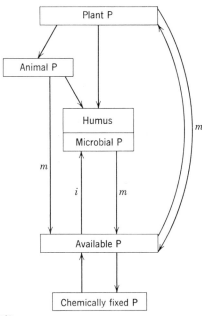

Figure 1. Mineralization (m) and immobilization (i) of phosphorus.

353

chemical fertilizers or it may be incorporated as plant or animal residues. Thus, phosphorus occupies a critical position both in crop production and in the biology of soil.

Microorganisms bring about a number of transformations of the element. These include: (a) altering the solubility of inorganic compounds of phosphorus; (b) mineralizing organic compounds with the release of orthophosphate; (c) converting the inorganic, available anion into cell protoplasm, an immobilization process analogous to that occurring with nitrogen; and (d) bringing about an oxidation or reduction of inorganic phosphorus compounds. Particularly important to the phosphorus cycle in nature are the microbial mineralization and immobilization reactions. By the continual interplay of the latter two processes, the availability of phosphorus, like that of nitrogen, is governed to no small degree. A general cycle of phosphorus may be visualized as shown in figure 1.

Chemistry of Soil Phosphorus

The chief source of organic phosphorus compounds entering the soil is the vast quantity of vegetation that undergoes decay. Agricultural crops commonly contain 0.05 to 0.50 per cent phosphorus in their tissues. In plants, this element is found in several compounds or groups of substances: phytin, phospholipids, nucleic acids and nucleoproteins, phosphorylated sugars, coenzymes, and related compounds. Phosphorus may also be present, especially in vacuoles and internal buffers, as inorganic orthophosphate.

In contrast with nitrogen and sulfur, for which the ions assimilated, nitrate or sulfate, are reduced within the cell to the amino ($-NH_2$) or sulfhydryl ($-SH$) functional groups, the plant does not reduce phosphate; this ion enters into organic combination largely unaltered. Thus, the phosphorus in phytin, phospholipids, and nucleic acids is found as phosphate. Phytin is the calcium-magnesium salt of phytic acid, the latter term being synonymous with inositol hexaphosphate.

phytic acid

Phospholipids are compounds in which phosphate is combined with a lipid. In the phosphatides, a class of phospholipids that includes lecithin and cephalin, the phosphate is esterified with a nitrogenous base. Lecithin, for example, is made up of glycerol, fatty acids, phosphate, and choline.

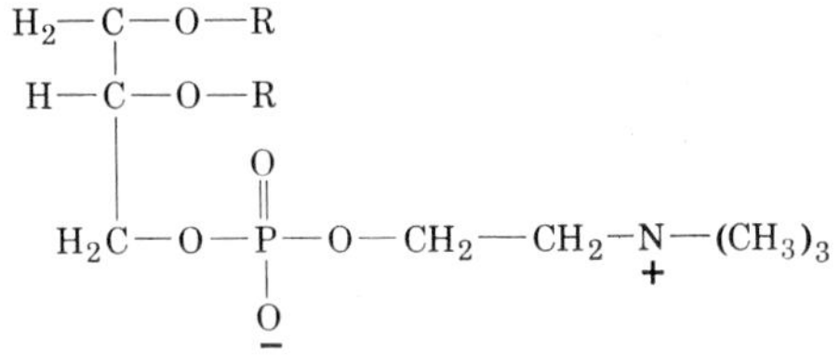

$$H_2-C-O-R$$
$$H-C-O-R$$
$$H_2C-O-\overset{\overset{O}{\|}}{\underset{\underset{O}{|}}{P}}-O-CH_2-CH_2-\overset{+}{N}-(CH_3)_3$$

lecithin–type compounds
(R: fatty acid)

Nucleoproteins are conjugates of proteins with nucleic acids, the molecule of the latter consisting of a number of purine and pyrimidine bases, a pentose sugar, and phosphate. There are two nucleic acids, ribonucleic acid (RNA) and deoxyribonucleic acid (DNA).

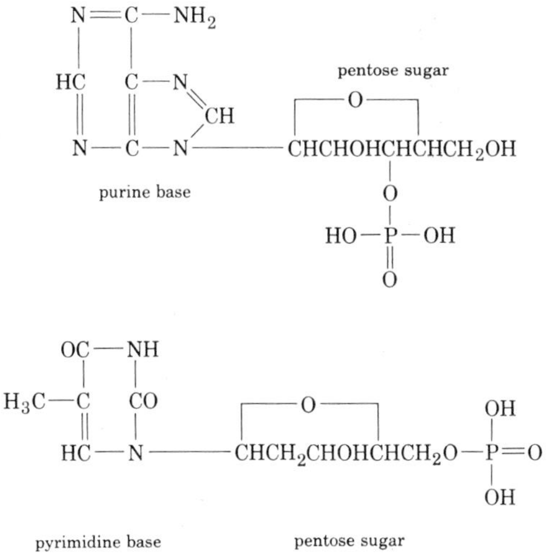

purine base

pentose sugar

$$CHCHOHCHCHCH_2OH$$
$$HO-\overset{\overset{O}{\|}}{P}-OH$$

pyrimidine base   pentose sugar

nucleotide units of RNA and DNA

The bulk of the phosphorus in the bacterial cell is in RNA, this nucleic acid usually accounting for one-third to one-half of all the phosphorus. Large quantities are found in acid-soluble compounds, both organic and inorganic, a total commonly of 15 to 25 per cent of the total cell phosphorus content. The acid-soluble fraction of bacterial protoplasm contains ortho- and metaphosphate, sugar phosphates, and many of the coenzymes and adenosine phosphates. The concentration of phospholipids in bacteria varies greatly, depending upon species and age of the microorganism, but phospholipids usually represent less than 10 per cent of the cell phosphorus. DNA contributes from 5 to 10 per cent of the total. Although there is no evidence for the presence in microorganisms of phytin, inositol phosphates may occur (11).

In soil, from 25 to 85 per cent of the total phosphorus is organic. The absolute quantity of organic phosphorus generally declines with increasing depth. At the same time, the proportion of total phosphorus that is organic is greater in surface than in subsurface horizons. Of the inorganic forms, large quantities occur in minerals wherein the phosphate is part of the mineral structure, as insoluble calcium, iron, or aluminum phosphates. The calcium salts predominate in neutral or alkaline conditions, the iron and aluminum salts in acid surroundings.

The organic compounds making up the humus fraction are derived from surface vegetation, microbial protoplasm, or metabolic products of the microflora. Thus, the components of humus are directly related to the constituents making up the tissues of plants and microorganisms or their derivatives. Of these substances, only phytin, the nucleic acids, and their derivatives seem to be part of the soil organic phosphorus fraction. Phospholipids may be present in low concentrations, but this material is never abundant. Phospholipids of the lecithin type comprise, at maximum, only about 0.5 to 2.5 per cent of the total organic phosphorus. Thus, within the limitations of present techniques, it seems that most of the phosphorus in humus is bound in inositol phosphates originating from phytin and in nucleic acids or degradation products thereof.

Phytin and related substances are estimated to constitute from as little as 25 to as much as 90 per cent of the soil organic phosphorus, the results varying with the analytical method and the soil under investigation. Despite these large amounts, phytin added to soil is mineralized very slowly, particularly in acid soils, so that plants derive little benefit from such amendments. Only at alkaline reactions is significant phytin phosphorus made available. The order of solubility of this compound in soil is low, and little appears in solution; inositol phosphates are known to react readily, with the formation of iron, aluminum, calcium, and magnesium salts, all having a poor solubility (10). Since phytin or inositol phosphates are relatively uncommon in microbial cell substance, their occurrence in soil indicates a plant origin.

The evidence for the existence of nucleic acids or nucleotide derivatives in soil is indirect. Typical of such results is the demonstration of purine and pyrimidine bases—constituents of the RNA and DNA molecules. Early reports suggested that nucleoproteins, nucleic acids, and nucleotides made up 20 to 60 per cent of the humus phosphorus, but recent data indicate that the early estimates were too high. In most localities, the nucleic acid–type compounds probably contribute less than 1 to a maximum of 10 per cent of the total organic phosphorus. As the microbial cell is rich in nucleic acids, it is possible that a reasonably large part of the nucleic acid in soil, which is undoubtedly primarily of the RNA type, is bound within the cells of viable members of the microflora. Once the cells die, the nucleic acids would be readily mineralized (2, 3).

At present, the balance sheet of organic phosphorus is far from complete. The known major components frequently do not account for the sum total of this substance. Other as yet unidentified compounds may be formed by microbial action or, alternatively, the inositol phosphates or nucleic acids may be modified to such an extent that existing analytical methods do not detect them.

Soils rich in organic matter contain abundant organic phosphorus. A good correlation, moreover, exists between the concentrations of organic phosphorus, organic carbon, and total nitrogen, almost all of the latter being organic (table 1). Ratios of organic carbon to organic phosphorus of 100 to 300:1 have been reported for mineral soils of many of the great soil groups. Similarly, the nitrogen:organic phosphorus ratio may range from 5 to 20 parts of nitrogen for each part of phosphorus; the ratio is commonly wider for virgin than for comparable cultivated land. The organic phosphorus level, therefore, is directly related to the concentration of other humus constituents, the phosphorus content being 0.3 to 1.0 and 5 to 20 per cent of the carbon and nitrogen concentration, respectively. It is interesting to note that the organic carbon:nitrogen:organic phosphorus ratio is 60:10:1 for the population developing in an acid soil and 45:11:1 for the microflora in a calcareous soil (21). These results are not inconsistent with the hypothesis that the relative constancy of the ratios in humus is governed by the composition and activities of the microflora. The higher relative carbon content in the soil organic fraction than in microbial tissue may result from resistant carbonaceous substrates remaining in the former. On the other hand, although microorganisms are the probable cause of these ratios approaching certain equilibrium values, it is not valid to conclude that any one of these

TABLE 1

Organic Phosphorus, Carbon, and Total Nitrogen in Several Iowa Soil Profiles (15)

Soil Type	Depth	Organic C	Total N	Organic P	C:N:P
	in.	%	%	%	
Carrington	0–6	2.40	0.20	0.0246	98:8.3:1
silt loam	6–9	2.28	0.20	0.0200	114:9.8:1
	12–15	1.43	–	0.0130	–
	18–21	0.81	0.076	0.0079	107:9.6:1
Grundy silt loam	0–6	2.84	0.21	0.0205	138:10.4:1
	6–10	2.36	0.16	0.0133	180:12.3:1
	14–18	1.64	0.12	0.0069	238:19.1:1
Garwin silty	0–5	5.11	0.41	0.0393	130:10.5:1
clay loam	5–14	1.74	0.12	0.0170	102:7.3:1
	14–22	0.68	0.06	0.0070	97:8.6:1

three constituents, carbon, nitrogen, or phosphorus, is present in soil largely or entirely in the cells of the microflora.

Much of the organic phosphorus in soil is not readily mineralized. This observation is unexpected because microbial enzymes usually degrade such compounds at a rapid rate. The slow decomposition in soil apparently results from adsorption of the phosphate-containing substrates. The removal of the compounds from solution is affected by soil texture, particularly by the clay in the sample. The more clay present, the greater is the adsorption. The type of adsorbent is also of importance, and certain clay minerals are more active in this regard than others. In addition, pH strongly affects the removal of the substrate from solution. Thus, the maximal adsorption of phytin takes place at pH 3.5 to 4.5 while the optimum for many other compounds is at 5.0 to 6.5. There is little adsorption at neutral to alkaline reactions (9).

Solubilization of Inorganic Phosphorus

Insoluble inorganic compounds of phosphorus are largely unavailable to plants, but many microorganisms can bring the phosphate into solution. This attribute is apparently not rare since one-tenth to one-half of the bacterial isolates tested are capable of solubilizing calcium phosphates. Species of *Pseudomonas, Mycobacterium, Micrococcus, Flavobacterium, Penicillium, Sclerotium, Aspergillus,* and others are active in the conversion. These bacteria and fungi grow in media with $Ca_3(PO_4)_2$, apatite, or similar insoluble materials as sole phosphate sources. Not only do the microorganisms assimilate the element but they also make a large portion soluble, releasing quantities in excess of their own nutritional demands. If the insoluble phosphate is suspended in an agar medium, the responsible strains are readily detected by the zone of clearing produced around the colony.

The major microbiological means by which insoluble phosphorus compounds are mobilized is by the production of organic acids. In the special case of the ammonium- and sulfur-oxidizing chemoautotrophs, nitric and sulfuric acids are responsible. The organic or inorganic acids convert $Ca_3(PO_4)_2$ to the di- and monobasic phosphates with the net result of an enhanced availability of the element to plants. The amount brought into solution by heterotrophs varies with the carbohydrate oxidized, and the transformation proceeds only if the carbonaceous substrate is one converted to organic acids.

Nitric or sulfuric acids produced during the oxidation of nitrogenous materials or inorganic compounds of sulfur react with rock phosphate, thereby effecting an increase in soluble phosphate. Sulfur oxidation was at one time investigated extensively as a possible means of providing utilizable phosphates. In the *Lipman process*, a compost is prepared of soil, manure, elemental sulfur, and rock phosphate; as the sulfur is oxidized to sulfuric acid by *Thiobacillus* spp., there is a parallel increase in acidity and a net release of soluble phosphate. Nitrification of ammonium salts also leads to a slight but significant liberation of soluble phosphorus from rock phosphate composts. Biological sulfur or ammonium oxidation has never been adopted on a commercial scale because of the availability of cheaper and more efficient means of preparing fertilizers. The studies of sulfur oxidation and nitrification have demonstrated, however, that chemoautotrophic reactions can release insoluble phosphorus.

Although phosphate solubilization commonly requires acid production, a second mechanism may account for ferric phosphate mobilization. In this instance, certain bacteria liberate hydrogen sulfide, which reacts with ferric phosphate to yield ferrous sulfide, liberating the phosphate (19). Likewise, phosphate is released from iron and

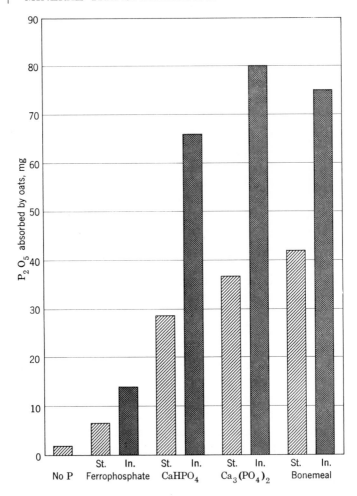

Figure 2. Phosphorus uptake by oats grown in sterile (St.) and in infected (In.) quartz sand. Inoculum: 1 per cent non-sterile soil (8).

aluminum phosphates when the environment becomes O_2-deficient. An explanation for the latter process is lacking.

Soil contains large numbers of phosphate-dissolving microorganisms. The population is especially abundant in the root zone, wherein the biochemical activities of the microflora may appreciably enhance phosphate assimilation by higher plants. The data cited in figure 2 demonstrate that the yield of oats grown in sterile and non-sterile conditions with the addition of phosphorus as ferrophosphate, $CaHPO_4$, $Ca_3(PO_4)_2$, and bonemeal is consistently greater in infected than in non-infected pots, the microorganisms solubilizing the added phosphate. Similar studies have been reported for other plants and for other inorganic phosphorus sources. Hence, it is probable that phosphate-dissolving microorganisms are of significance in the root zone of plants.

Mineralization of Organic Phosphorus

The existence in soil of a large reservoir of organic phosphorus that cannot be utilized by plants emphasizes the role of microorganisms in converting the organic phosphorus to inorganic forms. By their actions, the bacteria, fungi, and actinomycetes make the bound element in crop residues and soil organic matter available to succeeding generations of plants.

Mineralization is generally more rapid in virgin soils than in their cultivated counterparts. Not only is the total amount mobilized greater in virgin areas but the percentage of total organic phosphorus that is mineralized is higher in virgin than in cultivated land. The decomposition is likewise favored by warm temperatures. Below 30°C, the net release of mineral phosphate responds slightly to increases in temperature. Above 30°C, the rate of breakdown is markedly influenced by rising temperature (20); that is, the thermophilic range is more favorable than the mesophilic range. However, the net quantity of phosphate released does not necessarily parallel mineralization because immobilization rates are altered by temperature as well.

The rate of mineralization is enhanced by adjusting the pH to values conducive to general microbial metabolism, and a shift from acidity to neutrality increases phosphate release. Further, the rate of mineralization is directly correlated with the quantity of substrate; hence, soils rich in organic phosphorus will be the most active. However, for a constant content of humus-phosphorus, the amount of bound phosphorus that is decomposed is positively associated with pH (22). Of the added organic sources, nucleic acids are dephosphorylated most readily, phytin is the slowest to be degraded, while

TABLE 2

**Mineralization of the Phosphorus in Several Organic Substrates
by the Soil Microflora (14)**

Soil Amendment	Organic P	ppm Acid-Soluble Inorganic P			
		0 Days	5 Days	45 Days	90 Days
	%				
Untreated soil	–	24.0	27.0	30.5	33.0
Oat straw	0.060	44.5	45.5	52.5	49.0
Alfalfa	0.115	47.0	43.5	47.5	48.0
Soybean meal	0.526	28.5	32.0	41.5	45.5
RNA	7.80	25.5	79.0	56.0	62.5
Phytin	19.10	25.5	24.0	40.0	65.0

the rate of lecithin breakdown is intermediate between the two. Some typical data are presented in table 2. Bacterial cell phosphorus is mineralized quickly, and its acid-soluble organic phosphorus, phospholipid, and DNA are dephosphorylated in a short period. Phosphorus in microbial RNA is released more slowly (4).

The mineralization and immobilization of this element are related to the analogous reactions of nitrogen. As a rule, phosphate release is most rapid under conditions favoring ammonification. Thus, a highly significant correlation is observed between the rates of nitrogen and phosphorus conversion to inorganic forms, the nitrogen mineralized being from 8 to 15 times the amount of phosphate made available. There is also a correlation between carbon (CO_2 release) and phosphorus mineralization, a ratio of ca. 100 to 300:1 (22). These results show that the ratio of C:N:P mineralized microbiologically at the equilibrium condition is similar to the ratios of these three elements in humus.

The finding of phytin derivatives as well as phytin itself in the soil organic fraction suggests that a breakdown of the inositol hexaphosphate takes place. The enzyme phytase liberates phosphate from phytic acid or its calcium magnesium salt, phytin, with the accumulation of inositol.

phytic acid → inositol

$$\text{phytic acid} + 6H_2O \longrightarrow \text{inositol} + 6H_3PO_4 \quad (I)$$

Phytase activity is widespread and is enhanced by carbonaceous materials that increase the size of the microbial population. Species
of *Aspergillus, Penicillium, Rhizopus, Cunninghamella, Arthrobacter,*
and *Bacillus* can synthesize the enzyme. Yet, despite the great phytase potential, phytin is not readily metabolized in soil. The hydrolysis apparently is not limited by the phytase-producing capacity
of microorganisms, which is appreciable, but by the small amount of
phytic acid in the soil solution. The fact that phytate-phosphorus is
relatively unavailable to crops growing in acid soils when compared
with neutral environments is thus not a result of insufficient phytase
synthesis but rather is a consequence of the small amount of phytic
acid in the soluble phase of acid soils where the substrate is bound
into iron and aluminum complexes.

Pure nucleic acids added to soil are rapidly dephosphorylated.
Indeed, a large population can develop in media containing nucleotides as the sole sources of carbon, nitrogen, and phosphorus. The
mineralization is affected by pH, and the rate declines as the acidity
increases (14). If the major reserves of phosphorus in humus are
phytin and nucleic acids, it would seem that the latter is the more
active fraction in mobilization and immobilization reactions because
phytin is relatively resistant to decay while the nucleic acids are
highly susceptible to microbial attack.

Attempts have been made to exploit microbiological phosphate
release. When organisms known as phosphobacteria are inoculated
into soil or on the seeds of several crop plants, there allegedly are remarkable increases in yield and in phosphorus content of the crop
harvested (16, 24). Oats, wheat, millet, corn, and soybeans are
claimed to benefit from the inoculation. The use of bacterial fertilizers of this type may prove to be agronomically sound, but further
field investigations are required with adequate statistical controls.
It would be surprising, nevertheless, to find that inoculation without
soil amendment alters the microbial equilibrium to such an extent

that phosphorus uptake is enhanced. Inoculation per se rarely leads to the establishment of a new population.

Immobilization

Microbial growth requires the presence of available forms of phosphorus. Because this element is essential for cell synthesis, the development of the microflora is governed by the quantity of utilizable phosphorus compounds in the habitat. In environments where phosphorus is limiting, its addition will therefore stimulate microbiological activities. Deficiencies are not frequently encountered although they may be induced artificially by the addition of carbohydrates. By and large, phosphate amendments have little effect upon the microflora since the microscopic inhabitants appear to be highly efficient in mobilizing the large, natural reservoir of the element.

The assimilation of phosphorus into microbial nucleic acids, phospholipids, or other protoplasmic substances leads to the accumulation of non-utilizable forms of the element. Hence, during the decomposition of organic matter added to soil, the increase in the population size puts a great demand on the phosphate supply. Consequently, should the carbonaceous residue be deficient in phosphorus, the microbial assimilation of available phosphate may depress crop yields; such decreases in yield can be prevented by the application of phosphatic fertilizers. As the decomposition of phosphorus-deficient substrates proceeds, the percentage of phosphorus in the decaying residue increases, but the organic N:organic P ratio generally remains at approximately 10:1 (5).

Phosphorus, like nitrogen, is therefore both mineralized and immobilized. The process that predominates is governed by the percentage of phosphorus in the plant residues undergoing decay and the nutrient requirements of the responsible population. Should the concentration exceed that required for microbial nutrition, the excess appears as inorganic phosphate; if inadequate for the microflora, the net effect is one of immobilization. Consequently, in the decomposition of substrates poor in phosphorus or which have a wide C:P ratio, a portion of the available nutrient supply is immobilized from the surroundings. As the ratio narrows with time because of CO_2 volatilization, phosphate will be formed.

There have been many studies of the mineral composition of

bacterial and fungus cells. Commonly, phosphorus accounts for 0.5 to 1.0 per cent of fungus mycelium and 1.5 to 2.5 per cent of the dry weight of bacteria and probably of actinomycetes. Not infrequently, however, microorganisms exhibit a luxury consumption in culture media; i.e., they assimilate excessive quantities, so that the values reported from cultural studies are undoubtedly too high for organisms growing in nature. Consider a hypothetical case of organic matter decomposition in which 100 parts of carbonaceous material containing 40 per cent carbon are acted upon by fungal, bacterial, and actinomycete populations. Using the phosphorus composition of microorganisms cited above and assuming further that 30 to 40, 5 to 10, and 15 to 30 per cent of the substrate carbon is assimilated during decomposition by the fungi, bacteria, and actinomycetes, respectively, then the following calculations present a first approximation to the critical phosphorus content of organic materials:

$0.40 \times 100 = 40$ parts substrate C added

Fungi
   $(0.30$ to $0.40) \times 40 = 12$ to 16 parts cell C formed
   Fungi commonly contain 50 per cent C
      hence $(12$ to $16)/0.50 = 24$ to 32 parts fungal mass
   $(0.005$ to $0.01) \times (24$ to $32) = 0.12$ to 0.32 parts of P required
      per 100 parts of organic matter

Similar calculations give values of 0.06 to 0.20 and 0.18 to 0.60 parts of phosphorus needed for the decomposition of 100 parts of substrate by bacteria and actinomycetes.

In actual trials in culture media containing glucose as the carbohydrate source, *Aspergillus niger* assimilates 0.24 to 0.40 parts, *Streptomyces* sp. assimilates 0.27 to 0.63, while the figures for a mixed soil flora range from 0.16 to 0.36 parts of phosphorus for each 100 parts of glucose oxidized. With a carbohydrate like cellulose, from 0.35 to 0.45 parts of phosphorus are assimilated by the microflora for each 100 parts of cellulose (6, 12). A value of 0.3 may be taken as an average figure for aerobic conditions provided the substrate is readily and completely metabolized. Anaerobically, micoorganisms derive less energy from decomposition and, consequently, less tissue is synthesized; hence, less phosphate need be immobilized for the same quantity of fermentable carbon.

Although an approximation of 0.3 per cent may be generally valid for simple organic molecules, that is, phosphorus equivalent to

0.3 per cent of the weight of the organic compound is required for the population to develop to its full extent, not all the carbon in natural products is readily available. In the decomposition of natural substrates, the quantity of phosphorus immobilized is diminished because less of the total carbon is degraded in a finite time interval. As a consequence, the amount of phosphorus immobilized during the decomposition of plant residues is closer to 0.2 per cent of the dry weight of the organic matter. Therefore, the critical level of phosphorus in natural carbonaceous products which serves as a balance point between immobilization and mineralization is ca. 0.2 per cent (table 3). If the substrate contains more phosphorus than the critical level, some is released. If the material has less than the critical level, less than needed by the microflora, phosphorus disappears from the environment as the net effect is one of immobilization. On the other hand, as the phosphorus-poor organic matter is decomposed and the phosphorus content of the residue increases, a point is eventu-

TABLE 3

Influence of Phosphorus Content of Straw Residues Applied to Mohave Clay Loam on Phosphorus Uptake by Ryegrass (7)

P Content of Straw Residue	Yield of Ryegrass	P in Ryegrass	Total P Absorbed
%	g/pot	%	mg/pot
0.08	1.0	0.08	1.0
0.11	1.1	0.09	1.0
0.14	1.3	0.08	1.0
0.16	1.7	0.08	1.4
0.17	1.9	0.09	1.7
0.19	1.8	0.12	2.2
0.23	1.8	0.18	3.2
0.39	2.0	0.21	4.2
0.42	2.8	0.22	6.2
0.48	2.5	0.27	6.8
0.58	2.7	0.31	8.4
Unamended soil	1.5	0.21	3.2

ally reached when the 0.2 per cent figure is exceeded, and phosphate reappears.

As long as there is decay and microbial cell synthesis, both mineralization and immobilization are taking place. The phosphorus content governs not the absence of one or the other transformation but rather the greater rate of uptake or release of the nutrient. Nevertheless, few crop residues or animal manures bring about a net phosphorus immobilization. Only straw and certain similar materials are causes of biological phosphorus depletion (13). Because most plants contain 40 to 45 per cent carbon on a dry weight basis, mineralization will be the net effect when the C:P ratio of crop remains is less than about 200:1 while immobilization predominates during the initial stages of decomposition when the C:P ratio of the added organic matter is greater than approximately 300:1.

The relatively constant organic C:organic P ratio in soil organic matter may be associated with the comparatively fixed phosphorus demand by the microflora for each unit of organic matter metabolized. Likewise, the N:P ratios for humus and for microbial protoplasm are essentially identical at ca. 10:1. These observations on the composition of humus and of microbial cells are in conformity with the tenfold differences in critical levels in the immobilization-mineralization balance for nitrogen and for phosphorus, approximately 2.0 and 0.2 per cent respectively.

Oxidation-Reduction Reactions

Phosphorus, like nitrogen, may exist in a number of oxidation states ranging from the -3 of phosphine, PH_3, to the oxidized state, $+5$, of orthophosphate. In contrast to nitrogen, however, little attention has been given to the inorganic transformations of phosphorus, but there is some evidence for biologically catalyzed changes in the oxidation state of this element too.

Biological oxidation of reduced phosphorus compounds was demonstrated by Adams and Conrad (1) who noted that phosphite added to soil disappears with a corresponding increase in the concentration of phosphate.

$$HPO_3^= \rightarrow HPO_4^= \tag{II}$$

The conversion is brought about microbiologically since the reaction is eliminated upon the addition of a biological inhibitor such as toluene. A number of heterotrophic bacteria, fungi, and actinomycetes utilize phosphite as sole phosphorus source in culture media and oxidize the phosphite within the cell to organic phosphate compounds. Bacteria utilize phosphate in preference to phosphite so that, in media containing both anions, the former disappears first. There is no evidence that the oxidation is capable of providing energy for the development of chemoautotrophic bacteria.

The possibility of the reverse process, a reductive pathway, has received somewhat more attention. When a soil sample is incubated anaerobically in a mannitol-$NH_4H_2PO_4$ medium, the phosphate disappears relatively rapidly. This decrease is not a result of assimilation, which can only account for a small proportion of the loss. Phosphate apparently is reduced to phosphite and hypophosphite, and phosphine may possibly be evolved in the transformation.

$$\underset{+5}{H_3PO_4} \xrightarrow{2H} \underset{+3}{H_3PO_3} \xrightarrow{2H} \underset{+1}{H_3PO_2} \xrightarrow{4H} \underset{\substack{-3 \text{ (oxidation} \\ \text{state)}}}{PH_3} \qquad (III)$$

In the presence of nitrate or sulfate, phosphate reduction is retarded since the nitrate and sulfate seem to be more readily utilized as electron acceptors. Moreover, pure cultures of *Clostridium butyricum* and *Escherichia coli* form phosphite and hypophosphite from orthophosphate (17, 23). The process seems analogous biochemically to denitrification or to the bacterial conversion of sulfate to sulfide. It is unlikely that the reduction takes place in well-aerated environments. This process may be only of limited practical significance even in wet paddy soils, but there is as yet too little information to provide definite answers.

REFERENCES

Reviews

Askinazi, D. L. 1958. The possible role of microorganisms in increasing the effectiveness of ground rock phosphate as a fertilizer. *Soviet Soil Sci.*, 1958:372–379.

Black, C. A., and C. A. I. Goring. 1953. Organic phosphorus in soils. In W. H. Pierre and A. G. Norman, eds., *Soil and fertilizer phosphorus in crop nutrition.* Academic Press, New York, pp. 123–152.

Pierre, W. H. 1948. The phosphorus cycle and soil fertility. *J. Am. Soc. Agron.*, 40:1–14.

Stanford, G., and W. H. Pierre. 1953. Soil management practices in relation to phosphorus availability and use. In W. H. Pierre and A. G. Norman, eds., *Soil and fertilizer phosphorus in crop nutrition.* Academic Press, New York, pp. 243–280.

Literature cited

1. Adams, F., and J. P. Conrad. 1953. *Soil Sci.*, 75:361–371.
2. Adams, A. P., W. V. Bartholomew, and F. E. Clark. 1954. *Soil Sci. Soc. Am., Proc.*, 18:40–46.
3. Anderson, G. 1958. *Soil Sci.*, 86:169–174.
4. Bartholomew, W. V., and C. A. I. Goring. 1948. *Soil Sci. Soc. Am., Proc.*, 13:238–241.
5. Chang, S. C. 1939. *Soil Sci.*, 48:85–99.
6. Chang, S. C. 1940. *Soil Sci.*, 49:197–210.
7. Fuller, W. H., D. R. Nielsen, and R. W. Miller. 1956. *Soil Sci. Soc. Am., Proc.*, 20:218–224.
8. Gerretsen, F. C. 1948. *Plant and Soil*, 1:51–81.
9. Goring, C. A. I., and W. V. Bartholomew. 1950. *Soil Sci. Soc. Am., Proc.*, 15:189–194.
10. Jackman, R. H., and C. A. Black. 1951. *Soil Sci.*, 72:179–186.
11. Jones, A. S., S. B. H. Rizvi, and M. Stacey. 1958. *J. Gen. Microbiol.*, 18: 597–606.
12. Kaila, A. 1949. *Soil Sci.*, 68:279–289.
13. Kaila, A. 1954. *Z. Pflanzernahr. Dung.*, 64:27–35.
14. Pearson, R. W., A. G. Norman, and C. Ho. 1941. *Soil Sci. Soc. Am., Proc.*, 6:168–175.
15. Pearson, R. W., and R. W. Simonson. 1939. *Soil Sci. Soc. Am., Proc.*, 4: 162–167.
16. Pikovskaia, R. I. 1948. *Mikrobiologiya*, 17:362–370.
17. Rudakow, K. J. 1929. *Zent. Bakteriol.*, II, 79:229–245.
18. Sokolov, D. F. 1944. *Priroda*, 5-6:105–107.
19. Sperber, J. I. 1957. *Nature*, 180:994–995.
20. Thompson, L. M., and C. A. Black. 1947. *Soil Sci. Soc. Am., Proc.*, 12:323–326.
21. Thompson, L. M., C. A. Black, and F. E. Clark. 1948. *Soil Sci. Soc. Am., Proc.*, 13:242–245.
22. Thompson, L. M., C. A. Black, and J. A. Zoellner. 1954. *Soil Sci.*, 77:185–196.
23. Tsubota, G. 1959. *Soil and Plant Food*, 5:10–15.
24. Uarova, V. N. 1956. *Dokl. Vsesoyuz Akad. Selskokhoz. Nauk im. V.I. Lenina*, 21(6):22–26.

21

Microbial Transformations of Sulfur

Sulfur is an essential nutrient for members of the plant and animal kingdoms. Yet, despite its abundance in the earth's crust, sulfur is often present in soil in suboptimal quantities or in unavailable states so that responses to sulfur-containing fertilizers are not uncommon. The major reserve of the element in soil is the organic fraction, and the storehouse is only unlocked through biological decomposition. In the decomposition, there is a resemblance to the transformations affecting nitrogen availability, and the microscopic inhabitants are the sole agents converting the organic compounds of both elements into available, inorganic forms. The atmosphere also contains considerable sulfur from the burning of coal, the operation of factories, and from products of microbiological action in swamps.

Sulfur in its various organic and inorganic forms is readily metabolized in soil. The dominance of one or another transformation is governed to a large extent by the environmental circumstances that affect the composition and activity of the microflora. Four distinct processes can be delineated: (a) decomposition of organic sulfur compounds, a process in which large molecules are cleaved to smaller units and the latter in turn converted to inorganic compounds; (b) microbial assimilation or immobilization of simple compounds of sulfur and their incorporation into bacterial, fungal, or actinomycete cells; (c) oxidation of inorganic compounds such as sulfides, thiosulfate, polythionates, and elemental sulfur; and (d) reduction of sulfate and other anions to sulfide.

The individual steps and generalized reactions of the biological sulfur cycle are presented diagrammatically in figure 1. The earth's

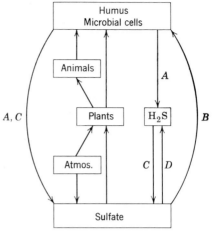

Figure 1. The sulfur cycle.

A. Mineralization   C. Sulfur oxidation
B. Immobilization   D. Sulfate reduction

vegetation gets the bulk of its sulfur from sulfate, but some may be obtained directly from the atmosphere. Animals, on the other hand, satisfy their demand for the element by feeding upon plants or other animals. When incorporated into soil, the proteins of plant and animal tissues are hydrolyzed by the microflora to the amino acid stage. Sulfate and sulfide in turn accumulate following the microbiological attack upon the amino acids and other sulfur-containing molecules. In aerated environments, the combined sulfur is ultimately metabolized to sulfate. Under waterlogged or other anaerobic circumstances, H_2S accumulates. Sulfide accumulation results in part from sulfate reduction and in part from the mineralization of organic sulfur. Between sulfide and sulfate in both the oxidative and reductive sequences are several intermediates, but these do not persist for extended periods, and their concentration in nature is usually low.

The transformations of sulfur resemble in many ways the microbial conversions of nitrogen. Since both elements are constituents of protoplasm, they must be assimilated during proliferation. Likewise, both nitrogen and sulfur are largely in organic combination in soil, and microbiological decomposition is therefore required to make the elements available. Inorganic sulfur compounds are oxidized in a fashion analogous to the nitrification of ammonium and nitrite, and the conditions necessary for the reduction of sulfate are essentially identical with those for nitrate. The similarity is not limited to environmental factors but extends also to the physiology and biochemistry of the responsible organisms.

Soil Sulfur

Sulfur enters the soil in the form of plant residues, animal wastes, chemical fertilizers, and rainwater. The element is also found as sulfide in several primary minerals. Occasionally, elemental sulfur is deliberately added for the control of certain plant pathogens or in the reclaiming of alkali soils. The quantity of volatile sulfur compounds returned to the earth's surface varies considerably. Figures for sulfur derived from the atmosphere range from 1 lb in parts of Africa, Australia, and New Zealand to more than 100 lb per acre per year in industrialized sections of Europe and the United States.

A large part of the sulfur in the soil profile is in organic combination, usually half to three-fourths. The inorganic sulfate concentration is invariably low, typically accounting for less than one-tenth of the total sulfur present. A common characteristic of virgin as well as cultivated land is the ratio between organic sulfur, carbon, and nitrogen. Considering sulfur as unity, the C:S ratio of the organic fraction is approximately 100:1, and the total N:organic S ratio is approximately 10:1 in different soils and in the several horizons at a single site (7, 24). Experimentally observed values, however, may range up to two-fold greater or less for the C:organic S or the N:organic S ratios.

Little is known of the chemistry of humus sulfur, but the soil organic fraction probably contains amino acids derived from proteins of microbial cells and plant tissues. The sulfur-containing amino acids are cystine, cysteine, and methionine. The organic fraction may also contain ethereal sulfates, thiourea, glucosides, and alkaloids originating in the tissues of plants, microorganisms, and animals. Sulfates dominate the inorganic fraction providing that aeration is adequate, but sulfides, elemental sulfur, thiosulfate, and tetrathionate have also been observed.

Mineralization

Sulfur is taken up by the plant root system largely as the sulfate ion although several amino acids may be assimilated without prior degradation. Atmospheric sulfur dioxide supplies some of the element as well. Within plant tissues, however, the sulfate is reduced to the sulfhydryl (—SH) form. Since agricultural crops and other vegetation require for growth the sulfate found in their rooting medium, the mineralization of organic sulfur plays an important part in the microbiological reactions required for higher life.

A diverse group of organic compounds containing sulfur are presented as substrates to the microflora. The element occurs in plant, animal, and microbial proteins in the amino acids, cystine and methionine, and in the B vitamins, thiamine, biotin, and thioctic acid. It is also found in the tissues and excretory products of animals as free sulfate, taurine and, to some extent, as thiosulfate and thiocyanate.

Cystine	$HOOCCHNH_2CH_2SSCH_2CHNH_2COOH$
Cysteine	$HSCH_2CHNH_2COOH$
Methionine	$H_3CSCH_2CH_2CHNH_2COOH$
Taurine	$H_2NCH_2CH_2SO_2OH$
Thiosulfuric acid	$HSSO_3H$
Thiocyanic acid	$HSCN$

Upon the addition to soil of plant or animal remains, the sulfur contained therein is mineralized. A portion of the inorganic products is utilized by the microflora for cell synthesis, and the remainder is released into the environment. Aerobically, the terminal, inorganic product is sulfate. In the absence of atmospheric O_2, particularly during the putrefaction of proteinaceous matter, H_2S and the odoriferous mercaptans accumulate. The ability to form H_2S from partially degraded proteins is a property common to many genera of bacteria. Hence, it is likely that sulfides are among the major inorganic substances released during the decomposition of proteinaceous substrates.

The sulfur in cystine and cysteine is recovered quantitatively as sulfate when either of these amino acids is applied to well-aerated soils. The conversion is rapid because many microorganisms attack the two compounds. The decomposition may proceed by any one of several known mechanisms. In soil, cystine can be formed by a chemical oxidation of added cysteine. The sulfur of the molecule in turn is oxidized to sulfate with cystine disulfoxide and possibly cysteine sulfinic acid as intermediates, a reaction sequence not involving H_2S (9).

$$\text{cysteine} \xrightarrow{\text{chem.}} \text{cystine} \rightarrow \text{cystine disulfoxide} \rightarrow$$

R-SH R-S-S-R R-SO-OS-R

$$(\text{cysteine sulfinic acid}) \rightarrow \text{sulfate} \quad (I)$$

R-SO₂H

In pure culture, many bacteria bring about a desulfhydration of cysteine by means of the enzyme cysteine desulfhydrase, which liberates equimolar quantities of pyruvic acid, H_2S and NH_3.

$$HSCH_2CHNH_2COOH + H_2O \rightarrow CH_3COCOOH + H_2S + NH_3 \quad (II)$$

Alternatively, fungi such as *Microsporeum gypseum* convert cysteine-sulfur to sulfate by a mechanism possibly involving the consecutive formation of cystine, the sulfenic and sulfinic acids, sulfite and sulfate (19). Other pathways have been reported for bacteria, but the distribution of the active species in nature is not known.

The transformation of methionine frequently proceeds in an entirely different manner. Sulfate is sometimes produced when this amino acid is applied to soil, but often none is detected since the decomposition proceeds largely by way of volatile compounds. The added sulfur is lost through volatilization of methyl mercaptan, CH_3SH, and dimethyl disulfide, CH_3SSCH_3. A similar conversion has been shown in culture media with species of *Microsporeum*, *Scopulariopsis*, and *Aspergillus* (8, 19), but other fungi can form

TABLE 1

Production of Sulfate from Organic Sulfur Compounds in Nixon Sandy Loam (8)

Compound	Organic S Applied	S Recovered as Sulfate, %		
		1 wk	10 wk	21 wk
	ppm			
Cystine	2670	28	63	85
Na taurocholate	600	74	89	102
Thiamine	950	1	62	65
Thiourea	4210	1	7	9
Sulfanilic acid	1680	2	0	0
Mercaptoethanol	4100	0	0	4
NH₄ sulfamate	2810	0	0	0

sulfate from methionine. Although bacteria of many genera produce H_2S readily from peptone, cystine, and cysteine in culture, methionine is characteristically more resistant to attack. In soil, there is also a fairly rapid mineralization of thiamine and taurocholate while thiourea, mercaptoethanol, and other compounds are slowly oxidized (table 1).

As in the ammonification of organic nitrogen, the extent of mineral sulfur formation is influenced by the sulfur content and the C:S ratio of the decomposing substrate. Sulfate accumulates only when the sulfur level in the organic matter exceeds the microbial needs. In lieu of precise data, it is likely that the percentage of sulfur mineralized per annum is similar to the figure for nitrogen, i.e., some 1 to 3 per cent of the total supply in soils of the humid-temperate zone. Therefore, in a field containing 0.02 per cent sulfur in the A horizon largely in organic combination, some 4 to 12 lb may be mineralized per acre per year. It is also likely that environmental factors that govern microbial growth in general would affect the rate of sulfur mineralization.

Microbial Assimilation

Many compounds serve as sulfur sources for microbial growth though any single strain may be limited to a few substances. Among the materials that may supply this element are sulfate, hyposulfite, sulfoxylate, thiosulfate, persulfate, sulfide, elemental sulfur, sulfite, tetrathionate, and thiocyanate of the inorganic substances and cysteine, cystine, methionine, taurine, and undecomposed proteins of the organic group. Sulfate is commonly included in culture media, but this anion is not known to be produced in environments devoid of O_2 so that anaerobes in soil probably assimilate reduced sulfur compounds. The sulfur content of most microorganisms lies between 0.1 and 1.0 per cent of the dry weight, and the most conspicious cellular constituents containing the element are the amino acids, cystine and methionine.

The microbiological immobilization of nitrogen is frequently of concern in field practice, but deficiencies of sulfur arising in the same way are uncommon. In greenhouse experiments, however, a deficiency can be induced in soil by treatment with readily metabolized carbohydrates. For example, the addition of starch to a sulfur-poor soil depresses crop yields, but the reduction in yield is prevented if sulfates are applied (5). The detrimental effect is probably a result of microbial utilization of the available sulfur during the decomposition of the starch, leading to an immobilization of the nutrient. As long as there is less sulfur in the organic matter than required for microbial proliferation, immobilization will be dominant; when the element is in excess, mineral sulfur will be liberated as a waste product. The critical C:S ratio in carbonaceous materials above which immobilization is dominant to mineralization is reported to be approximately 50:1 (2).

Inorganic Sulfur Oxidation

The inorganic compounds of sulfur that are transformed biologically represent various oxidation states from -2 of sulfide to $+6$ of sulfate. Not all of the reactions in soil are enzymatic, and many individual steps are non-biological. In soil, sulfides, elemental sulfur, and thiosulfate can be oxidized slowly by chemical means, but the microbiological oxidation is far more rapid when conditions are favorable (figure 2). At near-optimum moisture and temperature, chemical changes are insignificant in comparison to microbiological conversions.

Bacteria which oxidize inorganic sulfur compounds are usually obligate or facultative autotrophs, but certain heterotrophic fungi and bacteria also participate in the process. The bacteria utilizing inorganic sulfur compounds for energy are physiologically and morphologically diverse. They vary in shape from short rods to long filaments, and their metabolism ranges from aerobic to anaerobic. The sulfur oxidizers can be divided into four groups: (a) non-filamentous, chemoautotrophic bacteria of the genus *Thiobacillus*; (b) heterotrophic bacteria, fungi, and actinomycetes; (c) thread-forming bacteria represented by *Beggiatoa*, *Thiothrix*, *Thioplaca*, and others; and (d) photosynthetic green and purple sulfur bacteria. Of these, only the first two groups are prominent in soil. The filamentous forms are common in muds and possibly in flooded soil from which H_2S is evolved while the photosynthetic bacteria are largely aquatic.

The genus *Thiobacillus* contains nine species. Of these, five have been the subjects of considerable investigation. *T. thiooxidans* is a strict chemoautotroph which oxidizes elemental sulfur and is capable of active growth at pH 3.0. *T. thioparus*, on the other hand, is an acid-sensitive, obligate chemoautotroph. *T. novellus* cannot use elemental

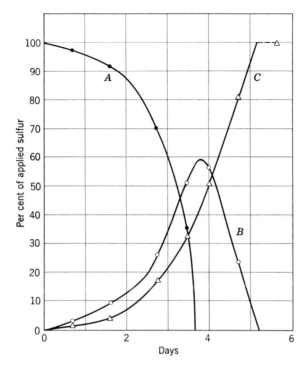

Figure 2. Oxidation of thiosulfate in soil. A: thiosulfate; B: tetrathionate; C: sulfate (10).

sulfur but will oxidize organic compounds as well as inorganic sulfur salts. The common species able to develop in the absence of O_2, *T. denitrificans*, uses nitrate as the electron acceptor in anaerobic conditions. The distinguishing trait of *T. ferrooxidans*, the fifth species, is its ability to use the oxidation of either ferrous or sulfur salts for energy. Elemental sulfur, sulfide, thiosulfate, tetrathionate, and thiocyanate serve as energy sources for one or more members of the genus, and CO_2 or bicarbonate supplies the carbon for chemoautotrophic growth.

Thiobacillus spp. are non-spore-forming, gram negative rods which are commonly 1 to 3 μ long and about 0.5 μ in diameter. Motility occurs in most species, and movement is by means of polar flagella. In their general morphological characteristics, the thiobacilli resemble the pseudomonads, but they differ by their chemoautotrophic nutrition. With the exception of *T. novellus*, the aforementioned species are obligate autotrophs, deriving no energy from the oxidation of organic carbon. *T. thioparus*, moreover, is distinctive in its ability to precipitate free sulfur at the surface of liquid media during the oxidation of thiosulfate. The pH optima also serve to distinguish the five species. The optimum for *T. thiooxidans* and *T. ferrooxidans* is at pH 2.0 to 3.5; the remaining three, *T. denitrificans*, *T. thioparus*, and *T. novellus*, prefer near-neutral or even slightly alkaline conditions.

Representatives of the group are generally obligate aerobes, the chief exception being *T. denitrificans*, which can utilize nitrate as the terminal electron acceptor. When grown thus anaerobically, the bacterium converts nitrate to gaseous nitrogen compounds and, at the same time, oxidizes thiosulfate or some other sulfur compound. There is also evidence that *T. thioparus* metabolizes thiosulfate anaerobically if nitrate is present (6). The latter organism, however, does not bring about volatilization of the nitrogen. In addition to the classical strains, thermophilic and halophilic variants of autotrophic thiobacilli are isolated with ease.

The following equations typify the transformations catalyzed by the thiobacilli:

T. thiooxidans and *T. novellus*

$$Na_2S_2O_3 + 2O_2 + H_2O \rightarrow 2NaHSO_4 \tag{III}$$

T. thioparus

$$5Na_2S_2O_3 + 4O_2 + H_2O \rightarrow 5Na_2SO_4 + H_2SO_4 + 4S \tag{IV}$$

$$Na_2S_4O_6 + Na_2CO_3 + \tfrac{1}{2}O_2 \rightarrow 2Na_2SO_4 + 2S + CO_2 \tag{V}$$

T. thiooxidans

$$S + 1\tfrac{1}{2}O_2 + H_2O \rightarrow H_2SO_4 \tag{VI}$$

T. denitrificans

$$5S + 6KNO_3 + 2H_2O \rightarrow K_2SO_4 + 4KHSO_4 + 3N_2 \tag{VII}$$

The abundance of chemoautotrophic sulfur-oxidizing bacteria can be measured by inoculating soil dilutions into mineral salts media containing inorganic sulfur compounds and observing the change in acidity. By such procedures, it has been shown that mineral soils usually have less than 100 or 200 thiobacilli per gram, but counts as high as 10,000 are occasionally encountered. In peats, the population is typically less than 500, and often 50 per gram is a maximum figure. The population, therefore, is never dense unless sulfur compounds are added deliberately.

Sulfur oxidation is not restricted to the genus *Thiobacillus*, for a number of other bacteria carry out the same transformation. These sulfur bacteria are found within six families of the class Schizomycetes.

I. Order Beggiatoales
    A. Beggiatoaceae. Cells occur within motile trichomes. Sulfur granules deposited in the trichomes. *Beggiatoa, Thiothrix, Thioplaca.*
    B. Leucotrichaceae. Sulfur may be deposited outside of cell. Not autotrophic. *Leucothrix.*
    C. Achromatiaceae. Globules of sulfur found within cells if sulfide present. Cells occur singly, not in trichomes. *Achromatium.*
II. Order Pseudomonadales
    A. Thiobacteriaceae. Non-filamentous, colorless bacteria oxidizing inorganic sulfur compounds. Chemoautotrophy not established. Elemental sulfur deposited either inside or outside of cell. *Thiobacterium.*
    B. Thiorhodaceae. Photoautotrophic, purple sulfur bacteria. Sulfur globules deposited in the presence of sulfides.
    C. Chlorobacteriaceae. Photoautotrophic, green sulfur bacteria. Sulfur globules usually deposited outside of cell.

Of the filamentous group, i.e., members of the Beggiatoales, only *Beggiatoa, Thiothrix,* and *Thioplaca* have been adequately investigated. Members of these three genera oxidize H_2S and, in the process, deposit elemental sulfur granules in the filaments. Despite the fact that the first sulfur-oxidizing bacterium described was *Beggiatoa* and that studies of this organism led Winogradsky (25) to propose the concept of chemoautotrophy, it is still not clear whether *Beggiatoa* indeed has an autotrophic nutrition. Possibly, the bacterium utilizes both inorganic and organic energy sources because several isolates have been cultivated upon organic nutrients. None of the genera of filamentous sulfur bacteria are present in well-aerated soils.

The autotrophy of the colored sulfur bacteria is dependent upon a source of light, and sulfur in these microorganisms participates in the photosynthetic reaction. The organisms are found in environments in which H_2S is released and light is available, and they are therefore of no importance in well-drained soils. In the presence of H_2S, the purple sulfur bacteria deposit sulfur within the cell, but the internal globules are converted to sulfate once the sulfides are gone. Many of the green sulfur bacteria carry the oxidation only to the free sulfur stage. The reactions may be expressed by equations VIII and IX.

$$CO_2 + 2H_2S \xrightarrow{\text{light}} (CH_2O) + 2S + H_2O \qquad \text{(VIII)}$$

$$2CO_2 + H_2S + 2H_2O \xrightarrow{\text{light}} 2(CH_2O) + H_2SO_4 \qquad \text{(IX)}$$

The oxidation of inorganic sulfur compounds is also carried out by a number of heterotrophic microorganisms. It is assumed that no energy is made available to the organism by such oxidations and that the transformations are incidental to the main metabolic pathways. For example, certain species of aerobic bacteria, actinomycetes, filamentous fungi, and yeasts oxidize powdered sulfur, and several heterotrophic bacteria convert thiosulfate to polythionates in the presence of organic nutrients (11, 17, 20). As a rule, these reactions are slower than the corresponding thiobacillus step. Filamentous fungi produce sulfate from organic substrates such as cystine, thiourea, methionine, and taurine; the active genera are represented by *Aspergillus, Penicillium,* and *Microsporeum,* but further investigation will undoubtedly disclose additional groups. The high rate of sulfate formation by fungi, the abundance and ubiquity of these organisms, and the few thiobacilli in many areas suggest that heterotrophs may be more important than chemoautotrophs in the production of sulfate from organic matter, but additional study is required.

In culture, a wide variety of inorganic sulfur compounds are metabolized by one or another microorganism. The same is true in vivo; for example, soils treated with colloidal sulfur, thiosulfate, trithionate, or tetrathionate form sulfate after an initial lag period lasting for several days. These reactions are biological as they are abolished by microbial inhibitors. Sulfides are readily oxidized in soil although this process may not be entirely microbiological because sulfides can be converted to elemental sulfur by chemical means. Dithionate, on the other hand, is resistant to attack by the microflora. It is interesting that tetrathionate appears prior to sulfate in soils perfused with thiosulfate (figure 2), an observation suggesting that tetrathionate is a naturally occurring intermediate in thiosulfate oxidation.

The oxidation of powdered sulfur produces considerable sulfuric acid, as shown by equation VI. The addition to soil of flowers of sulfur is essentially equivalent to sulfuric acid application, such is the activity of the thiobacilli. At high rates of application, the pH of a neutral soil may fall to as low as pH 2 after several months.

T. thiooxidans is usually the major organism responsible, but *T. thioparus* and *T. denitrificans* metabolize free sulfur as well.

The mechanism of chemoautotrophic sulfur oxidation still remains obscure. The great reactivity and chemical instability of many of the proposed intermediates make biochemical investigations difficult. Trudinger (22), however, has characterized an enzyme of one of the thiobacilli that converts thiosulfate directly to tetrathionate. Further, after exposure of the bacterium to S^{35}-thiosulfate for a 10-second period, all the metabolized thiosulfate is recovered as tagged tetrathionate. It thus seems that tetrathionate is an intermediate in the thiobacillus conversion of thiosulfate to sulfate.

$$2Na_2S_2O_3 + \frac{1}{2}O_2 + H_2O \rightarrow Na_2S_4O_6 + 2NaOH \qquad (X)$$

Other polythionates may be generated as well, and trithionate, $S_3O_6^=$, may be liberated during tetrathionate metabolism (23). The steps in the oxidation of elemental sulfur have not been investigated intensively; speculation has not been so retarded. One proposed pathway, advanced by Vishniac and Santer, is shown in figure 3.

There are several ways by which the thiobacilli can have a profound agricultural significance in addition to their possible role in the formation of the sulfate needed for plant nutrition. One such way is in the alteration of soil acidity to reduce the incidence or severity of potato scab or of the rot of sweet potatoes. These diseases are caused by acid-sensitive actinomycetes, *Streptomyces scabies* and *Streptomyces ipomoea* for the scab and rot, respectively. The diseases are not severe at reactions below ca. pH 5.0; therefore, the pathogens are often controlled by the addition of sulfur in quantities sufficient to bring the reaction to a point below the limiting level. With these streptomycete diseases, control is associated with the sulfuric acid formed by the thiobacilli. Similar treatments have been adapted to the

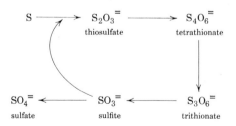

Figure 3. Biochemistry of chemoautotrophic sulfur oxidation.

reclamation of alkali land. If free sulfur is added to these soils, providing that thiobacilli are present, the sulfuric acid generated will neutralize the alkalinity and bring the soils into potential productivity. The corrosion of concrete may also result from the activities of *Thiobacillus* spp. Atmospheric H_2S is frequently the source of the element for the deterioration of concrete (15).

The oxidation of elemental sulfur causes a solubilization of soil minerals. The sulfuric acid formed reacts with minerals and other insoluble materials, leading to nutrient mobilization. Thus, the oxidation increases the quantity of soluble phosphate, potassium, calcium, manganese, aluminum, and magnesium (1). Indeed, manganese deficiency can be corrected by the application of sulfur or thiosulfate, treatments which increase the concentration of the divalent manganous ion. The composting together of colloidal sulfur, soil, and rock phosphate is one means of solubilizing phosphate, and composts of this type were at one time recommended for the preparation on the farm of available phosphate (14).

Reduction of Inorganic Sulfur Compounds

In soils that become deficient in O_2 as by flooding, the sulfide level increases to relatively high concentrations, often in excess of 150 ppm. At the same time, the sulfate concentration falls, and not infrequently a distinct zone of ferrous sulfide deposition appears in the profile. As these processes take place, there is a concomitant increase in the number of sulfate-reducing bacteria. The population of the sulfate reducers may become greater than several million per gram after about 2 weeks in wet paddy soils (21). Much of the sulfide that accumulates originates by sulfate reduction, but the mineralization of organic sulfur compounds leads to the same product.

The predominant microorganisms concerned with the reduction of sulfate are bacteria of the genus *Desulfovibrio*. Morphologically, the cells are curved rods that move about by means of a single polar flagellum. Physiologically, the bacteria are obligate anaerobes which produce H_2S from sulfate at a rapid rate. Although several species have been described, *Desulfovibrio desulfuricans* seems to be the most ubiquitous species in nature. Its pH range is narrow, and no growth occurs in media more acid than pH 5.5. This fact has a direct bearing on the lack of appreciable sulfide formation in many acid soils. At high temperatures, sulfates can still be converted to sulfides by the action of obligate anaerobes; the responsible organism, *Clostridium nigrificans,* differs from *D. desulfuricans* by its capacity to form endospores and its thermophilic habit. The mesophilic species has its optimum at approximately 30°C, the thermophile at about 55°C (4).

Desulfovibrio spp. use sulfite, sulfate, thiosulfate, tetrathionate, or colloidal sulfur but not atmospheric oxygen or organic sulfur compounds as electron acceptors for growth. The electron donors or energy sources for the reaction include a number of carbohydrates, organic acids, and alcohols.

$$2CH_3CHOHCOONa + MgSO_4 \rightarrow$$
$$H_2S + 2CH_3COONa + CO_2 + MgCO_3 + H_2O \quad (XI)$$

D. desulfuricans also utilizes molecular hydrogen as an energy source for growth. In the latter circumstance, the bacterium exhibits an autotrophic metabolism; hence, it is classified as a facultative autotroph which oxidizes either H_2 or organic substrates. Autotrophy is here determined by possession of the enzyme that activates H_2, hydrogenase, and by the utilization of inorganic rather than organic carbon. In its autotrophic nutrition, *D. desulfuricans* reduces sulfate, sulfite, and thiosulfate with the consumption of 4, 3, and 4 moles H_2 per mole of electron acceptor, respectively (16).

$$SO_4^= + 4H_2 \rightarrow S^= + 4H_2O \quad (XII)$$
$$SO_3^= + 3H_2 \rightarrow S^= + 3H_2O \quad (XIII)$$
$$S_2O_3^= + 4H_2 \rightarrow 2SH^- + 3H_2O \quad (XIV)$$

In addition to the anaerobic *Desulfovibrio* spp. and *Clostridium nigrificans,* there is evidence that *Bacillus megaterium* and *Pseudomonas zelinskii* liberate H_2S from sulfate (3, 18), but the significance of the latter two bacteria in soil has not been ascertained.

In spite of the few microorganisms adapted to reduce the most oxidized natural form of sulfur, sulfate, partially reduced inorganic sulfur compounds such as thiosulfate, tetrathionate, and sulfite are readily converted to sulfide by many bacteria, fungi, and actinomycetes. The active microorganisms are in no way unique, and numerous families and genera of aerobes and anaerobes are implicated. In each instance, an organic electron donor is required for the reduction of the inorganic sulfur compound.

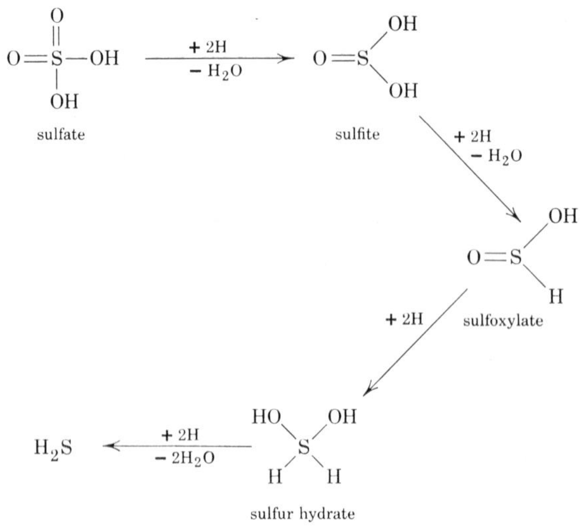

Figure 4. A pathway for sulfate reduction.

The mechanism of H_2S formation from sulfate has received scant attention. A likely mechanism involves the stepwise reduction via sulfite, sulfoxylate, and sulfur hydrate (figure 4). Provision must be made in any scheme for the microbial production of H_2S from thiosulfate and tetrathionate. A postulated biochemical pathway must also account for the finding of sulfites in addition to sulfides during the reduction of thiosulfate (12).

Microorganisms that reduce the availability of sulfate have a profound influence upon soil fertility because they diminish the supply of the major sulfur source for agricultural crops. Beyond this fact, however, the sulfate-reducing bacteria, chiefly *Desulfovibrio desulfuricans,* can have a great economic influence. Iron and steel pipes buried in the soil are frequently subjected to corrosion when the environment is anaerobic. The corrosion is associated not with iron bacteria but rather with *Desulfovibrio,* which, from sulfates, forms the sulfides that react with iron to yield ferrous sulfide. The organisms can completely destroy a $\frac{1}{5}$-in. pipe in a period of 7 to 8 years. Such anaerobic corrosion is particularly serious at about pH 7, but because of the acid-sensitivity of the sulfate-reducers, it is rarely a problem below pH 5.5. Deterioration is severe in areas that remain wet for long periods, especially in swampy sites. A similar corrosion occurs in submarine cables and in oil well equipment.

Sulfate-reducing bacteria also apparently participate in the formation of sulfur deposits. It is hypothesized that *Desulfovibrio* spp. form sulfide from sulfate, and then the sulfur is precipitated in the presence of O_2 either by chemical autooxidation or by biological means (13). Sulfides may also be implicated in the corrosion of stone and concrete, particularly in anaerobic tanks used for sewage treatment.

REFERENCES

Reviews

Butlin, K. R. 1953. The bacterial sulphur cycle. *Research (London)*, 6:184–191.

Starkey, R. L. 1950. Relations of microorganisms to transformations of sulfur in soils. *Soil Sci.*, 70:55–65.

Starkey, R. L. 1958. The general physiology of the sulfate reducing bacteria in relation to corrosion. *Producers Monthly*, 22(9):12–30.

Vishniac, W., and M. Santer. 1957. The thiobacilli. *Bacteriol. Rev.*, 21:195–213.

Walker, T. W. 1957. The sulphur cycle in grassland soils. *J. Brit. Grassland Soc.*, 12:10–18.

Literature cited

1. Ames, J. W. 1921. *Ohio Agric. Expt. Sta. Bull. 351.*
2. Barrow, N. J. 1958. *Nature*, 181:1806–1807.
3. Bromfield, S. M. 1953. *J. Gen. Microbiol.*, 8:378–390.
4. Campbell, L. L., Jr., H. A. Frank, and E. R. Hall. 1957. *J. Bacteriol.*, 73:516–521.
5. Conrad, J. P. 1950. *Soil Sci.*, 70:43–54.
6. De Kruyff, C. D., J. P. Van Der Walt, and H. M. Schwartz. 1957. *Ant. van Leeuw.*, 23:305–316.
7. Evans, C. A., and C. O. Rost. 1945. *Soil Sci.*, 59:125–137.
8. Frederick, L. R., R. L. Starkey, and W. Segal. 1957. *Soil Sci. Soc. Am., Proc.*, 21:287–292.
9. Freney, J. R. 1958. *Nature*, 182:1318–1319.
10. Gleen, H., and J. H. Quastel. 1953. *Applied Microbiol.*, 1:70–77.
11. Guittonneau, G. 1927. *Compt. Rend. Acad. Sci.*, 184:45–46.
12. Ishimoto, M., J. Koyama, and Y. Nagai. 1955. *J. Biochem. (Japan)*, 42:41–53.
13. Jones, G. E., and R. L. Starkey. 1957. *Applied Microbiol.*, 5:111–118.
14. Lipman, J. G., H. C. McLean, and H. C. Lint. 1916. *Soil Sci.*, 2:499–538.
15. Parker, C. D. 1945. *Austral. J. Exptl. Biol. Med. Sci.*, 23:81–90.
16. Postgate, J. R. 1949. *Nature*, 164:670–671.
17. Rippel, A. 1924. *Cent. Bakteriol.*, II, 62:290–295.
18. Shturm, L. D. 1948. *Mikrobiologiya*, 17:415–418.
19. Stahl, W. H., B. McQue, G. R. Mandels, and R. G. H. Siu. 1949. *Arch. Biochem.*, 20:422–432.

20. Starkey, R. L. 1934. *J. Bacteriol.*, 28:387–400.
21. Takai, Y., T. Koyama, and T. Kamura. 1956. *Soil and Plant Food,* 2:63–66.
22. Trudinger, P. A. 1959. *Biochim. Biophys. Acta,* 31:270–272.
23. Vishniac, W. 1952. *J. Bacteriol.*, 64:363–373.
24. Walker, T. W., and A. F. R. Adams. 1959. *Soil Sci.*, 87:1–10.
25. Winogradsky, S. 1887. *Botan. Zeitung,* 45:489–507.

22

Microbial Transformations of Iron

Despite the fact that it is only a minor nutrient for the growth of most of the microscopic life of the soil, iron is an element which readily undergoes transformation through the activity of the microflora. Iron is always abundant in terrestrial habitats, and it is one of the major constituents of the earth's crust. Yet, the element is often in a form unavailable for plant utilization, and serious deficiencies are occasionally encountered.

Microorganisms are implicated in the transformations of iron in a number of distinctly different ways, and the form of the element may be affected through a variety of biological means. (*a*) A group of bacteria, sometimes termed the *iron bacteria,* oxidizes ferrous iron to the ferric state, the latter precipitating in large masses about the cells as ferric hydroxide. (*b*) Many heterotrophic species attack soluble organic iron salts, and the iron, now in an inorganic and only slightly soluble form, is precipitated from solution. (*c*) Microorganisms alter the oxidation-reduction potential of their surroundings. Decreases in the oxidation-reduction potential resulting from microbial growth lead to the formation of the soluble ferrous from the insoluble ferric ion. (*d*) Innumerable bacteria and fungi produce acidic end-products such as carbonic, nitric, sulfuric, and organic acids. Increases in acidity bring iron into solution. (*e*) Under anaerobiasis, the sulfide formed from sulfate and organic sulfur compounds may remove iron from solution as ferrous sulfide. (*f*) The liberation by microorganisms of certain organic acids and other carbonaceous products of metabolism often results in the formation of soluble organic iron complexes. This process is the reverse of *b*.

Iron may thus be precipitated in nature by the iron bacteria, the action of heterotrophs in decomposing the organic moiety of salts of the metal, the liberation of O_2 by algae, and the creation of an alkaline reaction. Conversely, solubilization may occur through acid formation, the synthesis of certain organic products, or by the creation of reducing conditions. Chemically, the ferrous ion predominates in solution below pH 5 while the ferric ion is favored above pH 6. Even in culture media containing soluble ferrous salts, the formation of alkaline products causes an oxidation and, therefore, a precipitation of the metal as ferric iron. On the other hand, if the oxidation-reduction potential falls below 0.2 volts, most of the iron will be found in the ferrous state. At potentials greater than 0.3 volts, the ferric ion is the major form. Hence, an increase in reducing intensity leads to the accumulation of the soluble ferrous iron; the reverse occurs when the environment becomes more oxidized.

The Iron Bacteria

In 1888, S. Winogradsky, the eminent Russian microbiologist, reported the isolation of a bacterium from iron-containing spring water which would oxidize the ferrous ion and precipitate ferric hydroxide in its sheath. Although the organism, a strain of *Leptothrix*, was probably never pure, Winogradsky proposed that the bacterium was a chemoautotroph that obtained its energy from the oxidation of ferrous salts (figure 1). The formation of the ferric hydroxide sheath resulted in the development of a characteristic brown coloration surrounding the organism.

Bacteria that precipitate ferric iron occur almost universally in ferruginous waters, but some may be found in non-iron-bearing waters as well. These microorganisms are frequently detected in raw and even in treated drinking water. Typically, their usual habitat contains little soluble organic matter, adequate dissolved O_2, and either ferrous or manganous salts. The higher iron bacteria can grow and precipitate ferric hydroxide in streams where the iron content is less than 1.0 ppm. In water, such microorganisms occasionally produce fouling of pipes as a result of the accumulation of the large mass of ferric salts in which is embedded smaller amounts of cellular material. The

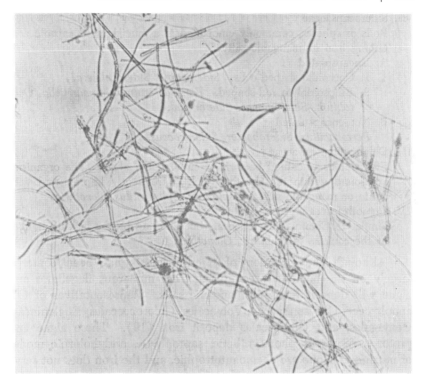

Figure 1. Photomicrograph of *Leptothrix ochraceae* (18).

plugging of water pipes, the formation of ferruginous slimes and the production of discolorations and unpleasant tastes typify their activities in drinking water. Iron may be obtained by the bacteria from the pipes themselves, and incrustations or pits will thereby develop. Because of the economic problems involved, considerable research has been done in the field of water works management for the control of these bacteria.

Many iron bacteria possess a distinctive morphology. Most but not all are filamentous and thread-like, somewhat resembling a spiral-shaped ribbon. They are placed in four families, Caulobacteraceae, Siderocapsaceae, Chlamydobacteriaceae, and Crenothrichaceae.

I. Caulobacteraceae
   Rod-shaped, non-filamentous bacteria occurring on stalks that are attached to the substratum. The stalks are the sites of ferric hydroxide accumulation. *Gallionella, Siderophacus.*

II. Siderocapsaceae

Rods or spheres, commonly embedded in a mucilaginous capsule containing iron or manganic salts.

A. Encapsulated

1. Coccoidal shaped cells. *Siderocapsa, Siderosphaera.*
2. Ellipsoidal to rod-shaped. *Ferribacterium, Naumanniella, Ochrobium, Sideromonas, Sideronema.*

B. Non-encapsulated

Ferrobacillus, Siderobacter, Siderococcus.

III. Chlamydobacteriaceae

Filamentous, sheathed bacteria resembling the algae. The organisms are found within the sheath, which is frequently impregnated with ferric or manganic salts. *Leptothrix, Sphaerotilus, Toxothrix.*

IV. Crenothricaceae

Similar to Chlamydobacteriaceae, but differing by the lack of motility of the conidia. *Crenothrix, Clonothrix.*

Although the attention of microbiologists has been centered largely on the bacteria precipitating iron, numerous flagellates and algae will deposit ferric or manganic salts. Representatives of Cyanophyceae, Chrysophyceae, Volvocales, Chlorococcales, Euglenineae, Conjugales, and Ulothricales deposit iron (19). These algae and protozoa represent photosynthetic, saprophytic, and holozoic modes of nutrition. None are chemoautotrophic, and the iron does not serve as an energy source for growth.

Few definitive physiological investigations have been carried out upon the higher iron bacteria because they are difficult to cultivate in laboratory media. The group is composed of aerobic species, and proliferation is not possible in environments devoid of free oxygen. In the presence of iron, the accumulation of ferric hydroxide about the cells imparts to them a brown to rust-red color. Many of the same organisms that oxidize ferrous iron will oxidize manganous salts and form precipitates of manganic rather than ferric compounds about the cells. Stalk-forming and related iron bacteria grow best in environments of neutral to slightly alkaline reaction, circumstances in which the ferrous ion undergoes a spontaneous oxidation to ferric; therefore, the microorganisms that presumably bring about a biological oxidation of the ferrous ion are found only in surroundings where an analogous chemical conversion occurs. This effect of pH on growth and on the ferrous-ferric equilibrium makes it difficult to interpret the nature of the process of iron precipitation, i.e., whether it be enzymatic or merely chemical. In the latter case, the sheath or capsule may serve as a selective accumulating structure. Should the higher iron bacteria be autotrophic and obtain their energy by ferrous oxidation, they do so by deriving energy from a process which takes place at a considerable pace in the absence of living systems.

It is likely that few of the large group of bacteria depositing ferric hydroxide obtain energy from the process. Indeed, with the exception of a few genera, chemoautotrophy among the iron bacteria has not been conclusively demonstrated. Among the heterotrophs, ferric accumulation may be a surface adsorption phenomenon or a result of secondary metabolic reactions. The iron-depositing bacteria are tentatively placed in three divisions: (a) obligate chemoautotrophs that utilize ferrous oxidation as the sole energy-yielding reaction for growth; (b) facultative chemoautotrophs oxidizing organic matter when available but also utilizing ferrous salts as energy sources; and (c) heterotrophic organisms that accumulate ferric hydroxide but obtain no energy from iron oxidation.

Present evidence indicates that only *Gallionella ferruginea* (21), *Thiobacillus ferrooxidans,* and *Ferrobacillus ferrooxidans* are obligate iron autotrophs. These three do not develop in organic media, but they are able to obtain carbon for cell synthesis from CO_2 and energy from ferrous oxidation. *Leptothrix ochraceae,* on the other hand, grows in media containing organic substrates in the absence of significant amounts of iron. In these media, the sheath of the bacterium is not brown, as in iron solutions, but rather it is colorless. Nevertheless, growth also apparently occurs in the absence of organic carbon, demonstrating the facultative autotrophic behavior of the organism (18). In most of the remaining iron bacteria, growth is entirely dependent upon organic matter decomposition, the nutrition is heterotrophic, and iron oxidation is not a requisite for proliferation.

The structurally complex iron organisms discussed above are almost entirely aquatic in distribution. There is no evidence for their importance in arable land, and it seems doubtful that they would be numerous or of consequence in soil. Crawford (9) has reported that higher iron bacteria were rarely encountered in the hardpan of a podzol profile, and the same result might be expected in other soil types.

Ferrous Oxidation

One way of investigating the microbiological oxidation of ferrous iron is to add an appropriate salt to sterile media or quartz sand

and measure the rate of ferrous oxidation when soil is introduced. As the chemical oxidation is appreciable at near-neutral pH, the non-biological changes are estimated by means of controls containing soil inocula subjected to sterilization. The results of such studies suggest that normal soil effects a greater change than the sterile sample, i.e., an apparent microbial ferrous oxidation (5). The data are, even in the best of circumstances, difficult to evaluate because of the dominant non-biological action.

An unequivocal demonstration of the biological oxidation of ferrous salts in soil has been provided by Gleen (10, 11), who used the fact that ferrous iron is stable at pH 3.0. An oxidation at the acid reaction, therefore, must be catalyzed by living agents. By perfusing soil with $FeSO_4$ solution at pH 3.0, Gleen showed that the soluble ferrous iron was oxidized to the ferric form, the latter precipitating upon the soil column. An initial lag was observed in the rate of oxidation during the $FeSO_4$ perfusion, but no such lag period was noted upon subsequent treatment with a fresh solution (figure 2). The lag in the first treatment and its elimination upon the addition of fresh substrate are indications of a microbiological conversion, the initial lag reflecting the time necessary for the population to become sufficiently large to produce chemically detectable changes and the subsequent absence of the lag indicating that the soil has been enriched with an active population. That the oxidation is biological was further demonstrated by adding low concentrations of a biological poison like sodium azide, which eliminated the transformation.

In bituminous coal deposits, an interesting process takes place through the metabolism of iron bacteria. In such deposits, vast quantities of sulfuric acid are produced microbiologically, the acid entering the mine waters and creating a highly corrosive drainage effluent. The acid mine effluent frequently completely destroys the aquatic life and makes the vegetation along adjacent stream banks scarce. In addition to sulfuric acid, a considerable amount of ferrous iron is present in the mine waters, both the iron and the sulfate being derived from iron disulfides in the coal veins. It has been estimated that the bituminous mines of western Pennsylvania alone add about a million tons of sulfuric acid each year to the Ohio River drainage area (15).

Iron pyrite, a typical disulfide, is slowly oxidized by non-biological means, yet the addition of a small amount of acid mine water brings about a rapid liberation of iron from the sulfide ore.

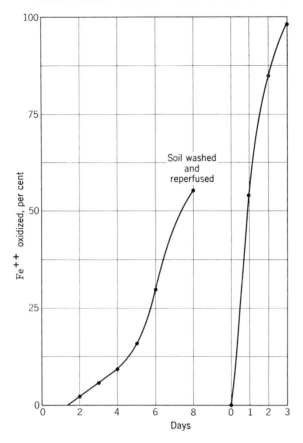

Figure 2. Ferrous oxidation in soil maintained at pH 3.0. After the initial oxidation was completed, the soil column was washed and fresh $FeSO_4$ added (11).

This activity is eliminated by sterilization and is negligible at 0°C. Paralleling the release of iron into solution is an increase in acidity and the appearance of sulfate (6).

The formation of sulfuric acid from iron disulfide ores at low pH could be attributed, as a first approximation, to the bacterium *Thiobacillus thiooxidans.* Despite its presence in acid mine drainage, *T. thiooxidans* is unable to generate sulfate or acidity from the disulfides. A second chemoautotroph, however, is found in the mine waters, an organism obtaining its energy by the oxidation of ferrous iron. The fact that it oxidizes ferrous salts at pH 3.5 in the absence

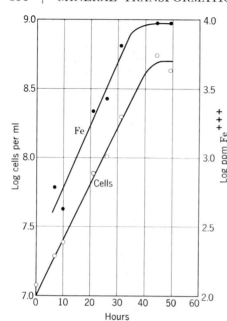

Figure 3. Growth and ferrous oxidation by *Ferrobacillus ferrooxidans* (22).

of organic materials (figure 3) is clear evidence of the autotrophic nutrition of the organism, a fact difficult to establish for higher iron bacteria growing in solutions of neutral pH. The bacterium, *Ferrobacillus ferrooxidans*, is a short, gram negative rod which utilizes no organic materials. Indeed, its growth is retarded by carbohydrates and peptones. Although resembling the thiobacilli, *F. ferrooxidans* does not oxidize inorganic sulfur compounds. Ferrous oxidation proceeds at pH 2.0 to 4.5 with an optimum at 3.5 (14, 15). Another bacterium isolated from the acid drainage of a coal mine converts not only ferrous iron to ferric but also utilizes thiosulfate as its sole energy source. Because it lives autotrophically by the transformation of inorganic sulfur as well as iron salts, it has been named *Thiobacillus ferrooxidans*. The iron autotrophy here too is beyond question as the bacterium oxidizes ferrous iron in media too acid for chemical autooxidation (8, 27). Both *Thiobacillus ferrooxidans* and *Ferrobacillus ferrooxidans* are simple rods that reproduce by binary fission. These two species are closely related but differ markedly from the higher iron bacteria, which possess a more complex morphology.

The energy for growth of the iron autotrophs is obtained from an oxidation of the type shown in equation I.

$$4FeCO_3 + O_2 + 6H_2O \rightarrow 4Fe(OH)_3 + 4CO_2 + 40,000 \text{ cal} \quad (I)$$

The energy yield, 10,000 cal per gram atom of iron (55.8 g), is small so that appreciable substrate turnover is necessary for cell synthesis. According to the calculations of Starkey (24), iron autotrophy entails the deposition of ferric hydroxide in quantities equivalent to about 500 times the weight of the cells; hence, only a small proportion of the total material in the growth mass is microbial protoplasm.

Iron Precipitation from Organic Salts

Many physiologically distinct microbial species are concerned in transformations of iron. Moreover, organisms not defined as iron bacteria are important in the reactions of the element. Frequently, the iron itself does not function in the cellular metabolism of these non-specific microorganisms. The classical iron bacteria are not as important in such changes as their name might indicate whereas common heterotrophic species are of unquestioned significance in soil.

The precipitation of the iron found in certain water-soluble organic compounds is a major means of altering the availability of the element. The organic portion of the molecule provides energy for microbial proliferation, and as the carbonaceous moiety is decomposed, the iron is released and precipitates as insoluble ferric salts. The precipitation thus results from a direct action upon the organic portion of the compound rather than upon the iron.

When a sample of soil is added to a solution containing ferric ammonium citrate, the decomposition of the citrate portion of the molecule results in a rapid accumulation of ferric hydroxide. The reaction proceeds in the presence or absence of air. In addition to its release from ferric ammonium citrate, iron is precipitated from solutions of the citrate, lactate, acetate, and albuminate salts (13). The responsible microorganisms, chiefly bacteria, are found abundantly in soil but also can be demonstrated in well, lake, or river water. Strains of diverse genera and families can in this manner remove iron from solution by attacking the organic portion of the salts. Representatives of the bacterial genera *Aerobacter, Pseu-*

domonas, Bacillus, Serratia, and *Corynebacterium,* several types of filamentous fungi, and species of *Nocardia* and *Streptomyces* are active in the conversion (9, 16).

Organic iron complexes appear to have a role in podzolization. The microflora may influence podzol formation by producing the active organic materials that function in the development of the typical soil profile. In his study of the microbiological aspects of podzolization, Crawford (9) incubated samples of various horizons of a podzol profile under carefully controlled conditions. Samples of the raw humus or A horizon were found to have had an increase in the soluble iron level when incubated in air. The amount of soluble iron in the B horizon aliquots, however, decreased upon aerobic incubation. At the same time, the population of heterotrophs precipitating iron from ferric ammonium citrate increased markedly in the B horizon. Hence, it is possible, though far from fully established, that iron moving down the podzol profile in organic combination is attacked by such heterotrophs, the microorganisms thereby causing an accumulation in the B horizon of the iron oxides. It has also been suggested that the abundance in hardpans (irreversibly cemented soil horizons) of bacteria that precipitate iron from ferric ammonium citrate may be indicative of a microbiological role in the formation of hardpans (17).

Iron Reduction

In soils that are well-drained, most of the iron occurs in the higher oxidation state, and only small amounts of the ferrous ion are found. Should the soil become waterlogged or otherwise subjected to anaerobiasis, its ferrous iron content rapidly rises. This process is entirely the result of biological agencies as no change occurs if the soil is sterilized prior to waterlogging. The data cited in table 1 are typical of the transformations in waterlogged habitats—the drop in oxidation-reduction potential (E_h) and the rapid reduction of iron in the first week or two following flooding. Treatment with organic matter enhances the reduction, and the quantity of ferrous iron appearing in the soil solution is directly related to the amount of fermentable substrate added and the length of submergence (7). In terms of the oxidation-reduction potential, ferrous becomes prominent at E_h values below ca. 0.2 volt during periods of intense microbio-

TABLE 1

Microbial Reduction Processes in Paddy Soils (26)

Time	E_h	Ionic Fe^{++}	Acid Soluble $Fe^{++}/(Fe^{++} + Fe^{+++})$
days	volts	ppm	%
0	0.45	0	43
1	0.22	0	47
2	−0.05	200	59
3	−0.20	—	66
5	−0.23	940	73
8	−0.25	1030	76
13	−0.25	1140	84
21	−0.25	950	78

logical action. When the water status of poorly drained soils is improved, there is a reversion to the +3 oxidation state.

Certain microorganisms likewise bring about a solubilization of metallic iron filings provided that a utilizable carbon source is present and O_2 is excluded. If the anaerobic cultures that have solubilized metallic iron are exposed to the air, an immediate chemical reaction takes place leading to the precipitation of the ferric salt (12).

Several mechanisms may account for the microbiological ferric reduction and the stimulatory effect of fermentable substrates. For example, an increase in acidity accompanying fermentation favors iron mobilization. Further, the depletion of O_2 as a consequence of microbial metabolism will tend to lower the E_h and lead to ferric reduction. Another possible mechanism for the transformation is the direct reaction of fermentation products with ferric hydroxides and oxides. Alternatively, reduction may be the result of electron transport, the iron functioning as an electron acceptor in cell respiration in a manner analogous to the reduction of nitrate by denitrifying bacteria.

Many bacteria, when growing in organic media at suboptimal O_2 levels, bring a portion of the added $Fe(OH)_3$ into solution. Transformations resulting in ferrous production are not peculiar to any single family or genus but are attributes of a variety of organisms, and as many as 10^4 to 10^5 bacteria per gram of soil have the capacity

TABLE 2

Bacterial Reduction of Ferric Hydroxide (3)

Bacterium	ppm Ferrous Iron Formed in 3 Media		
	Soil Extract	GS [*]	SYS [†]
Escherichia freundii	19	19	3
Bacillus cereus	3	1	0
Aerobacter aerogenes	3	16	9
Bacillus polymyxa	5	1	25
Bacillus circulans	—	1	40
Control	4	1	0

[*] Glucose–inorganic salts medium.
[†] Sucrose-yeast extract–inorganic salts medium.

to reduce iron actively. Among the bacteria converting ferric to ferrous iron are *Bacillus polymyxa, Bacillus circulans, Escherichia freundii,* and *Aerobacter aerogenes* (table 2). The first two species, neither of which make the medium more acid than pH 5.5 to 6.0, are especially active. The last two, however, produce divalent iron only in media that become distinctly acid so that, for these at least, pH is probably responsible for the transformation.

The reduction by *Bacillus circulans,* the organism most intensively investigated, is not brought about by metabolic waste substances excreted into the medium since culture filtrates have no effect upon ferric salts. If cell suspensions of the bacillus are incubated with certain organic compounds in the presence of $Fe(OH)_3$, however, ferrous iron appears. In these conditions, the relative rates of reduction are the same whether an artificial electron acceptor or $Fe(OH)_3$ is present. Further, respiratory poisons inhibiting the reduction of the artificial acceptor suppress the analogous reaction with trivalent iron. The evidence suggests, therefore, that the conversion of tri- to divalent iron by *B. circulans* is intimately linked to cell respiration and, because of the similarity to the organic substrate-artificial acceptor system, the ferric ion probably serves in respiration as an electron acceptor (3, 4, 20).

A phenomenon possibly associated with the microbial metabolism of iron is known as *gleying.* Sites in the soil profile that have undergone gleying are sticky and exhibit a gray or light greenish-blue coloration. Gleys are common where the water table is high, and such horizons are characteristically associated with waterlogged areas. The color of the gleyed zone is attributed to the ferrous sulfide produced under anaerobiasis by the reaction of the end-products of the microbial reduction of sulfate and iron. In a model system designed to simulate gleying, a clay soil is incubated with a sugar solution under partial or complete anaerobiasis; as a consequence of bacterial action, the clay becomes bleached, and iron is observed in the fermentation liquor. The color of the bleached clay varies with the soil; sometimes it is white, sometimes gray, and occasionally brown. In flooded soils treated with glucose, the rate of disappearance of the sugar and the formation of ferrous iron give the sigmoid curves characteristic of bacterial growth, and the most rapid rates of both processes occur at the same time. This suggests that bacteria are the responsible agents, and gleyed clays may indeed contain as many as 10^7 iron-reducing bacteria per gram. There is therefore evidence that, where fermentable organic matter is available, gleying may at least in part be a result of bacterial action (1, 2, 3).

In the absence of O_2, another biological process of importance to the transformations of iron may take place. This is the production of sulfide either through organic sulfur mineralization or by the reduction of sulfate by *Desulfovibrio* spp. Microorganisms which thus form H_2S cause the precipitation of iron as ferrous sulfide by a reaction of the H_2S with iron salts. The responsible organisms can be easily recognized on agar media containing iron lactate and $(NH_4)_2SO_4$ because the colonies become surrounded by a dark halo of FeS. A precipitate will also be formed in iron-rich media by the release of H_2S during the decomposition of proteins or other sulfur-containing molecules (12, 13).

Iron and steel materials buried underground are subject to corrosion in conditions of O_2 deficiency. Corrosion of this type may be so severe that iron pipes become useless after a few years, and the economic loss through deterioration of buried pipes is in the hundreds of millions of dollars per annum. At least part of the effect is brought about by microorganisms. Corrosion is particularly severe in poorly drained soils which remain wet for long periods. There is, moreover, a direct correlation between the oxidation-reduction potential and the occurrence and severity of anaerobic deterioration of iron pipes. The corrosion does not appear in soils whose potential is greater than 400 mv, it is usually slight at potentials from

200 to 400 mv, moderate at E_h of 100 to 200 mv, and almost always severe in environments with potentials below 100 mv.

The optimum conditions for the destruction of iron pipes in soil are moderate temperatures, pH values greater than 5.5, low concentrations of free O_2, and the presence of sulfate. The population concerned can be deduced from the stimulatory role of sulfate, and there is no question that it is the sulfide formed by sulfate-reducing *Desulfovibrio* spp. which effects a change in the iron by precipitation of ferrous sulfide. As the bacteria are strict anaerobes utilizing sulfate as electron acceptor for growth, the need for sulfate, low E_h, and anaerobiasis can be understood. The pH range for these bacteria parallels that of the iron corrosion, i.e., ca. pH 5.5 and above. The net reaction is best represented by the equation

$$4Fe + SO_4^= + 4H_2O \rightarrow FeS + 3Fe(OH)_2 + 2OH^- \qquad (II)$$

with ferrous sulfide and ferrous hydrate as products. The individual steps have yet to be characterized (23, 25).

REFERENCES

Reviews

Cholodny, N. 1926. *Die Eisenbakterien.* Gustav Fisher, Jena.
Pringsheim, E. G. 1949. Iron bacteria. *Biol. Rev.*, 24:200–245.
Starkey, R. L. 1945. Transformation of iron by bacteria in water. *J. Am. Water Works Assoc.*, 37:963–984.

Literature cited

1. Bloomfield, C. 1949. *J. Soil Sci.*, 1:205–211.
2. Bloomfield, C. 1949. *Soils and Fert.*, 12:319–321.
3. Bromfield, S. M. 1954. *J. Soil Sci.*, 5:129–139.
4. Bromfield, S. M. 1954. *J. Gen. Microbiol.*, 11:1–6.
5. Brown, P. E., and G. E. Corson. 1916. *Soil Sci.*, 2:549–573.
6. Bryner, L. C., J. V. Beck, D B. Davis, and D. G. Wilson. 1954. *Ind. Eng. Chem.*, 46:2587–2592.
7. Clark, F. E., and J. W. Resnicky. 1956. *Rapports, 6th Intl. Cong. Soil Sci.*, Paris, C:545–548.
8. Colmer, A. R., K. L. Temple, and M. E. Hinkle. 1950. *J. Bacteriol.*, 59:317–328.
9. Crawford, D. V. 1956. *Rapports, 6th Intl. Cong. Soil Sci.*, Paris, C:197–202.
10. Gleen, H. 1951. *J. Gen. Microbiol.*, 5:XV.
11. Gleen, H. 1950. *Nature*, 166:871–872.
12. Halvorson, H. O. 1931. *Soil Sci.*, 32:141–165.
13. Harder, E. C. 1919. *Professional Paper No. 113, U. S. Geological Survey.*

14. Leathen, W. W., S. A. Braley, Sr., and L. D. McIntyre. 1953. *Applied Microbiol.*, 1:65–68.
15. Leathen, W. W., N. A. Kinsel, and S. A. Braley, Sr. 1956. *J. Bacteriol.*, 72:700–704.
16. Lewis, I. M. 1928. *Cent. Bakteriol.*, II, 75:45–52.
17. Mudge, C. S. 1927. *Soil Sci.*, 23:467–473.
18. Präve, P. 1957. *Arch. Mikrobiol.*, 27:33–62.
19. Pringsheim, E. G. 1946. *Phil. Trans., Royal Soc. London*, B, 232:311–342.
20. Roberts, J. L. 1947. *Soil Sci.*, 63:135–140.
21. Sartory, A., and J. Meyer. 1948. *Compt. Rend. Acad. Sci.*, 226:443–445.
22. Silverman, M. P., and D. G. Lundgren. 1959. *J. Bacteriol.*, 77:642–647.
23. Starkey, R. L. 1958. *Producers Monthly*, 22(9):12–30.
24. Starkey, R. L. 1945. *Science*, 102:532–533.
25. Starkey, R. L., and K. M. Wight. 1945. *Anaerobic corrosion of iron in soil*. Am. Gas Assoc., New York.
26. Takai, Y., T. Koyama, and T. Kamura. 1956. *Soil and Plant Food*, 2:63–66.
27. Temple, K. L., and A. R. Colmer. 1951. *J. Bacteriol.*, 62:605–611.
28. Winogradsky, S. 1888. *Botan. Zeitung*, 46:261–270.

23

Transformations of Other Minerals

Microorganisms affect the availability of plant nutrients in numerous ways. The principles set forth with regard to the metabolism of nitrogen frequently can be extended to the transformations of other elements, and consideration of the various steps of the nitrogen cycle will lead to some understanding of the microbiologically induced changes of other mineral substances.

On the basis of the biological reactions of nitrogen, phosphorus, sulfur, and iron discussed in the previous chapters, six general mechanisms of mineral transformations can be delineated.

a. The release of inorganic ions during the decomposition of organic materials. As in ammonification and phosphorus mineralization, the accumulation of the inorganic ion is dependent upon the concentration of the element in excess of the microbiological demand.

b. Removal of inorganic ions from solution and the disappearance of the available form of the element to satisfy the nutrient demands of the microflora. Immobilization into microbial tissue for the purposes of cell synthesis is in continuous competition with mineralization, one process supplying the element for plant use, the other removing it.

c. Utilization of inorganic ions as energy sources, resulting in an oxidation. This type of transformation has been described for the oxidation of ammonium, nitrite, inorganic sulfur compounds, and ferrous iron by species of *Nitrosomonas*, *Nitrobacter*, *Thiobacillus*, and *Ferrobacillus*, respectively.

d. Reduction of an oxidized state of the element in the absence of adequate O_2. Among the substances serving as electron acceptors are nitrate, sulfate, carbonate, and ferric ions.

e. Indirect transformations resulting from the activities or the products of microorganisms; for example, changes in acidity and alkalinity or alterations in the partial pressure of O_2 by respiration modify the oxidation state of several elements.

f. Changing the total quantity of an element in the soil. Nitrogen fixation and chemoautotrophic CO_2 assimilation increase the amount of nitrogen and carbon while denitrification and H_2S formation diminish the nitrogen and sulfur levels.

It may be taken as a general principle in mineral metabolism that the microflora is usually active in interconverting various of the oxidation states of elements which exist in more than one valence state in soil provided that toxicity is not a hindrance. As one or more of the ions may be unavailable or even toxic to agronomic or horticultural crops, inorganic transformations can exert important effects upon plant development.

Many elements undergo microbiologically induced transformations. Several of the more conspicuous changes have been discussed in previous chapters. In addition to the elements already cited, there is ample evidence for direct or indirect biological alterations in the availability, solubility, or oxidation state of potassium, manganese, selenium, tellurium, arsenic, zinc, copper, calcium, magnesium, alumi-

TABLE 1

The Influence of Rice Straw on Release of Inorganic Ions in a Submerged Silty Clay Loam (16)

Period of Submergence	No Rice Straw			0.8% Rice Straw		
	K	Ca	Mg	K	Ca	Mg
days	ppm	ppm	ppm	ppm	ppm	ppm
1	6	9	2.0	12	10	3.5
11	8	26	4.5	20	45	11
21	10	18	7.5	23	64	23
35	10	32	11	24	108	43
49	10	48	16	21	138	50

num, molybdenum, and various halogens. Some typical data illustrating the release of three elements during the decomposition of rice straw are shown in table 1. Not infrequently the cause of the transformation is obscure, and studies of mineral metabolism should, therefore, be a highly fruitful area for future investigation.

Potassium Mobilization

A major cation that plants must obtain from the soil is potassium. Because the quantity in soil is often inadequate, the element is one of the macronutrients supplied in chemical fertilizers. Despite the potential agricultural importance of microbial transformations of this element, little is known of the conversions of potassium that can be effected by the microscopic inhabitants.

Potassium is readily adsorbed by soil constituents, but the various reactions are inadequately delineated. A portion of the soil's reserve of the element is soluble while a large part is bound in the structure of various minerals where it is non-exchangeable. The external sources of potassium are agricultural fertilizers and the tissues of plants and animals. In crop residues, the element is not strongly bound in organic combination so that microbial action is not as critical to the release of potassium during organic matter breakdown as it is in the mineralization of bound nitrogen or sulfur. Moreover, the element exists in only the monovalent state in biological systems, and there are thus none of the inorganic oxidations and reductions that typify the microbiological transformations of nitrogen, sulfur, and iron.

The microflora does have an influence on the level of available potassium, however. The cation is solubilized through the liberation of organic or inorganic acids that react with potassium-containing minerals. Alternatively, the element disappears through the assimilation necessary for the formation of new microbial cells. Some may be released during the decomposition of plant residues, but approximately two-thirds of the potassium of plants is not strongly bound and is immediately soluble in water (14) so that only about one-third of the total amount requires microbial intervention for its release. Only that portion of the plant-potassium which occurs in organic complexes needs to be liberated biologically.

Certain bacteria are capable of decomposing aluminosilicate minerals and releasing a portion of the potassium contained therein.

These organisms grow in potassium-deficient media to which is added the insoluble aluminosilicate. Typical of this group of microorganisms is the aerobic spore-former *Bacillus siliceus.* It has been reported that the yields of wheat and corn planted in sterile soil are increased as a result of inoculation with *B. siliceus,* increases equivalent to those observed in KCl-fertilized treatments. Apparently, the so-called silicate bacteria attack potassium silicates in soil, releasing the potassium and making it available for crops (1). Fungi such as *Aspergillus niger* also use clay minerals as sole potassium sources in culture media, but not all clays provide appreciable quantities of the element. Biotite and muscovite supply the greatest amounts, greensand is not as effective, and microcline provides the least to the fungus (19). In addition to the silicates cited, microorganisms liberate potassium from nephelite, leucite, orthoclase, and undoubtedly a number of others.

Acid production is the major mechanism for solubilization of the insoluble potassium in minerals. The important acids in the solubilization are carbonic, nitric, sulfuric, and several organic acids. Carbonic acid is formed from the CO_2 produced by the vast heterotrophic population, and many cultures that produce no organic acids mobilize potassium through the release of CO_2. Microorganisms such as *Clostridium pasteurianum* and *Aspergillus niger* are active because of the organic acids they synthesize. The production of nitric and sulfuric

TABLE 2

Effect of Nitrification and Sulfur Oxidation on Water-Soluble Cations in a Silt Loam (3)

Addition	Concentration of Water-Soluble Cations, ppm				
	K	Ca	Mg	Al	Mn
None	18	111	30	0	0
$CaCO_3$, 0.4%	7	270	13	0	0
$(NH_4)_2SO_4$, 0.8%	30	355	80	0	38
$(NH_4)_2SO_4 + CaCO_3$	26	1067	85	0	18
Sulfur, 0.4%	18	370	103	660	468
Sulfur + $CaCO_3$	53	785	64	413	471

Incubated for 19 weeks at 30°C.

acids in autotrophic metabolism has the same effect in releasing potassium. This is illustrated by the results of table 2 wherein the sulfuric and nitric acids from sulfur and ammonium sulfate are the active principles. The autotrophic oxidation has been used to release potassium from greensand, which, if composted with sulfur, has its potassium made soluble. The potash released can then bring about an increase in crop yield.

Some potassium may be released from clay minerals by a shift of the equilibrium between soluble and insoluble forms as microorganisms remove the cation from solution.

$$\text{K in protoplasm} \leftarrow \text{soluble-K} \leftrightharpoons \text{mineral-K} \qquad (\text{I})$$

Where this mechanism is operative, the potassium obtained from clay minerals to satisfy the demands of microbial nutrition ultimately becomes available, as the soluble cation is liberated at the time of decomposition of the microbial cells.

Potassium Immobilization

As a rule, microorganisms require the same inorganic ions as higher plants, and they may therefore be expected to compete with the macroorganisms in environments in which the nutrient supply is suboptimal. It is simple to demonstrate a competition for nitrogen between the microscopic soil inhabitants and field crops; potassium competition, on the other hand, is quite difficult to establish.

The quantity of water-insoluble, non-exchangeable potassium in soil fluctuates even when the physical and chemical environment is maintained relatively constant. Because of these fluctuations, a hypothesis has been advanced that part of the non-exchangeable potassium fraction is microbial in origin; that is, the potassium is immobilized into protoplasmic constituents. Therefore, it would seem that the microflora is participating in reducing the concentration of available potassium. In the same vein, a stimulation of microbial transformations was proposed to be the cause of the decrease in exchangeable potassium noted upon liming.

The validity of these hypotheses is questionable because of chemical reactions which tend to obscure biological changes. Thus, the concentration of available potassium varies as the moisture level fluctuates, both in sterile and in non-sterile soil. Such changes cannot be biological. Further, the alterations in exchangeable potassium resulting from liming can be duplicated in sterile samples; therefore, this phenomenon also cannot be attributed to the microflora (33, 47). On theoretical grounds, the detection of microbial potassium immobilization should be difficult in the absence of added organic matter since even with nitrogen, a nutrient required in much greater amounts, immobilization in the absence of supplemental carbon is never appreciable.

The situation is entirely different when large quantities of energy materials are undergoing decay. Under these conditions, cell synthesis is rapid, and the demand for inorganic nutrients is great. Thus, more potassium is taken up by *Aspergillus niger* from sterile, glucose-amended soil than from parallel samples which had been inoculated with a soil suspension after sterilization and incubated for 5 months. The observation that the concentration of leachable potassium is diminished by the addition to a silt loam of sweet clover and oat straw may be explained by this mechanism (17, 26).

Potassium is essential for the growth of all microorganisms. During their proliferation in soil, they must assimilate the ion, even if they must themselves render it soluble. In order to predict the extent of immobilization, the amount of decomposable organic matter, the efficiency of converting substrate-carbon to microbial-carbon, and the potassium content of the microbial cells must be known. In bacteria, up to about 2.0 per cent of the dry weight is potassium while the mycelium of fungi may contain as little as 0.1 per cent. Consider an example in which 5 tons of readily oxidizable organic matter containing 40 per cent carbon are added to an acre of soil. A total of 4000 lb of carbon are present for oxidation. Assume that an aerobic population containing 50 per cent carbon in its total mass assimilates 30 per cent of the substrate-carbon so that 1200 lb of microbial carbon are formed or a total of about 2400 lb of tissue mass. If this population as a whole has a potassium content of 0.2 to 0.5 per cent, then some 5 to 12 lb of potassium are assimilated, an immobilization of consequence but far less than the 200 lb occasionally reported.

The figures cited above are hypothetical, but they do serve as a first approximation, in the absence of definitive experimental results, to the order of change to be expected. Precise data on the potassium content of the soil flora would permit greater accuracy in the estimates. Nevertheless, even when immobilization is proceeding rapidly, it is unlikely that there would be serious competition for potassium between microorganisms and plants.

Oxidation of Manganese

An essential micronutrient for the growth and development of higher plants is the element manganese. Because the element exists in several oxidation states of dissimilar availability to plants, the ability of the microflora to transform manganese has considerable importance. Manganese occurs in soil in the tetravalent form and as the exchangeable divalent manganous ion. Plants are known to assimilate the divalent manganous form, while the tetravalent manganic ion presumably is not utilized. The exchangeable cation, Mn^{++}, is water-soluble while Mn^{++++} is essentially insoluble, the latter typically occurring as the manganic oxides, represented as MnO_2.

Of the two major ionic species, the ion that predominates is a function of the pH. At reactions more acid than pH 5.5, manganese is present largely as exchangeable Mn^{++}. At reactions more alkaline than about pH 8.0, Mn^{++} is unstable and is oxidized to manganic oxides. Because manganic oxides are not assimilated appreciably by plants, alkaline conditions frequently are associated with deficiencies of the element. Below pH 8.0, there is little chemical oxidation of divalent manganese, the process of Mn^{++} autooxidation being characteristic of low hydrogen ion concentrations.

$$MnO_2 + 4H^+ + 2e^- \underset{\text{alkaline}}{\overset{\text{acid}}{\rightleftharpoons}} Mn^{++} + 2H_2O \qquad (II)$$

In the intermediary ranges, between pH 5.5 and 8.0, the prominence of microbiological phenomena becomes evident.

When a solution of $MnSO_4$ is perfused through a neutral or slightly alkaline soil in the perfusion apparatus, there is an initial adjustment between the concentration of the cation in solution and that in the soil phase. This initial stage is followed by a disappearance of the manganous ion from the liquid. The loss of divalent manganese from solution is accompanied by an increase in the soil of the quantity of insoluble, oxidized manganese compounds (figure 1). The process is biological because (a) the oxidation exhibits the logarithmic transformation typical of the bacterial growth curve, (b) the disappearance is most rapid at relatively low concentrations of added $MnSO_4$ whereas chemical reactions are typically faster at high levels of reactants, and (c) manganous oxidation is eliminated by inhibitors such as sodium azide, iodoacetate, and chloretone (28, 34). Inhibitors of this type are convenient tools for the differentiation

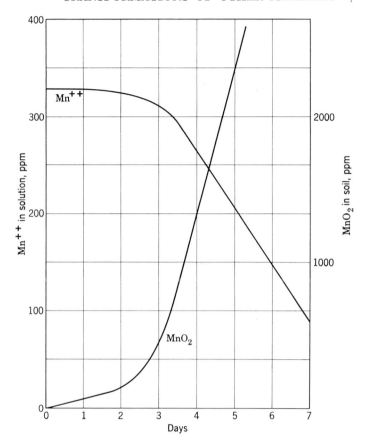

Figure 1. Oxidation of manganous in soil perfused with $MnSO_4$ (34).

of biological and non-biological reactions provided that the in-hibitors have no effect on the chemical transformations.

The first definitive work on manganous oxidation was that of the Dutch microbiologist, M. W. Beijerinck (5, 6), who described a number of bacteria and fungi obtained from garden soil that oxidized $MnCO_3$. The oxidation process can be demonstrated readily by the addition of a soil sample to an agar medium containing $MnCO_3$; the products of microbiological action are seen as brown spots develop-ing in the agar. It is characteristic of the active organisms to form dark brown specks in media containing $MnSO_4$ or $MnCO_3$, a result of manganic oxide accumulation. The active organisms include strains of the bacterial genera *Aerobacter, Bacillus, Corynebacterium,* and *Pseudomonas* and of the fungal genera *Cladosporium, Curvularia, Helminthosporium,* and *Cephalosporium.* A number of nocardias and streptomycetes also exhibit the same capacity (11, 43). Occasionally, two organisms are required for the oxidation to the insoluble MnO_2. For example, pure cultures of a *Corynebacterium* sp. and a *Chromobacterium* sp. are incapable of manganous oxidation whereas a mixture of the two is able to carry out the transformation. The mixed culture effect is not a result of the production of a diffusable substance by one of the bacteria as no oxidation occurs when the two cultures are separated by a membrane; further, neither of the two species oxidizes the manganous ion in the presence of heat-killed cells of the other (9). The cause of the mixed culture phenomenon is unknown.

Several of the higher iron bacteria and related microorganisms which precipitate ferric hydrate also accumulate MnO_2, the latter compound resulting in a zone of darkening around the cells. Some of the colorless, alga-like bacteria such as *Leptothrix* spp., *Crenothrix polyspora,* and *Clonothrix putealis* may have either iron or manganic oxides in their sheaths. Likewise, certain flagellates and algae that deposit iron can cause the precipitation of manganese (38).

There is little conclusive evidence that microorganisms obtain energy for growth by the oxidation of the manganous ion, and proliferation of the active species usually requires organic carbon. Therefore, although the oxidation does release energy, the existence of chemoautotrophic manganese bacteria is subject to doubt. There are indications, however, that there may indeed be a manganese chemoautotrophy (37, 40), but further study is necessary in order to establish firmly the nutritional characteristics of these bacteria.

The number of manganese-oxidizers varies considerably between soil types, but they often account for some 5 to 15 per cent of the total viable microflora. The size of the population is affected by proximity to plant roots as the number of active organisms is increased in the zone under the influence of the root system (table 3). Manganous oxidation is brought about by microorganisms in conditions as acid as pH 5.5 and as alkaline as pH 8.9. The biological transformation is not too sensitive to acidity, but it is generally most rapid at pH 6.0 to 7.5 (31). Individual species will be more or less sensitive to the hydrogen ion concentration, and several isolates carry out the oxidation in slightly acid circumstances.

TABLE 3

Microbiological Population in Rhizosphere * of Oats Resistant and Susceptible to Manganese Deficiency (42)

Oat Variety	Soil Treatment	Bacteria/g $\times 10^3$	Actinomycetes/g $\times 10^3$	Mn Oxidizers $\times 10^3$	Mn Oxidizers % of Total
		Rhizosphere Soil			
Resistant	None	266,000	2,500	41,800	15.7
	Manure, $MnSO_4$	509,000	2,100	42,200	8.3
Susceptible	None	564,000	2,300	255,000	42.2
	Manure, $MnSO_4$	638,000	1,200	181,000	28.2
		Non-rhizosphere Soil			
	None	129,000	1,500	8,000	6.2
	Manure, $MnSO_4$	224,000	600	9,400	4.2

* Soil associated with the plant root system.

The precise chemical structure of the manganic oxides is not understood despite their usual designation as MnO_2. Manganese dioxide or similar compounds do exist in soil, but there is also some evidence for the presence of Mn_2O_3 and Mn_3O_4. The three oxides Mn_3O_4, Mn_2O_3, and MnO_2 have progressively increasing oxidation states in addition to different physical and physiological properties. The oxides produced microbiologically seem to be intermediary between the trivalent and tetravalent forms, Mn_2O_3 and MnO_2. While it is usually assumed that only the divalent ion is available to plants, the higher oxidation states presumably not being assimilated, certain of the manganic oxides may indeed serve as nutrient sources. For example, the oxide produced by a *Corynebacterium* sp. is slowly utilized by oats without microbial intervention (10).

Several mechanisms for manganese oxidation have been proposed. One involves the oxidation of the manganous ion by hydroxy acids. This reaction occurs in alkaline solution containing citrate, tartrate, lactate, malate, or gluconate, all of which are produced during the decomposition of carbohydrates. This hypothesis is supported by observations that pure cultures of a number of organisms transform soluble compounds of manganese to insoluble, brown oxides when grown on agar media containing salts of various hydroxy acids; the same reaction is noted when a sterile sodium carbonate solution is added to the surface of the agar in order to increase the alkalinity

(41). From this, it would seem that microorganisms contribute to manganese oxidation by the production of hydroxy acids or by decreasing the hydrogen ion concentration, or both. In either instance, the initial step in forming the organic acid or in altering the pH is biological, but the subsequent oxidation of the cation is chemical. Thus, in the presence of a hydroxy acid, a strain that creates an alkaline environment will bring about a non-biological oxidation; alternatively, the production of hydroxy organic acids in alkaline systems effects the same change.

A second mechanism, similar to one reported in plant tissues and in purified enzymes, may account for the reaction in other microorganisms. In the presence of enzymes which produce H_2O_2, the enzyme peroxidase brings about an oxidation of manganous ions (29). A coupling of H_2O_2-liberating enzymes with peroxidase has not been demonstrated in microorganisms, but bacteria, actinomycetes, or fungi which produce the necessary catalytic systems may yet be discovered.

Manganese Deficiency

Deficiencies of trace metals are often a significant factor in reducing crop yields. Manganese is no exception since it is an essential element for growth. Deficiencies of manganese occur commonly in soils rich in organic matter and at pH values of 6.5 to 8.0. Heavy applications of $MnSO_4$ may alleviate the condition, yet such additions frequently have no or, at best, a transitory effect as the element becomes oxidized in the soil. Alternatively, dilute $MnSO_4$ solutions are sometimes sprayed on the foliage to reverse the deficiency. The availability of manganese can also be increased by the use of sulfur or $(NH_4)_2SO_4$, which, by the autotrophic formation of sulfuric or nitric acids, alter the pH to favor the available state of the element. Flooding the soil also increases the amount of assimilable manganese.

A deficiency of manganese is responsible for the gray speck disease of oats and for marsh spot in peas, but similar nutrient imbalances have been reported in other cereals, various grasses, a wide variety of vegetable crops, and for several fruit trees. A biological influence upon these deficiencies is readily demonstrated. Thus, when oats are grown in solution culture, gray speck symptoms do not appear, but the symptoms develop quickly if the culture solution is inoculated with a small amount of the "diseased" soil. Should the diseased soil be sterilized with formaldehyde, a treatment which has a minimum of effect on the manganese status, the oats developing therein are healthy. When the sterile soil is subsequently reinfected with a small quantity of infested soil and then planted to oats, the gray speck reappears (23). Thus, biological agencies are super-imposed upon the simple mineral deficiency and intensify the condition.

Ample evidence can be cited to support the contention that the manganese-oxidizing microflora is associated with the gray speck of oats. The data of table 3, for example, show a correlation between the severity of the condition and the numbers of Mn^{++} oxidizers in the oat rhizosphere. The microorganisms presumably reduce the available manganous level in soil. Fumigants such as chloropicrin and formaldehyde reduce or eliminate the symptoms and also markedly suppress the responsible population; a straw mulch, on the other hand, intensifies the condition and produces a large number of manganous-oxidizers (42). Gray speck disease serves as an excellent example of the saprophytic flora causing a plant disorder by virtue of its peculiar biochemical properties rather than through the more common means of inducing pathological responses.

Manganese Reduction

In the cyclic sequence of manganese interconversions, the divalent ion may be regenerated through acid production or by bacterial reduction. Hence, a decrease in pH, lowering of the oxidation-reduction potential, or removal of O_2 as a result of microbial metabolism will increase the level of exchangeable manganese. Soil organic matter itself, with no direct biological intervention, also reduces the higher oxides (30). In field practice, when soils are waterlogged and the partial pressure of O_2 in them declines, MnO_2 is reduced to Mn^{++}, and the content of manganese in the liquid phase rises. The appearance of the soluble divalent cation is stimulated by the addition of available carbohydrates or plant residues, and the amount of the element in solution is related to the quantity of organic matter added and the length of the flooding period. Not only in poorly drained areas does this occur, for the addition of glucose to a well-drained soil results in a decrease in manganic oxides (figure 2); once the sugar has been entirely metabolized, however, the microflora or chemical auto-oxidation reforms the insoluble manganic compounds (16, 34).

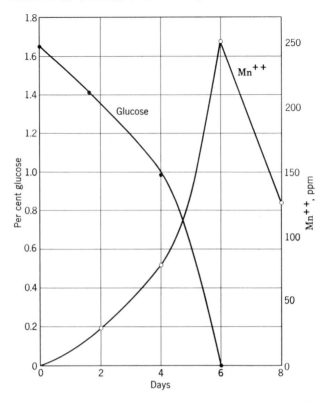

Figure 2. Reduction of manganic oxides in a soil perfused with glucose (34).

In pure culture, many bacteria reduce MnO_2 in the presence of an oxidizable organic nutrient. MnO_2 may serve herein as an electron acceptor for respiratory enzymes, replacing molecular oxygen in this regard.

$$RH_2 + MnO_2 \rightarrow Mn(OH)_2 + R \qquad (III)$$

Cell respiration can in this way be linked with the manganic-manganous system when O_2 is absent (24). It is likely that carbonaceous nutrients in soil function metabolically in the same manner for manganic oxide reduction, i.e., by providing a need for electron acceptors.

As pointed out above, microbiologically synthesized acids increase manganese availability because of the effect of the hydrogen ion upon the manganous-manganic equilibrium. It is not surprising, therefore, that the divalent manganese content of soil rises following sulfur or thiosulfate application, the biogenesis of sulfuric acid making more of the element available to crops and frequently relieving symptoms of manganese deficiency. An anomaly is noted, however, during the oxidation of sulfur by *Thiobacillus thiooxidans* grown in media containing MnO_2; more soluble manganese is released than in the uninoculated control medium to which is added sulfuric acid to bring the pH to the level produced during growth of the bacterium. A similar phenomenon occurs in soil. Consequently, only part of the MnO_2 solubilization can be accounted for in terms of acid formation by thiobacilli, and pH is not the sole cause of Mn^{++} release under these conditions. The additional effect may arise from the coupling of manganic reduction with sulfur oxidation, that is, the Mn^{++++} serves as an alternate electron acceptor for the bacteria (22, 45).

It is clear from the foregoing discussion that there is a manganese cycle in soil, a cycle involving divalent, tetravalent, and probably other oxidation states of the element. The form which is favored depends upon the acidity, the population, the presence of O_2, and the availability and abundance of organic matter. In soils of pH below 5.5, Mn^{++} predominates because of the chemical equilibrium. Increasing pH brings biological forces into play, and the microbiological production of MnO_2 and other oxides becomes apparent. In the same general pH range, biological reduction regenerates exchangeable manganese. At reactions higher than pH 8.0, chemical autooxidation favors the oxidized states of the element.

$$\underset{\text{(exchangeable)}}{Mn^{++}} \quad \underset{\substack{\text{biological} \\ H^+}}{\overset{\substack{OH^- \\ \text{biological} \\ \text{autooxidation}}}{\rightleftharpoons}} \quad \underset{(MnO_2)}{Mn^{++++}} \qquad (IV)$$

In the microbiological transformations of manganese, immobilization is of no consequence since microbial cells rarely contain more than 0.005 per cent of the element. Consequently, the net amount assimilated would not greatly affect the more general processes of oxidation and reduction.

Reduction of Inorganic Compounds

A number of bacteria, actinomycetes, and fungi bring about the reduction of selenium salts. In filamentous microorganisms and in bacteria, the end-product of the reaction commonly is elemental selenium which is deposited within the mycelium or the bacterial cell. Aerobic, facultatively anaerobic, and obligately anaerobic bacteria are represented in the group which reduces selenite and selenate salts to the metallic state. The reduction typically leads to a color change, the colonies taking the brick-red coloration of the selenium metal. Active species are simple to detect by the red coloration associated with their growth.

The ability to precipitate metallic selenium from selenite salts is not an uncommon attribute. Fewer organisms reduce selenate, and the deposition of the metal is slower from selenate than from selenite. Species of *Clostridium, Corynebacterium,* and *Rhizobium* effect the transformation. The formation of elemental selenium can be detected microscopically because the metal is deposited within the cell as distinct, red granules. In contrast to sulfate reduction in which the final product is H_2S, selenium rather than selenide, H_2Se, accumulates. The transformation is not restricted to culture media, moreover, since selenium is evolved from shales treated with selenite or selenate (table 4). Bacteria do not seem to be capable of using the reaction to permit anaerobic growth, i.e., to use selenate or selenite as an electron acceptor for proliferation as the denitrifying bacteria use nitrate when O_2 is unavailable. Considerations of comparative biochemistry would suggest that such organisms do exist, but experimental verification is lacking.

A similar phenomenon has been demonstrated with oxidized forms of tellurium. Bacterial colonies growing on agar media con-

TABLE 4

Selenium Volatilization from Pierre Shale (21)

Soil Amendment	% Selenium Volatilized from	
	Selenite	Selenate
None	0.39	18
Oat straw	5.5	100
Astragalus residue	70	53

Selenite and selenate added to give 6.4 and 1.5 mg selenium, respectively. Incubated for 2 months.

taining tellurium oxide are often dark gray to black as a consequence of the accumulation of elemental tellurium. In the presence of small quantities of potassium tellurite, several bacteria, fungi, and actinomycetes form elemental tellurium by reduction. As with selenium, metallic tellurium is deposited within the bacterial cell or in the hyphae of filamentous microorganisms, the accumulation of the metal resulting in the black colony (7).

Because the reduction of selenium and tellurium salts yields inorganic products, the same might be expected of all such reductive processes. The comparison, however, does not hold. Arsenite reduction, for example, is known to be biological, but the experimental evidence has resulted in the rejection of the early concept that the final product is arsine, AsH_3.

Many instances of human poisoning have been attributed to volatile compounds associated with the use of wallpapers containing arsenical pigments. The gas released has a typical garlic-like odor and is commonly termed Gosio gas. When moisture is adequate, the wallpaper itself supports a fungal growth which liberates the volatile arsenic compounds. The fungi participating in the conversion include species of *Aspergillus, Mucor, Scopulariopsis, Fusarium,* and *Paecilomyces.* It is not difficult to show that soil microorganisms likewise produce gaseous arsenic-containing compounds and that such substances are released from soils treated with salts of arsenic (36, 46).

The product of the reaction is not arsine but trimethylarsine, $(CH_3)_3As$. This was first demonstrated for *Scopulariopsis brevicaulis,* a fungus liberating trimethylarsine from arsenious oxide. The process involves a one-carbon transfer in which the methyl of methionine or similar compounds is transferred to arsenious acid to yield the monomethyl-, the dimethyl-, and finally the trimethylarsine. The overall process may be visualized as shown in figure 3 although the detailed steps have not been finally established.

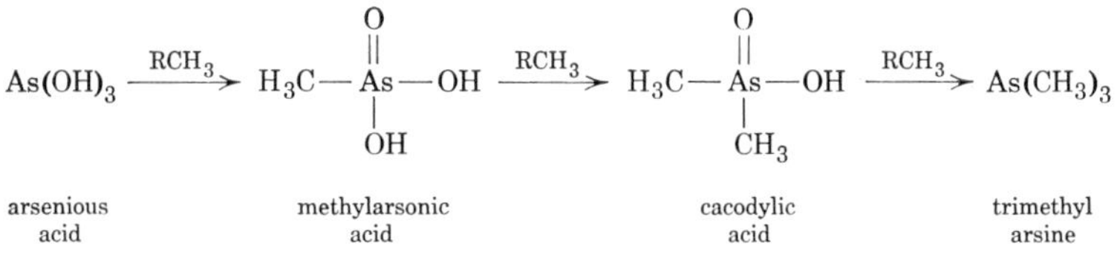

Figure 3. Postulated reaction sequence in the formation of trimethylarsine (13).

Many and probably most microorganisms that act upon the inorganic salts of selenium and tellurium do so with the ultimate production of the metal, yet some species carry out a methylation of the molecule in a fashion entirely analogous to that observed with arsenic. Occasionally, both transformations may take place in the same culture. For example, in the reduction of selenate or selenite in organic media, the volatile substance evolved by S. brevicaulis or Aspergillus niger is dimethylselenide, $(CH_3)_2Se$. In its action upon soluble tellurium compounds, on the other hand, S. brevicaulis forms either dimethyl telluride, $(CH_3)_2Te$, or elemental tellurium. Dimethyl telluride can also be synthesized from potassium tellurite by Penicillium spp. The generation of dimethyl selenide from selenate or selenite and dimethyl telluride from tellurite appears to result from an enzymatic addition of methyl groups by the fungus as in the formation of trimethylarsine from inorganic salts of arsenic (7, 18).

An anion chemically different from those discussed but one which is also reduced biologically is chlorate. Chlorate disappears from treated soils at rates exceeding the anticipated leaching loss. The rate of diminution in concentration is enhanced by added glucose, but the loss is largely prevented by microbial inhibitors, results indicating that chlorate destruction is biological. The likeliest mechanisms for the conversion are either a direct, enzymatic reduction or a reaction of chlorate with reducing substances formed by the microflora. The rate of chlorate reduction may be quite rapid or moderately slow depending upon the availability of decomposable organic materials, the aeration status, and the temperature of the environment. High temperature and a poor O_2 supply are the most favorable conditions. The final product of chlorate reduction seems to be chloride, but neither the organisms involved nor the chemical steps have been investigated (27, 35). It is interesting that sodium chlorate, a chemical once recommended for weed control, is a potent inhibitor of nitrate production by Nitrobacter spp. and that its toxicity to plants is reduced by nitrate. Therefore, there appears to be an interaction between nitrate and chlorate in the physiology of both plants and microorganisms.

Oxidation of Inorganic Compounds

Though the salts of selenium and sulfur are alike in many of their chemical properties, sulfur transformations have received considerable attention while those of selenium have been largely neglected. True, the oxidized forms of both can be reduced biologically, but the intensive investigations of the autotrophic sulfur oxidizers of the genus *Thiobacillus* have no counterpart in studies of the metabolism of selenium. Some evidence bearing on similarities in oxidation does, however, exist. Two bacteria have been reported to be capable of satisfying their energy requirements from the oxidation of selenides or metallic selenium although organic materials could replace the inorganic energy substrate of one. The alleged selenium-oxidizing bacterium was isolated from an enrichment culture following the observation that the metal was oxidized in soil with a resultant increase in acidity, and the rod-shaped bacterium was purified in mineral media containing elemental selenium as the sole energy source (8, 32). Because litle work has been done with the group, the validity of a selenium autotrophy must await confirmation.

Arsenite oxidation has been the subject of more close scrutiny. If applied at low rates to soil, arsenite disappears and arsenate is produced; the reaction is biological as it is abolished by enzyme

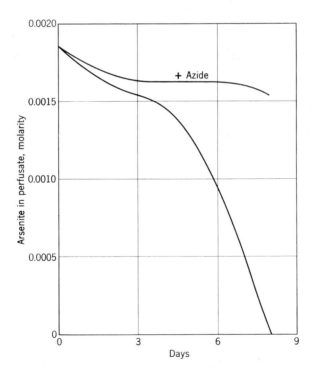

Figure 4. Arsenite oxidation measured in the soil perfusion apparatus (39).

poisons such as sodium azide. Moreover, the transformation follows the logarithmic rate typical of the growth of bacterial cultures (figure 4). A soil enriched with an arsenite-metabolizing flora rapidly acts upon the substrate and, at the same time, consumes O_2. The amount of O_2 utilized is in agreement with that predicted by equation V (39).

$$2NaAsO_2 + O_2 + 2H_2O \rightarrow 2NaH_2AsO_4 \qquad (V)$$
$$\text{arsenite} \qquad\qquad\qquad \text{arsenate}$$

Repeated perfusion of soil with arsenite leads to an ultimate diminution in the rate of oxidation. This unexpected decline in rate is suggestive of a heterotrophic process that requires a reserve of available organic matter although arsenite oxidation would seem to be an autotrophic parallel to the *Nitrobacter* metabolism of nitrite.

Attempts to isolate chemoautotrophs capable of deriving energy from the conversion of arsenite to arsenate have failed, the reaction in enrichments being abolished when organic carbon is absent (2). However, bacteria have been obtained from animal dipping tanks in which arsenate is formed from the arsenite ion. The responsible bacteria are all heterotrophic *Pseudomonas* strains that convert arsenite to the more oxidized state (44). In this process, therefore, the inorganic transformation is clearly the result of heterotrophic metabolism, and the possibility of autotrophy has been excluded.

Transformation of Other Minerals

Zinc availability may be altered by the microscopic inhabitants of soil. The evidence for an effect of this type comes largely from results obtained in investigations of the "little-leaf" condition of several fruit trees, an abnormality resulting from zinc deficiency. When soils supporting fruit trees with little-leaf symptoms are brought to the laboratory, sterilized, and seeded with a suitable test plant, none of the symptoms appear. The inoculation of the sterile sample with a small amount of diseased soil or with certain bacteria, however, leads to a redevelopment of the deficiency. The condition can be prevented by supplementation with $ZnSO_4$. The appearance of zinc deficiencies in flax has also been attributed to microbiological activities (4, 20). Thus, under certain conditions, the microflora may have an influence, direct or indirect, upon the availability to crops of zinc.

The copper level also may be affected by the metabolism of the microflora. For example, the concentration of soluble copper decreases during the decomposition of certain crop residues, the change being most marked at moderate temperatures. The effect on copper is indirect and results from changes in the soluble constituents of the organic matter. On the other hand, the decay of readily available carbonaceous materials such as glucose or asparagine may lead to an appreciable increase in the quantity of water-soluble copper, this effect probably resulting from metabolic products which react chemically with the bound forms of the element (15, 25). Copper is also liberated biologically from chalcopyrite, a release that parallels the formation of sulfuric acid from constituents of the ore (12).

Flooding of soils, particularly when readily oxidizable organic nutrients are available, leads to significant mobilization of certain mineral elements. Typically, the amount of soluble calcium, magnesium, iron, and manganese in submerged soils increases following flooding, and the quantity solubilized rises slowly with time. If supplemental organic carbon is provided, these four elements appear more rapidly in the soil solution. The quantity mobilized in this manner is thus related to the supply of added organic matter and the duration of the flooding period. Flooding, however, does not enrich the soil solution with copper, aluminum, or boron regardless of the incorporation of crop residues (16). The biological production of sulfuric and nitric acids from sulfur and ammonium salts in well-drained land can also affect the solubilization of calcium, aluminum, and magnesium. Frequently, neither the biochemical nor the microbiological basis of individual mineral transformations is understood, but the changes probably result from direct as well as indirect actions of the population upon the inorganic substances.

REFERENCES

1. Aleksandrov, V. G., and G. A. Zak. 1950. *Mikrobiologiya*, 19:97–104.
2. Alexander, M. Unpublished data.
3. Ames, J. W., and G. E. Boltz. 1919. *Soil Sci.*, 7:183–195.
4. Ark, P. A. 1936. *Proc. Am. Soc. Hort. Sci.*, 34:216–221.
5. Beijerinck, M. W. 1913. *Folia Microbiol.*, 2:123–134.
6. Beijerinck, M. W. 1913. *Verslag Akad. Wetenschappen*, 22:415–420.
7. Bird, M. L., and F. Challenger. 1939. *J. Chem. Soc.*, pp. 163–168.
8. Brenner, W. 1916. *Jahrb. Wiss. Bot.*, 57:95–127.
9. Bromfield, S. M. 1956. *Austral. J. Biol. Sci.*, 9:238–252.
10. Bromfield, S. M. 1958. *Plant and Soil*, 9:325–337.
11. Bromfield, S. M., and V. B. D. Skerman. 1950. *Soil Sci.*, 69:337–348.
12. Bryner, L. C., and A. K. Jameson. 1958. *Applied Microbiol.*, 6:281–287.

13. Challenger, F. 1951. *Adv. Enzymol.*, 12:429–491.
14. Chaminade, R. 1955. *Potassium Symposium*, Rome, pp. 203–214.
15. Ciferri, R., and G. Scaramuzzi. 1937. *Atti 1st Bot. Univ. Lab. Crittog. Pavia*, Ser. 5, 3:233–237.
16. Clark, F. E., and J. W. Resnicky. 1956. *Rapports, 6th Intl. Cong. Soil Sci.*, Paris, C:545–548.
17. Dean, H. C. 1936. *Iowa Agric. Expt. Sta. Research Bull. 197.*
18. Dransfield, P. B., and F. Challenger. 1954. *Biochem. J.*, 58:XXVIII.
19. Eno, C. F., and H. W. Reuszer. 1955. *Soil Sci.*, 80:199–209.
20. Ferres, H. M. 1949. *Brit. Commonw. Sci. Off. Conf.*, *Sp. Conf. Agric. Australia.*
21. Ganje, T. J., and E. I. Whitehead. 1958. *Proc. S. Dak. Acad. Sci.*, 37:81–84.
22. Garey, C. L., and S. A. Barber. 1952. *Soil Sci. Soc. Am.*, *Proc.*, 16:173–175.
23. Gerretsen, F. C. 1937. *Ann. Botany*, 1:207–230.
24. Hochster, R. M., and J. H. Quastel. 1952. *Arch. Biochem. Biophys.*, 36:132–146.
25. Hurwitz, C. 1947. *Soil Sci. Soc. Am.*, *Proc.*, 12:195–197.
26. Hurwitz, C., and H. W. Batchelor. 1943. *Soil. Sci.*, 56:371–382.
27. Jensen, S. T., and S. Larsen. 1957. *Tidsskr. Planteavl*, 61:103–118.
28. Jones, L. H. P. 1957. *Plant and Soil*, 8:315–327.
29. Kenten, R. H., and P. J. G. Mann. 1952. *Biochem. J.*, 52:125–130.
30. Kosegarten, E. K. 1957. *Landw. Forsch.*, 10:214–222.
31. Leeper, G. W., and R. J. Swaby. 1940. *Soil Sci.*, 49:163–169.
32. Lipman, J. G., and S. A. Waksman. 1923. *Science*, 57:60.
33. Litvinov, L. S., and E. V. Astafieva. 1957. *Mikrobiologiya*, 26:167–171.
34. Mann, P. J. G., and J. H. Quastel. 1946. *Nature*, 158:154–156.
35. Nelson, R. T. 1944. *J. Agric. Research*, 68:221–237.
36. Perotti, R., and O. Verona. 1939. *Ann. Fac. Agrar, Univ. Pisa*, 2:32–38.
37. Präve, P. 1957. *Arch. Mikrobiol.*, 27:33–62.
38. Pringsheim, E. G. 1946. *Phil. Trans., Royal Soc. London*, B232:311–342.
39. Quastel, J. H., and P. G. Scholefield. 1953. *Soil Sci.*, 75:279–285.
40. Sartory, A., and J. Meyer. 1947. *Compt. Rend. Acad. Sci.*, 225:541–542.
41. Sohngen, N. L. 1914. *Cent. Bakteriol.*, II, 40:545–554.
42. Timonin, M. I. 1946. *Soil Sci. Soc. Am.*, *Proc.*, 11:284–292.
43. Timonin, M. I. 1950. *Trans. 4th Intl. Cong. Soil Sci.*, Amsterdam, 3:97–99.
44. Turner, A. W. 1949. *Nature*, 164:76–77.
45. Vavra, J. P., and L. R. Frederick. 1952. *Soil Sci. Soc. Am.*, *Proc.*, 16:141–144.
46. Vinogradov, A. P. 1948. *Pochvovedenie*, pp. 33–38.
47. York, E. T. 1949. Ph.D. Thesis, Cornell University, Ithaca, N. Y.

ECOLOGICAL INTER-RELATIONSHIPS

24

The Biological Equilibrium

In natural environments, a number of relationships exist between individual microbial species and between individual cells. The inter-relations and interactions of the various microbial groups making up the soil population, however, are in a continual state of change, and this dynamic state is maintained at a level characteristic of the flora. The composition of the microflora of any habitat is governed by the biological equilibrium created by the associations and interactions of all individuals found in the population. Environmental changes temporarily upset the equilibrium, but it is re-established, possibly in a modified form, as the population shifts to become acclimated to the new circumstances.

In soil, many microorganisms occur in close proximity, and they interact in a unique way that is in marked contrast to the behavior of pure cultures studied by the microbiologist in the laboratory. Members of the microflora rely upon one another for certain growth substances, but at the same time they exert detrimental influences so that both beneficial and harmful effects are evident. The sum total of all of the individual interactions establishes the equilibrium population, the native flora typifying a given habitat.

A number of possible interactions may occur between two species. Odum has proposed the following relations: (*a*) *neutralism*, in which the two microorganisms behave entirely independently; (*b*) *symbiosis*, the two symbionts relying upon one another and both benefiting by the relationship; (*c*) *protocooperation*, an association of mutual benefit to the two species but without the cooperation being obligatory for their existence or for their performance of some reaction; (*d*) *commensalism*, in which only one species derives benefit while the other is unaffected; (*e*) *competition,* a condition in which there is a suppression of one organism as the two species struggle for limiting quantities of nutrients, O_2, space, or other common requirements; (*f*) *amensalism,* in which one species is suppressed while the second is not affected, often the result of toxin production; and (*g*) *parasitism* and *predation,* the direct attack of one organism upon another.

Because of these interrelationships, the introduction of an alien organism into soil rarely leads to its establishment. The fact that the species introduced is scarce or absent indicates of itself that the habitat is unfavorable for the microorganism's development. Bacteria and fungi not indigenous to a soil type rapidly die out when added, and changes resulting from the introduction of foreign organisms are always transient. This is observed routinely in the decline of the large numbers of microorganisms entering soil from animal droppings. The ecological axiom that *the population reflects the habitat* is an excellent rule in microbial ecology.

Beneficial Associations

The three beneficial relationships cited above, symbiosis, proto-cooperation, and commensalism, are found to operate among the soil inhabitants. Because of the high population density in a restricted ecological zone, microorganisms in time develop certain relations that are beneficial and others that are detrimental. Sometimes the benefit is mutual, but commensal relationships are quite frequent.

One of the more important beneficial associations is that involving two species, one of which can attack a substrate not available to the second organism, but the decomposition results in the formation of products utilized by the second. This type of commensalism is not infrequent in nature, and it is the way many polysaccharides are transformed to nutrients supporting non-specialized microorganisms; e.g., cellulolytic fungi produce from cellulose a number of organic acids that serve as carbon sources for non-cellulolytic bacteria and fungi. A second beneficial association arises from the need of many microorganisms for accessory growth substances. These growth factors are synthesized by certain microorganisms, and their excretion permits the proliferation of nutritionally complex soil inhabitants. The microbial decomposition of biologically produced inhibitors that prevent the proliferation of sensitive species is another instance of a beneficial relationship. Aerobes may permit the growth of obligate anaerobes by consuming the O_2 in the environment. In addition to these instances of commensalism and protocooperation, several well-documented examples of true symbiosis are in evidence, particularly those concerned with N_2 fixation.

The decomposition of a number of natural products is usually more rapid in mixed than in pure culture. The explanation for the phenomenon is obscure. The greater rate may be the result of a removal of fermentation products that deter the primary organism or it may arise from the production by the secondary population of growth factors required by the primary flora. This type of nutritional protocooperation is not uncommon, and it probably is important in many habitats. Occasionally, the interaction may be sufficiently close to warrant the term *nutritional symbiosis*.

Nutritional symbiosis or protocooperation has been demonstrated frequently in two- and three-membered cultures. For example, in a medium deficient in phenylalanine and folic acid, neither *Streptococcus faecalis* nor *Lactobacillus arabinosus* will grow as the former bacterium requires folic acid and the latter, phenylalanine. In mixed culture in the same medium, however, both grow since the partner bacterium synthesizes the missing vitamin or amino acid (21). Similar nutrient interactions between bacteria and fungi have been reported for various vitamins, amino acids, and purines. In each instance, the partner is capable of synthesizing the appropriate growth factor. Many hitherto anomalous symbiotic effects can now be explained on the basis of the excretion of specific nutrients by one of the two microbial partners.

In soil, mutual feeding assumes great prominence. A large proportion of the indigenous bacteria requires or is stimulated by water-soluble B vitamins and amino acids. They will not grow in simple laboratory media unless supplemented with the appropriate substances. The occurrence of nutritionally exacting species in nature is rather surprising because the organisms must be supplied continuously with the deficient nutrients in order for them to compete effectively for the limited amount of carbonaceous and inorganic nutrients. The results of table 1 show that 27.1 per cent of the bacteria in a Canadian soil require one or more vitamins for growth. Thiamine is the most frequently required vitamin, but biotin and vitamin B_{12} also are essential for a large number of bacteria. Similarly, many isolates will not grow in the absence of amino acids.

The presence of fastidious microorganisms would appear inexplicable except for the fact that vitamins occur in soil. Thiamine,

TABLE 1

Growth Factors and the Development of Soil Bacteria (15, 16)

Vitamin Required or Excreted	Percentage of Total Bacteria Which	
	Require the Vitamin	Excrete the Vitamin
Thiamine	19.4	35.5
Biotin	16.4	19.6
Vitamin B_{12}	7.2	29.9
Pantothenic acid	4.6	—
Folic acid	3.0	—
Nicotinic acid	2.0	—
Riboflavin	0.6	39.2
Terregens factor	—	22.4
One or more vitamins	27.1	50.5

biotin, riboflavin, pyridoxine, inositol, and p-aminobenzoic acid have been demonstrated. It is likely that these substances are produced by the microflora because the vitamins in plant residues are destroyed during decomposition. Numerous bacteria synthesize and excrete amino acids which serve to support proliferation of the more fastidious types. Further, thiamine, riboflavin, and vitamin B_{12} are produced by more than one-fourth and biotin and the terregens factor (an unidentified growth-stimulating compound) are formed by about one-fifth of the soil bacteria (table 1). Bacteria commonly excrete several vitamins, not just one. The synthesis of vitamins and amino acids in vitro does not signify the same occurs in the field, yet it does suggest that potentiality. Thus, the prevalence of organisms requiring growth factors probably results from the synthesis and release by other microorganisms of these substances. Undoubtedly, the effect is non-specific —i.e., the organisms synthesizing the compounds do not have symbiotic partners; rather the association is fortuitous. Because of the importance of such substances in nutrition, the interactions arising from the excretion of and need for growth factors probably are among the major biological determinants of the floral composition.

Protocooperation has also been of interest in studies of the N_2-fixing bacteria. *Azotobacter* spp. assimilate N_2, but they require simple organic compounds as carbon sources.   However, N_2 can be fixed by azotobacter with cellulose as energy source provided that a cellulose decomposer is present to convert the polysaccharide to simple sugars or organic acids (12).   Analogous instances of protocooperators providing assimilable organic products for azotobacter have been reported for starch and xylan, both of which are unavailable to most azotobacter strains.   Similarly, the partner for the bacterium may be an alga which provides the carbon by CO_2 fixation.

Symbiosis occurs between certain bacteria or fungi and plants. Agronomically, the *Rhizobium*-legume symbiosis is the most important as it results in appreciable nitrogen gains.   This is a true symbiosis as neither plant nor bacterium utilizes N_2 in the absence of the second symbiont.   The mycorrhizal, fungus-plant root association is another instance of a symbiosis.   There is also an association between bacteria and plants in which the leaves are the site of interaction.   The leaves of the tropical genera *Pavetta, Grumilea, Ardisia,* and *Psychotria* contain bacteria localized in nodular structures, but the function of the swellings is not clear.

Microbial Competition

Microorganisms inoculated into sterile soil develop rapidly and attain large population sizes; similar inoculations into non-sterile soil lead to poor growth, and often the seeded species is eliminated in a period of days or weeks.   The difference is entirely the result of biological interrelationships of an injurious nature.   Detrimental effects of one species upon its neighbors are quite common in soil, and they are detected by the decrease in abundance or metabolic activities of the more susceptible organism.   The compounding of simple interactions found in two culture systems into the multi-organism complex of the soil results in a diversity of harmful associations.   As a consequence, there is a permanent struggle for existence in the habitat, and only those species most fitted for the specific environment survive.

The categories of deleterious interactions are summarized by the terms competition, amensalism, parasitism, and predation, that is, (a) the rivalry for limiting nutrients, (b) the release by one species of products toxic to its neighbors, and (c) the direct feeding of one organism upon a second.   Because the supply of nutrients in soil is perennially inadequate, competition for carbon, minerals, or O_2 is quite common.   Alteration of the environment to the detriment of certain microbial groups may occur through the synthesis of metabolic products that are bacteriostatic or bactericidal, by the utilization of O_2 which leads to the suppression of obligate aerobes, or by the autotrophic formation of nitric and sulfuric acids which affects the proliferation of acid-sensitive microorganisms. Predatory and parasitic activities likewise are not rare. Predation and parasitism are observed in the feeding upon bacteria by protozoa and myxobacteria, the attack on nematodes by predacious fungi, the digestion of fungal hyphae by bacteria, and the lysis of bacteria and actinomycetes by bacteriophages.

In mixed cultures of several microorganisms in laboratory media or in partially sterilized soil, some species are suppressed while others survive, multiply, and assume dominance. The usual cause of this phenomenon is the competition for nutrients, space, or O_2. In competition, certain microorganisms dominate through their capacity to make most effective use of the limiting factors in the environment. Therefore, when large populations of alien bacteria are added to soil, the invaders do not become established and soon die out (25). The habitat is foreign, and the invader fails to find a niche. The disappearance itself is probably the result of competitive effects since specific toxic substances active against the alien bacteria are difficult to demonstrate.

The competitive phenomenon has been studied using *Fusarium oxysporum* as the test organism. A large proportion of the soil bacteria is observed to effectively inhibit the fungus. Under the experimental conditions, the major mechanism of the suppression is nutrient competition, particularly for nitrogen. This is shown in figure 1 for sterile soil inoculated simultaneously with *F. oxysporum* and *Agrobacterium radiobacter*. Indeed, the suppression can usually be reversed by the addition of nitrate. The most effective competitors for *F. oxysporum* apparently are organisms with simple nutrient requirements (19). Competition for nitrogen as reported for *F. oxysporum* is not uncommon. The presence of assimilable nitrogen, for example, prolongs the persistence of *Ophiobolus graminis*, cause of the take-all disease of wheat, and a lowering of the available nitrogen content by cropping practices decreases the incidence of the disease in the following crop (7). Soil amendment with organic materials also inhibits *Rhizoctonia solani*, and nitrogen supplementation here too mitigates the suppression (2). Microbiological competition for available carbon, however, is probably one of the more important

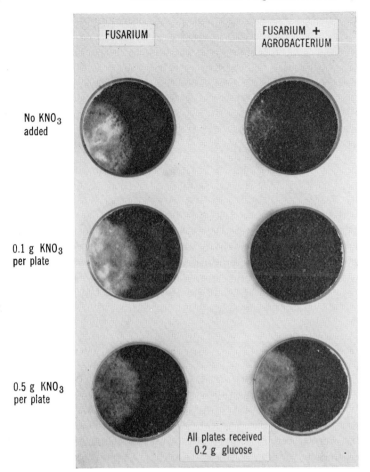

Figure 1. Suppression of *Fusarium oxysporum* by *Agrobacterium radiobacter* in sterilized soil and reversal of the suppression by nitrogen (19).

interactions between organisms. It is likely that the role of an element in modifying the biological equilibrium is determined by the demand of the microflora and the supply in the soil.

As a first approximation, the ability of an organism to compete is probably governed by its capacity to utilize the carbonaceous substrates found in soil, its growth rate, and its nutritional complexity. A simple nutrition could be advantageous, but the presence in soil of growth factors suggests that effective competitors need not be nutritionally independent, for they can develop at the expense of growth factors obtained from the environment.

Antibiosis

When a diluted soil suspension is plated upon a rich agar medium, many of the individual bacterial, actinomycete, and fungal colonies appearing on the petri dishes are found to be in close proximity. Nevertheless, one or more of the colonies occasionally is surrounded by a clear zone in which no other organism appears. This halo devoid of growth is good presumptive evidence that the colony surrounded by the zone of clearing is producing an *antibiotic*. An antibiotic is a substance formed by one organism which, in low concentrations, inhibits the growth of another organism. The capacity of an individual colony on a dilution plate to produce an antibiotic is confirmed by streaking the culture upon fresh agar, and, after 2 to 3 days, crossing the line of growth with perpendicular streaks of one or more test species. Following a suitable period of incubation, antibiosis is observed as a suppression of the test organism. Antibiotic synthesis can also be demonstrated by ascertaining the toxicity of culture solutions following the development of the suspected microorganisms.

Many soil inhabitants produce inhibitory substances in laboratory media, and it is not difficult to isolate strains which, when tested in pure culture, antagonize a variety of bacteria, fungi, or actinomycetes. The frequent isolation of antibiotic-producers demonstrates their wide distribution in soil. A variety of actinomycetes, bacteria, and fungi are able to synthesize antibiotics. Actinomycetes are particularly active in this regard, and streptomycin, chloramphenicol, cycloheximide, and chlortetracycline are but a few of the important chemotherapeutic substances synthesized by them. Most industrially prominent actinomycetes originally were obtained from soil. Antibiosis is especially common among *Streptomyces* isolates, but numerous strains of *Nocardia* and *Micromonospora* are likewise active. The most frequently encountered bacteria synthesizing antibiotics are aerobic, spore-forming *Bacillus* spp. and strains of *Pseudomonas* that liberate pyocyanin and related compounds. Species of *Penicillium, Trichoderma, Aspergillus, Fusarium,* and other fungi also excrete antibiotic substances.

Antibiotics are effective in inhibiting or killing susceptible fungi, bacteria, and actinomycetes. Representative data are presented in

TABLE 2

Antibiotic Production by Actinomycetes, Fungi, and Bacteria

Antibiotic-Producers *	Susceptible Organisms	Reference
1.7% of actinomycetes	*Sclerotium rolfsii*	20
21% of *Streptomyces*	*Escherichia coli*	11
12.2% of actinomycetes	*Streptomyces scabies*	17
16.0% of fungi	*Pythium arrhenomanes*	18
3.5% of fungi	*Sclerotium rolfsii*	20
3.6% of bacteria	*Pythium arrhenomanes*	18
0.2% of bacteria	*Sclerotium rolfsii*	20

* Per cent of isolates producing antibiotics effective against the test species.

table 2. The relative abundance of organisms suppressing any individual test species varies markedly with the locality from which the soil sample was obtained. Further, estimates of the numbers of antagonistic isolates will depend upon the species used for sensitivity determination because some organisms are inhibited by a large number of isolates while others are relatively immune to antibiotics. The degree of suppression therefore depends upon the soil sampled, the producing strain, and the test species. In addition, many microorganisms produce more than one toxic metabolite in culture media, and each may act upon a different group of organisms.

Despite the high proportion of soil inhabitants producing antibiotics in culture, the role of these organisms in the population equilibrium and their significance in determining the composition of the soil microflora are unknown. Thus, though most chemotherapeutic antibiotics originate from soil-borne saprophytes, the significance of the toxic compounds in the natural environment of the active species remains a point of considerable controversy.

One of the strongest arguments for antibiosis as a natural phenomenon arises from the assumption that products synthesized by so many organisms must have some beneficial effect for the cells producing them. Because of the abundance and ubiquity of the responsible microorganisms, it is necessary either to accept the importance of antibiosis or to postulate that the toxic products have no ecological value, being metabolic errors maintained through innumerable generations. There are several lines of evidence which may be indicative of the importance of antibiotic-producers in soil. Four will be cited to illustrate the type of information presently available: (a) the abundance of microorganisms which, when isolated from soil and tested in culture media, inhibit the growth of test species; (b) the greater persistence in soil of indigenous than of alien fungi in the presence of antibiotic-forming bacteria—i.e., soil fungi have been naturally selected for antibiotic resistance (22); (c) those *Streptomyces* having the greatest antibiotic potency against certain test fungi in laboratory media generally have the most marked effect on the fungi when tested in sterile soil (24); and (d) the formation of antibiotics in normal soil amended with 1 or more per cent organic matter (13).

The sheer abundance of these microorganisms in soil may have led to an overemphasis of their ecological significance. The weight of numbers has been highly suggestive of a significant position for antibiotic-producing strains in microbial population equilibria. On closer examination, however, the picture is not entirely clear. There is little evidence that antibiotics are formed in normal soil to bring about some of the antagonistic or detrimental interactions resembling those in sterile soil or in culture media. The arguments opposing the view of antibiosis as a major factor regulating the microbiological equilibrium may be summarized by the following five points. (a) There is no evidence that the ability to produce antibiotics favors survival of the active cultures. Toxin synthesizers, despite their apparent competitive advantage, are not particularly more common than the innocuous organisms. (b) No relationship has been demonstrated between the predominant species in soil and their sensitivity or resistance to antibiotics as might be expected. Indeed, the predominant bacteria are generally quite sensitive to antibiotics. (c) The rapid disappearance in soil of alien microorganisms is not associated with the build-up of toxins effective against the invaders. Clearly, the mechanism of elimination is by means other than antibiosis. (d) Following the addition of antibiotic-forming organisms to natural soil, the active principle presumably synthesized cannot be detected. Often, the population in the inoculum dies off. Certain antibiotics are synthesized when the appropriate microorganism is added to sterile soil, but organic amendments are frequently required even in sterile samples. At this point, however, the habitat is no longer soil but only a laboratory medium containing sand, silt, clay, and organic matter. (e) Antibiotics introduced into or formed in soil may be inactivated through adsorption, by chemical reaction, or by biological decomposition. Clay minerals adsorb basic antibiotics such as streptomycin, but there is little adsorption of acidic or neutral compounds. Actinomycin, chloramphenicol, chlortetracycline, cycloheximide, griseofulvin, patulin, penicillin, streptomycin, and others are degraded by the microflora.

Nevertheless, none of the arguments cited eliminates the possible microecological significance of antibiosis. Antibiotics may be a powerful force in small locales immediately surrounding the active organisms. The release of toxic products may indeed take place at those sites where conditions are favorable and the quantity of substrate adequate. In spite of the rapid biological and chemical inactivation of many of these compounds, the zone immediately surrounding the active species may conceivably contain a concentration sufficient to exert a marked local effect yet be too small for detection by present techniques. According to this hypothesis, the influence of antibiotics is expressed only in the vicinity of the antagonist, and the phenomenon of antibiosis can be considered not as a general environmental characteristic but as a restricted although important microbial interaction.

The ability of a species to colonize a microscopic locale could well be conditioned by its ability to suppress its neighbors at that individual site. In this sense, therefore, antibiotic production is one of the several weapons in the struggle for existence in microenvironments, and it can be classified together with rapid growth, nutritional complexity, and physiological adaptability as mechanisms favoring colonization and survival in mixed populations. The hypothesis that antibiotic production likely occurs in microenvironments has little relationship to the possibility of harnessing the antibiotic-forming microflora for the control of soil-borne pathogens. Commercial production of these toxic chemicals should be viewed as analogous to man's selection of certain plants as food crops. In both instances, man has applied his ingenuity to select organisms from nature and to cultivate them under artificial conditions for his own benefit. The environment in one instance is farm land; for the microorganism, the artificial environment is the industrial fermentation tank.

Toxic materials have, however, been observed in a wide variety of soils. These substances are inhibitory to bacteria and to spore germination and vegetative growth of fungi (6, 10). The effective principles are detected readily in ether and alcoholic extracts, but aqueous leachates also have antimicrobial activity. The factor or factors are widespread, but there are qualitative and quantitative variations in different soil types. The toxins may yet be associated with some unknown or inadequately described inhibitory substance produced in small amounts by certain common microorganisms.

Predation and Parasitism

Predation is one of the more dramatic interrelationships among microorganisms in nature. Of the many microscopic inhabitants of soil, the bacteria stand out as particularly prone to the attack of predators. The most numerous predators upon bacteria are the protozoa, which, by feeding upon the millions of true bacteria, undoubtedly affect the population balance. The prey, however, is never overwhelmed as the protozoa themselves are governed by the biological equilibrium. In the predator-prey relationship between protozoa and bacteria, a change in either group will bring about a qualitative and quantitative change in the other. The presence of a nutrient supply in the form of bacteria is essential for the development of soil protozoa, and large numbers of bacteria must be ingested for one protozoan cell division. In well-manured fields, the daily increases in bacteria and protozoa seem to be inversely related, one group increases as the other decreases (4). Protozoa, therefore, are undoubtedly a key factor in limiting the size of the bacterial population, probably reducing the abundance of edible cells and serving as a biological antagonist in maintaining the equilibrium.

Myxobacteria and myxomycetes also affect the true bacteria by feeding directly upon them. Both of these predacious groups are common in arable land. Prior to its digestion, the bacterial cell is usually destroyed by extracellular lytic enzymes produced by the myxobacteria, but the myxomycetes may be holozoic. Of the two predatory groups, the myxobacteria are numerically preponderant so that their significance is probably greater. The survey by Anscombe and Singh (1) has revealed that more than half of the soil bacteria are edible by amoebae, myxobacteria, and myxomycetes. Bacteria edible by one micropredator type are often edible by others, but not a few bacteria are relatively resistant to predation. The information on predation is too scant, however, to help account for the dominance of certain bacterial genera and the scarcity of others.

The capacity to lyse microorganisms is not restricted to myxobacteria. The feeding upon fungus mycelium is common among the bacteria, and bacterial development at the expense of mold hyphae is frequently noted upon microscope slides that have been buried in

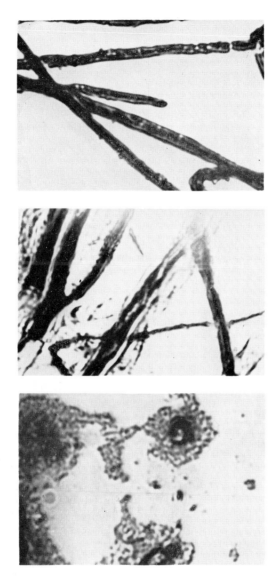

Figure 2. Lysis of *Fusarium oxysporum* mycelium by *Bacillus* sp. Top: original hyphae; center: partial disintegration; bottom: total lysis, bacteria alone remain.

the soil. The lytic association may serve as a natural control measure for fungus proliferation. Certain *Bacillus* spp. are capable of liberating extracellular enzymes that lyse the fungus mycelium, probably by digestion of the cell wall (9). The lysis leads to a complete disintegration of the mycelium (figure 2). A number of *Streptomyces* strains also cause a distinct lysis of fungal hyphae and bacterial cells; with some of the actinomycetes, the action is due to antibiotics, but frequently the effect results from the formation of extracellular enzymes by the streptomycetes (3).

Fungi are capable of parasitizing one another, and the parasitized species is thereby often eliminated. The parasitism may entail a penetration into the host's mycelium or a coiling around the host's hyphae. The virulence of individual fungi varies greatly even in a single species. Certain fungi are predacious, capturing and consuming nematodes or amoebae, and the study of the nematode-trapping fungi may prove of practical value in the control of plant diseases caused by nematodes.

Microbial Associations and Plant Pathogens

Soil-borne plant pathogens, with few exceptions, are more destructive to their hosts in sterile than in normal soil. Moreover, the virulence of pathogens introduced into sterile soil is markedly reduced if saprophytes are added to the inoculum. These and other facts demonstrate that the normal, saprophytic microflora helps regulate the incidence or severity of plant disease. The population of non-pathogens competes with or antagonizes the disease-producing microorganism and slows its rate of spread. Because of the practical significance of the pathogen-microflora interaction, many attempts have been made to modify the microbiological equilibrium in the hope of controlling specific plant pathogens. Two approaches to biological control have been studied: (*a*) the direct inoculation into soil of organisms producing antibiotics effective against pathogens in culture and (*b*) the modification of the environment to effect an alteration in the microflora such that the activities of the altered flora will be deleterious to the pathogen, without regard to the mechanism of the suppression.

In the first approach, isolates are chosen on the basis of their ability to exhibit antibiosis to the pathogen in laboratory media. The strains selected are then tested to determine whether they control the pathogen in the absence of a competing microflora, that is, in sterile soil. The latter procedure provides a means of assessing whether soil organic matter supplies the required carbonaceous nutrients, but it also shows whether the toxic factor is produced under conditions approaching normality. In investigations in which pathogen and antibiotic-producer are inoculated into sterile soil or sand planted to the susceptible host, significant control of many diseases has been reported. For example, *Pythium* damping off can be controlled with strains of *Trichoderma* and *Streptomyces* (8), and selected actinomycetes will reduce the severity of the root-rot of wheat caused by *Helminthosporium sativum* (23).

The ultimate test is to ascertain whether the antibiotic synthesizer will control the pathogen in natural soil where the indigenous population is functioning. In order for antibiotic production by introduced organisms to be of significance in the control of pathogens, the antagonist must be established, the antibiotic must be produced, the toxin must accumulate to levels that are inhibitory, and it must then persist for periods sufficiently long for effectiveness to be assured. In the final test in natural soil, almost all antagonistic inocula fail to carry out their desired purpose, and reports of successful field control are rare. The failures probably result from the inability of the introduced organism to establish itself and to produce the desired compounds under the stress of competition by the native population. Needless to say, the pathogen is already surviving in a habitat containing many organisms able to produce antibiotics. Further, it is unlikely that significant changes in the composition of a population will result from the mere addition of an organism. Competition with indigenous groups readily eliminates such invaders. The native population together with the physical and chemical characteristics of the environment define the composition of the microflora, and the addition of large populations has little effect in causing permanent biological alteration.

Success in the use of inocula of antibiotic-producing strains may be achieved in the suppression of seed- and seedling-infecting pathogens because the antagonists can be applied in large numbers to the small area where the pathogen must grow, at the seed surface, and where nutrients are probably relatively abundant. Thus, the damping off of Scots-pine seedlings, caused by *Fusarium* spp., has been controlled by treating the seeds with antibiotic-forming bacteria (14), and *Pythium* infection of white mustard seeds has been controlled by dusting the seeds with spores of *Trichoderma viride* and other fungi (26).

TABLE 3

Influence of Organic Amendments on the Pathogenicity of *Rhizoctonia solani* to Snap Beans (5)

	Infection Index *	
Amendment	Mature Residues	Immature Residues
None	4.31	2.88
Oak sawdust	4.05	—
Timothy	2.69	1.51
Wheat straw	2.37	—
Buckwheat	2.26	3.28
Soybeans	1.90	1.77
Sudan grass	1.69	1.72
Corn	—	2.30

* Mean severity rating of surviving bean plants on a scale of 0 (no disease) to 5 (hypocotyls completely girdled).

Of greater practical promise is the application to soil of various organic amendments. These treatments do reduce disease severity even in natural conditions (table 3). The incorporation of crop residues leads to a marked increase in the abundance and activities of non-pathogenic microorganisms and often a concomitant decrease in the pathogen's numbers. The rapid rise of the former population may make conditions unfavorable for the latter through competition for nutrients or O_2, by building up the CO_2 concentration to a deleterious level, or by antibiotic biosynthesis. Technical problems have prevented precise experimentation, and most approaches to these studies, therefore, have been largely empirical. Hence, the mechanism of the biological control of soil-borne pathogens by organic amendments remains unresolved.

REFERENCES

Reviews

Brian, P. W. 1957. The ecological significance of antibiotic production. In R. E. O. Williams and C. C. Spicer, eds., *Microbial ecology*. Cambridge Univ. Press, Cambridge, pp. 168–188.

Duddington, C. L. 1957. The predacious fungi and their place in microbial ecology. In R. E. O. Williams and C. C. Spicer, eds., *Microbial ecology.* Cambridge Univ. Press, Cambridge, pp. 218–237.

Lochhead, A. G. 1958. Soil bacteria and growth-promoting substances. *Bacteriol. Rev.,* 22:145–153.

Odum, E. P. 1959. *Fundamentals of ecology.* W. B. Saunders Co., Philadelphia.

Pramer, D. 1958. The persistence and biological effects of antibiotics in soil. *Applied Microbiol.,* 6:221–224.

Waksman, S. A. 1956. The role of antibiotics in natural processes. *Giorn. Microbiol.,* 2:1–14.

Wood, R. K. S., and M. Tveit. 1955. Control of plant diseases by use of antagonistic organisms. *Botan. Rev.,* 21:441–492.

Literature cited

1. Anscombe, F. J., and B. N. Singh. 1948. *Nature,* 161:140–141.
2. Blair, I. D. 1943. *Ann. Applied Biol.,* 30:118–127.
3. Carter, H. P., and J. L. Lockwood. 1957. *Phytopathol.,* 47:154–158.
4. Cutler, D. W., and L. M. Crump. 1935. *Problems in soil microbiology.* Longmans, Green and Co., London.
5. Davey, C. B., and G. C. Papavizas. 1959. *Agron. J.,* 51:493–496.
6. Dobbs, C. G., and W. H. Hinson. 1953. *Nature,* 172:197–199.
7. Garrett, S. D., and H. H. Mann. 1948. *Ann. Applied Biol.,* 35:435–442.
8. Gregory, K. F., O. N. Allen, A. J. Riker, and W. H. Peterson. 1952. *Phytopathol.,* 42:613–622.
9. Horikoshi, K., and S. Iida. 1958. *Nature,* 181:917–918.
10. Jackson, R. M. 1958. *J. Gen. Microbiol.,* 18:248–258.
11. Jagnow, G. 1956. *Arch. Mikrobiol.,* 25:274–296.
12. Jensen, H. L., and R. J. Swaby. 1941. *Nature,* 147:147–148.
13. Krasilnikov, N. A. 1954. *Dokl. Akad. Nauk S.S.S.R.,* 94:957–960.
14. Krasilnikov, N. A., and E. A. Raznitsina. 1946. *Agrobiologiya,* 1946(5/6): 109–121.
15. Lochhead, A. G. 1957. *Soil Sci.,* 84:395–403.
16. Lochhead, A. G., and M. O. Burton. 1957. *Canad. J. Microbiol.,* 3:35–42.
17. Lochhead, A. G., and G. B. Landerkin. 1949. *Plant and Soil,* 1:271–276.
18. Luke, H. H., and T. D. Connell. 1954. *Phytopathol.,* 44:377–379.
19. Marshall, K. C., and M. Alexander. 1960. *Plant and Soil,* 12:143–153.
20. Morton, D. J., and W. H. Stroube. 1955. *Phytopathol.,* 45:417–420.
21. Nurmikko, V. 1953. *Symp., Nutrition and growth factors, 6th Intl. Cong. Microbiol.,* Rome, pp. 97–112.
22. Park, D. 1957. *Trans. Brit. Mycol. Soc.,* 40:283–291.
23. Stevenson, I. L. 1954. *Nature,* 174:598–599.
24. Stevenson, I. L. 1956. *J. Gen. Microbiol.,* 14:440–448.
25. Waksman, S. A., and A. Schatz. 1946. *J. Bacteriol.,* 51:305–316.
26. Wright, J. M. 1956. *Plant and Soil,* 8:132–140.

25

Microbiology
of the Rhizosphere

The root system of higher plants is associated not only with an inanimate environment composed of organic and inorganic substances but also with a vast population of metabolically active microorganisms. The microflora that responds to the presence of living roots is distinctly different from the characteristic soil population, the plant creating a unique subterranean habitat for microorganisms. The plant, in turn, is markedly affected by the population it has stimulated since the root zone is the site from which mineral nutrients are obtained and through which pathogens must penetrate. Consequently, interactions between the macro- and the microorganism in this locale can have a considerable significance for crop production and soil fertility. This unique environment under the influence of plant roots is called the *rhizosphere*.

The rhizosphere is often divided into two general areas, the inner rhizosphere at the very root surface and the outer rhizosphere embracing the immediately adjacent soil. The microbial population is larger in the inner zone where the biochemical interactions between microorganisms and roots are most pronounced. The root surface and its adhering soil is sometimes termed the *rhizoplane*. In the rhizosphere and rhizoplane, several relationships between macroorganisms and microorganisms can be recognized. Symbiotic phenomena are observed between legumes and rhizobia and in the mycorrhizal associations. Pathogenic relationships are not uncommon because roots are attacked by a number of fungi, bacteria, and nematodes. Commensalism and protocooperation, however, are usually the dominant types of interaction between the plant and its rhizosphere inhabitants. In the subterranean partnership, the higher organism contributes excretory products and sloughed-off tissue; the dominant subterranean flora probably has no detrimental influence upon the plant harboring it. More likely, certain benefits are derived from the microscopic population.

Microflora of the Root Zone

The rhizosphere region is a highly favorable habitat for the proliferation and metabolism of numerous microbial types. The population has been investigated intensively by microscopic, cultural, and biochemical techniques. For microscopic studies of the environment, various modifications of the buried slide method of Rossi and Cholodny have been introduced. Commonly, the glass slide is inserted into the soil in such a way that the root ultimately grows up to and along the surface of the glass. The slides are then removed, stained, and examined. Microscopic characterizations are of considerable value for they show the types of organisms present and their physical association with the outer tissue surface. For cultural investigations, the plant is carefully removed from the field or from the greenhouse pot and the superfluous soil dislodged by gentle agitation. The roots and the adhering soil are placed in a tared flask containing a known volume of sterile diluent. Dilution series are prepared and plate counts made. The biochemical techniques used in rhizosphere investigations are numerous, and they are designed to measure a specific change brought about by the plant or by the microflora.

Microscopic examination reveals the presence of a vast microbial population surrounding and upon the surfaces of roots and root hairs. Bacteria are found to be localized in colonies and chains of individual cells. Filamentous fungi and actinomycetes are observed but not as frequently. Protozoa are relatively conspicuous, particularly the small flagellates and large ciliates; they are situated in the water films on the root hairs and on the epidermal tissue (14, 27). Microscopic studies show further that the population at a short distance from the root is little affected by the plant while soil immediately adjacent to the root contains an abundance of bacteria.

Plate counts likewise reveal the stimulation. Cultural methods, at the same time, show the selective enhancement of certain categories of bacteria. The root influence, as measured by plating techniques, is often expressed as a *rhizosphere effect,* a stimulation which can be put on a quantitative basis by the use of the R:S relationship. The R:S ratio is defined as the ratio of microbial numbers per unit weight of rhizosphere soil, R, to the population in a unit weight of the adjacent non-rhizosphere or control soil, S. The rhizosphere effect is consistently greater for bacteria than for the other microbial inhabitants. This is apparent from the higher R:S ratios for bacteria than for algae, protozoa, and fungi (table 1). Soil samples taken progressively closer to the root system have increasingly greater bacterial numbers while the fungi and actinomycetes may become more abundant, but the rise in viable counts of the filamentous microorganisms is usually slight.

The bacteria reacting to the presence of the root belong to several distinctly different physiological, taxonomic, and morphological groups. Those responding most markedly are the short, gram negative rods, which almost invariably make up a larger percentage of the rhizosphere than of the normal soil flora. The percentage incidence of short, gram positive rods, coccoid rods, and spore-forming bacteria (*Bacillus* spp.) declines. There apparently is no selective

TABLE 1

Rhizosphere Effect on Various Microbiological Groups in Soils Planted to Mangels (9)

Group	R:S Ratio			
	Unfertilized Soil		Manured Soil	
	80 days	117 days	80 days	117 days
Bacteria, total	35	45	26	120
Anaerobic bacteria	19	40	12	46
Nitrosomonas spp.	0.9	2.2	6.0	1.4
Ammonifiers	17	9	29	167
Denitrifiers	43	15	29	230
Azotobacter spp.	0.4	5.3	0.9	1.5
Fungi	2.5	6	2.5	19
Algae	0.4	1.5	1.4	2.3
Protozoa	2.4	4.0	1.2	23

stimulation or inhibition of the gram variable rods, the *Arthrobacter* group, cocci, or of the long, non-spore-forming rods. For example, 44 per cent of the bacteria in the tobacco plant rhizosphere are short, gram negative rods as compared to 13 per cent of the bacteria in the control soil. If to this percentage increase is added the fact that there are several-fold more bacteria about the roots than away from them, the magnitude of the stimulation can be appreciated (15). Even when, for the purposes of experimentation, artificial rhizospheres are created by cultivation of plants in nutrient solutions or by the addition of excretion products to fallow soil, it is the gram negative bacteria which are favored over the gram positives and the non-spore-formers over the spore-formers (22).

The short, gram negative rods of this habitat are classified largely as strains of *Pseudomonas, Achromobacter,* and occasionally *Agrobacterium.* It is upon these three genera that the root effect appears to be most pronounced. Many other bacteria are found in the root zone, particularly species of *Arthrobacter, Mycoplana, Brevibacterium, Flavobacterium, Serratia, Sarcina, Alginomonas, Bacillus,* and *Mycobacterium,* but they apparently are not as well suited to the environment (25). The stimulation of *Pseudomonas, Achromobacter,* and *Agrobacterium* has been verified in studies of agronomic and horticultural crops in addition to non-agricultural species. Because of the interest in bacteria related to *Rhizobium,* the abundance of *Agrobacterium radiobacter* cells in the vicinity of legumes was quickly established. The stimulation of this species is greatest with cowpeas, less with field peas and vetch, and the response is least with soybeans (24). Anaerobic bacteria also are affected by the root influence (table 1); this may be attributed to the reduced O_2 tension resulting from root and microbial respiration. Pigment-producing *Arthrobacter globiforme* and *Chromobacterium* strains frequently benefit from their proximity to living roots whereas the number of aerobic spore-formers (*Bacillus* spp.) is either unaltered or slightly reduced. However, there seems to be a qualitative difference between soil and rhizosphere *Bacillus* species; thus, *Bacillus circulans, B. brevis,* and *B. polymyxa* are generally more common on plant roots than outside of the rhizosphere zone (4).

Because the bacterial density in the rhizosphere is so great, frequently in excess of 10^9 cells per gram, there must be a high degree of microbiological competition. In the stress resulting from a large population, fast-growing organisms might be favored as their rapid growth would enable them to compete more effectively. Indeed, representative isolates from the rhizospheres of many crops tend to develop more rapidly than bacteria from fallow soil. At the same time, the biochemically more active organisms are favored to the detriment of less versatile strains (10, 20). This suggests that the rhizosphere flora has a greater ability to effect rapid biochemical changes than the organisms of uncropped land.

The scheme for grouping bacteria by their nutritional complexity (Chapter 2) has been especially useful in studies of the rhizosphere microflora. This classification system divides bacteria into seven groups on the basis of requirements for or stimulation by (a) no special factors, (b) amino acids, (c) B vitamins, (d) amino acids and B vitamins, (e) yeast extract, (f) soil extract, and (g) yeast extract plus soil extract. Applied to the bacteria surrounding the root, the nutritional classification reveals a consistent, preferential stimulation of organisms stimulated by or requiring amino acids and those proliferating in the absence of preformed growth factors (table 2). The preferential enhancement is seen in the greater percentage abundance of these two nutritional groups in rhizosphere than in control soil, a stimulation that is superimposed upon the general increase in numbers. Simultaneously, the proportion of bacteria with a com-

TABLE 2

Incidence of Nutritional Groups of Bacteria in the Rhizosphere of Oats (32)

Requirements for Maximum Growth	Percentage of Total		Total Count/g $\times 10^3$	
	Control	Rhizo-sphere	Control	Rhizosphere
None [*]	12.6	33.1	31,500	688,000
Amino acids	2.2	11.0	5,500	229,000
B vitamins	8.9	11.7	22,300	244,000
Amino acids, B vitamins	1.5	<1	3,800	<20,000
Yeast extract	26.7	18.6	66,800	387,000
Soil extract	23.0	17.9	57,600	372,000
Yeast extract, soil extract	24.4	7.6	61,000	158,000

[*] Grow in medium with sugar and inorganic salts.

plex nutrition, particularly those requiring soil extract or yeast extract plus soil extract, declines although their actual numbers increase.

The selection for bacteria whose development is enhanced by amino acids undoubtedly is associated with an increased level of amino acids in this environment. The amino compounds may be derived from plant exudates, from the decomposition of the nitrogenous constituents of dead root tissue and microbial cells, or from excretions of the microscopic inhabitants. Non-sterile sand or sand-soil mixtures supporting plant growth contain a number of amino acids including glutamic acid, aspartic acid, proline, leucine, alanine, cysteine, glycine, lysine, and phenylalanine. Plants cultivated under asepsis also liberate amino substances but in much smaller quantities. These compounds are utilized by microorganisms to satisfy their amino acid demand (11). Moreover, many of the bacteria that require no added growth factors excrete amino acids; therefore, the stimulation in the root zone may arise from the activities of the microorganisms as well as of the macroorganisms.

In contrast to their effects upon bacteria, roots do not alter appreciably the total counts of fungi. On the other hand, specific fungal genera are stimulated; i.e., the influence is selective to the type rather than the total number. Continuous cultivation of a single crop frequently favors *Aspergillus, Fusarium, Penicillium, Rhizopus,* or *Chaetomium,* but the genera dominating the environment vary with the crop, the soil, and the climate. Differing from the relatively high proportion of the fungal colonies on soil dilution plates which arise from spores, the fungus units in the rhizosphere occur to a large extent in the vegetative state (1).

As a rule, actinomycetes, protozoa, and algae are not significantly benefited by their proximity to roots, and the R:S ratios rarely exceed 2 or 3:1. Under certain circumstances such as around roots of old plants, R:S ratios for these microbial groups may become high. Because of the large bacterial population, an increase in the number or activity of protozoa is not unexpected.

The flora of the rhizosphere is affected by a number of factors. Proximity of the soil sample to the root is particularly important, and the bacterial count increases in samples taken progressively closer to the tissue surface. Simultaneously, the total activities of the population, measured by CO_2 evolution, are enhanced by closeness to the root. The depth of sampling is another important ecological variable. To study the influence of depth, a trench is made to expose the roots in vertical section, and samples are taken at various points for analysis. In agreement with results obtained for fallow soil, the population of bacteria, fungi, algae, and of most physiological categories of bacteria declines with depth (30).

Different plant species often establish somewhat different subterranean floras. The differences are attributed to variations in rooting habits, tissue composition, and excretion products of the macroorganism. The primary root population is determined by the habitat created by the plant; the secondary flora, however, depends upon the activities of the initial population. As a rule, legumes engender a more pronounced rhizosphere effect than grasses or grain crops, and alfalfa and several clovers have an especially pronounced influence on bacteria. Biennials, because of their long growth period, exert a more prolonged stimulation than annuals. At the same time, individual crops cause a striking response in one or two bacterial genera, e.g., *Pseudomonas* or *Agrobacterium*. The cause of the qualitative and quantitative differences among plants is not known.

The age of the plant also alters the underground flora, and the stage of maturity controls the magnitude of the rhizosphere effect and the degree of response by specific microorganisms. A stimulation is detectable in 3-day-old seedlings, the R:S ratios ranging from 12 to 23:1. As the seedlings develop, the R:S ratios generally increase (29). Because of the beneficial influences exerted by very young seedlings, it would seem that the microorganisms are responding to root excretions rather than to decomposable, dead tissues. During later development, however, dead and sloughed-off tissue may contribute appreciably to the microbiological composition of the environment. On the other hand, near the very end of the growing season when the roots are dying, the readily available carbohydrates are quickly metabolized, and the population declines. In time, the large rhizosphere population gradually fades, becoming indistinguishable from the normal soil flora. There is little if any residual microbiological effect carried over to the following year; the new crop largely determines its own rhizosphere composition. The results of the biochemical transformations, nevertheless, may persist; e.g., the contribution of *Rhizobium* spp. to the nitrogen status of soil is reflected in the yields of succeeding crops. But the composition of the microflora itself reverts to its original state with a diminution in the number of non-spore-formers and an increase in the relative abundance of spore-forming bacilli.

The microscopic inhabitants of fallow land and non-rhizosphere habitats respond greatly to additions of organic materials, but the same is not true within the root zone. Crop residues, animal manures, and chemical fertilizers cause no appreciable qualitative or quantitative changes in the microflora of the root region (31). Other soil treatments likewise have little influence on the total number of organisms. In general, the nature of the crop is more important than the fertility level of the soil. Different plant species in the same field have widely divergent numbers of organisms in their rhizospheres while the composition and size of the population under the same species cultivated in fields of greatly differing fertility status fluctuate only to a moderate extent.

Because the crop plays a greater role than the soil, the nature of the plant's excretions and the chemical constituents of its tissues probably determine to a large extent the microbiological composition of the environment. The vast number of viable cells so close to the root indicates that the plant is excreting and sloughing off large quantities of organic substances. The mechanism of greater importance, excretion or sloughing off, has yet to be ascertained. Regardless of the precise explanation, however, the products ultimately encountered by the microorganisms vary from plant to plant. For example, azotobacter fails to develop in the root zone of corn but is able to grow in the wheat rhizosphere (12). Some of the substances released by plants have been characterized, but the list is far from complete. The excreted compounds include amino acids, simple sugars, and nucleic acid derivatives. These substances are largely true excretions, not the result of sloughing off or decomposition, since the compounds are isolated from aseptically grown plants in the early phases of development. It is of interest that sterile root exudates stimulate the growth of organisms isolated from both rhizosphere and non-rhizosphere soil, but the response to the excreted materials is commonly greater for the isolates from the root zone. For some of the microorganisms, yeast extract provides the same degree of growth promotion as root excretions, suggesting that factors in the excretions are similar to or identical with substances in yeast extract (21).

Influence of the Plant

The microflora is affected in many ways by the growing plant, and microbial reactions important to fertility may be more rapid in the root environment than in non-rhizosphere soil. Undoubtedly, the most important plant contribution to the rhizosphere flora is the provision of excretion products and sloughed-off tissue to serve as sources of energy, carbon, nitrogen, or growth factors. At the same time, the macroorganism assimilates inorganic nutrients, thereby lowering the concentration available for microbial development. Microorganisms are also affected by root respiration, which alters the pH or the availability of certain inorganic nutrients by the evolution of CO_2. Root penetration likewise improves soil structure, and the improved structural relationships favor microbial oxidations.

In the respiration of the root, O_2 is consumed and CO_2 liberated. The utilization by the large microbial population of carbonaceous substrates also leads to the release of CO_2 and the utilization of O_2. Therefore, the respiration of both macro- and microorganisms results in a greater CO_2 production from rhizosphere than from non-rhizosphere soil. To assess factors affecting the microbial contribution to the gaseous exchange, CO_2 production of soil removed from around the roots is compared with that of soil taken at a distance away or from comparable fallow sites. In this manner, it has been shown that the stimulation of organic matter breakdown in soil of the root zone is far more pronounced with mature than with young plants (26). To determine with greater accuracy the microbial contribution, the rate of CO_2 evolution from sterile and non-sterile roots is measured. Comparisons of this type reveal that one-third to two-thirds of the carbon mineralized is the result of microbial respiration.

The large quantities of CO_2 liberated by the rhizosphere inhabitants undoubtedly influence crop nutrition. By forming carbonic acid, the gas can cause a solubilization of insoluble, inorganic nutrients not readily available to the plant. This would effectively increase the supply of assimilable mineral nutrients. By this means, the level of available phosphorus, potassium, magnesium, and calcium may rise. The solubilization phenomenon can be demonstrated by allowing sterile seedlings to grow in sterile soil containing polished marble. Under these conditions, the seedlings etch the marble surface but only to a slight extent. If the sterile system is duplicated except for the introduction of an inoculum of selected bacteria, the etching becomes far more pronounced. The greater change in the presence of the bacteria arises from the increased production of carbonic acid from the CO_2 respired by the microorganisms (6).

One of the physiological groups characteristically responding to the presence of living roots is the ammonifying bacteria. R:S ratios for these bacteria are quite high, varying up to several hundred to one. The stimulation may arise in part from organic nitrogen compounds present in the environment, but ammonifying bacteria are not substrate specific, and their response may be attributable to other environmental factors. Should the selective enhancement be directly related to the capacity to mineralize nitrogenous materials, then the large ammonifying flora should bring about a rapid decomposition of organic nitrogen in the rhizosphere. As predicted, soil samples taken from the root zone produce nitrate more rapidly from humus nitrogen when incubated in the laboratory than samples from fallow sites (26). Such results do not seem to conform with field data as less nitrate is found in cropped than in uncropped soils even if the nitrogen removed by the crop is included in the calculations as mineral nitrogen (figure 1). The field evidence supports the hypothesis that cropping diminishes nitrogen mineralization. On the other hand, the inorganic nitrogen status at any given time represents a balance between immobilization and mineralization. Commonly, the net amount of nitrogen mineralized is significantly lower in cropped than in fallow soils, an apparently reduced mineralization rate when the microflora is under the influence of the plant. However, the lower *net* mineralization can result from an enhancement of immobilization reactions by the large population associated with the roots. Immobilization can be appreciable because organic substances are abundant surrounding the root, and nitrogen is required for their decomposition. The final answer on the fate of nitrogen necessitated the use of N^{15}. Investigations performed with the isotopic tracer have revealed that, despite the fact that the net amount of nitrogen mineralized in soils cropped to non-legumes is about half that in fallow soils, the total quantity of nitrogen mineralized is greater in cropped than in uncropped soils. The differences between the two environments is attributable to the high immobilization rates associated with the root population (2).

Efforts to increase the amount of nitrogen made available to crops by stimulating the N_2-fixing flora of the rhizosphere are of great agricultural importance. The association of rhizobia with leguminous plants provides a dramatic example, but this is a highly specialized relationship in which the nodule provides a selective habitat wherein the rhizobium can develop. Yet, the root population influences the nature of the symbiotic association as shown by observations that some *Rhizobium* strains which are ineffective in sterile soil become effective for N_2 assimilation in non-sterile environments. Likewise, nodulation and N_2 fixation by some partially effective *Rhizobium* strains are enhanced by simultaneous inoculation with several

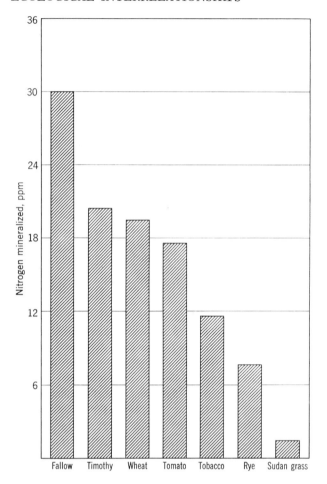

Figure 1. Nitrogen mineralized after 13 weeks in fallow and in cropped soil. The nitrogen content of the crop is included in the calculation of nitrogen mineralized (7).

rhizosphere bacteria and fungi whereas effective cultures are not improved in identical circumstances (8).

It has been reported frequently that the addition of non-symbiotic N_2-fixers to soil effects an increase in the amount of nitrogen made available to the plant or, alternatively, a greater crop yield. The arguments for and against azotobacter inoculation have been discussed previously, but brief mention may be made here of the occurrence of the non-symbionts in the rhizosphere. Larger populations of azotobacter, according to some investigators, are found near and on the root than at a distance away; the rhizospheres of beets, tobacco, mustard, and several legumes seem to exert a favorable effect on azotobacter whereas the bacteria are uncommon under onions, wheat, and corn. The results of many other studies indicate either that the aerobic, non-symbiotic N_2-fixers are unaffected by proximity to the root system or that the increase is too slight to be of consequence for crop production. Climatic or soil differences may account for some of the conflicting views. There is little doubt that, for certain crops in a number of areas, the root exerts a favorable influence upon *Azotobacter* spp. Whether this stimulation is economically important, however, is still subject to question.

The rhizosphere of many plants contains a much greater population of denitrifying bacteria than control soils, and the R:S ratios occasionally exceed 100:1. Although the stimulation could lead to a decline in the concentration of nitrate, there is no chemical evidence that denitrification itself is more pronounced. By contrast, the number of ammonium- and nitrite-oxidizing autotrophs is not markedly influenced by cropping, and the nitrification of ammonium salts proceeds at similar rates in samples from the root environs and from fallow areas (26). Cellulolytic bacteria, on the other hand, are more prevalent in the root zone and decrease in density in samples taken at a distance from the plant. The dominant cellulose-digesting bacteria of the rhizosphere frequently are the cytophagas and short rods (13). The cellulolytic flora may well be responding to the availability of large quantities of cellulosic tissues, and this population is undoubtedly a factor concerned with the degradation of the sloughed-off root material. The products of the metabolism of cellulolytic organisms can provide carbonaceous substrates for other microorganisms.

Root excretions have a pronounced influence on germination of the spores of several fungi. If, for example, the oospores of *Pythium mamillatum* are placed in soil beneath growing turnip seedlings, the oospores germinate. Little or no germination occurs in non-rhizosphere soil or in distilled water, but a stimulatory factor is introduced when developing turnip seedlings are placed in the water (3). Similarly, the germination in soil of the sclerotia of *Sclerotium cepivorum* is benefited by the presence of onions, and aqueous extracts of the onion enhance the rate of germination (5). These and similar results with other fungi demonstrate that roots liberate water-soluble compounds which activate the germination of spores of many fungal types. Such excretions may contribute to the rhizosphere effect upon fungal populations, but the phenomenon assumes particular importance for plant pathogens. Root excretions also are capable of inducing the hatching of nematode cysts. In contrast, roots liberate certain antimicrobial agents which may also play a prominent role in microbial ecology.

Influence of the Microflora

The rhizosphere population may have either a favorable or a detrimental influence upon plant development. Because the microflora is so intimately related with the root system, partially covering its surface, any beneficial or toxic substance produced can cause an immediate and profound response. In the previous discussion, the plant-induced changes in the root zone microflora have been reviewed. Modifications in the abundance of microorganisms or in the relative proportions of individual groups will in turn affect the plant through the microbiologically catalyzed reactions. The production of CO_2 in the rhizosphere and the formation of organic and inorganic acids aid in the solubilization of inorganic plant nutrients. At the same time, the vast microscopic population demands a variety of anions and cations for its own development, and immobilization of nitrogen or phosphorus may assume prominence. Aerobic bacteria remove O_2 from the environment, and O_2 depletion affects root respiration and ion uptake. The rhizosphere microflora may, however, favor plant development by producing growth-stimulating substances, contributing to the development of a stable soil structure, releasing elements in inorganic forms through the mineralization of organic complexes, and by entering into symbiotic root associations. Proposing a mechanism for a beneficial or detrimental relationship is far simpler than providing the experimental results, but evidence for several specific associations has been obtained.

The most direct approach to the establishment of the significance of rhizosphere microorganisms is by a comparison of plant growth in sterile and non-sterile environments. Typically, the rate of development is more rapid in sterile soil receiving an inoculum of organisms than in the uninoculated, sterile controls. Explaining the response, nevertheless, is very difficult. It is known that several bacteria, actinomycetes, and fungi produce, in culture media at least, considerable amounts of growth substances that have an influence on plant development. Because of the large microbial population in the root area, the concentration of products of this type can be quite high. Roberts and Roberts (19) report that substances inducing an auxin-like response in *Avena* coleoptiles were produced in agar media by 77 per cent of the bacteria, 66 per cent of the actinomycetes, and 46 per cent of the soil fungi investigated. Indoleacetic acid, one of these growth promoters, is synthesized by species of *Pseudomonas* and *Agrobacterium*, common rhizosphere bacteria, as well as by other microorganisms. Many bacteria produce large quantities of indoleacetic acid in the presence of tryptophan, but some synthesize the auxin in its absence. Bacterial formation of indoleacetic acid is affected by the presence of roots, and some plants may appreciably alter the microbial synthesis of the compound (23). Auxins have been detected in soil in low concentrations, but the favoring of microbial metabolism by organic amendments increases the level of growth promoters. It is possible, therefore, that auxin biosynthesis may be an important means of plant stimulation.

Phosphorus availability is influenced by the microscopic rhizosphere inhabitants, and because crops require appreciable quantities, changes in the assimilable phosphate concentration are of considerable consequence. It appears that organic phosphorus mineralization, using glycerophosphate and nucleic acid as substrates, is more rapid in the rhizosphere than in soil free of roots (17). However, the net quantity of inorganic phosphorus liberated is governed by the relative rates of mineralization and immobilization. Because of the abundance of bacteria, phosphorus immobilization is probably more rapid within the rhizosphere.

Another phosphorus transformation of agronomic significance is the solubilization of insoluble phosphate-containing compounds. Bacteria associated with the root system may be of assistance in rendering available substances that are poorly soluble. A comparison of the yields of plants grown in sterile and in non-sterile environments containing insoluble phosphate sources reveals that the response to the chemicals is greater where microorganisms are active. Support for the hypothesis that the root microflora is important in this transformation is found in the selective stimulation in the rhizosphere of microorganisms capable of dissolving $Ca_3(PO_4)_2$ (18).

Microorganisms in the rhizosphere probably also alter the solubility of iron and manganese. Iron is utilized in the ferrous form, and the conversion of the ferric to the ferrous state is brought about by an increase in acidity or by a fall in the oxidation-reduction potential accompanying microbial metabolism. However, the accumulation of certain organic acids commonly associated with carbohydrate decomposition can modify the soluble iron level because the organic acids chelate the cation. The acids may also make manganese less available for plant nutrition. Evidence for a relationship between manganese-oxidizing bacteria and deficiencies of the element has already been reviewed.

Products of microbial metabolism often have a detrimental effect upon higher plants. For example, many bacteria, when inoculated onto agar media containing aseptically cultivated tobacco seedlings, release soluble toxins. These inhibitory agents evoke symptoms from the seedlings typical of a number of deleterious substances (28). Thus, common non-pathogenic bacteria produce harmful effects through the release of soluble toxic factors. The intimacy of the association between bacteria and root would magnify any such inhibitions.

Since the rhizosphere has an immense population, much larger than in normal soil, mutual antagonisms are more pronounced. Moreover, if antibiotic formation is of consequence in natural habitats, one of the more likely environments for their production is the root zone, where the supply of energy substrates is particularly large. Several antibiotics are assimilated by higher plants through the root systems and then are translocated to above-ground portions. Should antibiotics be synthesized in the rhizosphere, their production may affect the development of root pathogens and, if translocated to stems and leaves, the development of disease in above-ground tissues. Antibiotics are also known to affect the physiology of the plant entirely apart from any antimicrobial actions they might have.

Plant Pathogens and the Rhizosphere

The population of the rhizosphere is composed mainly of non-pathogenic microorganisms. But the very density and the increased microbial interactions—competitive, antagonistic, and beneficial—can be especially important for soil-borne pathogens because the disease-producing organism must penetrate the rhizosphere in order to initiate infection. The intense biological interactions may lead to the elimination or suppression of the pathogen or, under certain conditions, they may be beneficial. The root excretions and sloughed-off tissues themselves affect the pathogen directly or, by the changes brought about in the saprophytic flora, indirectly. The common observation that soil-borne pathogenic fungi are more destructive in sterile than in normal soil indicates a role for the microflora in the development of disease; the ecological site of greatest saprophytic activity, the root surface, is undoubtedly the locale where interference with the pathogen is maximal.

The reasons for the differences in disease resistance between varieties of a single plant species remain largely obscure. Resistance often resides in a physiological or biochemical difference between the resistant and the susceptible varieties. The dissimilarity may be expressed, at least in part, by modifications in the root excretions or root tissue composition. Therefore, it is not too difficult to visualize a condition in which resistance or susceptibility is linked with the microflora of the rhizosphere. For example, the resistance of one variety may be dependent upon the excretion through the roots of a substance which induces the development of a flora competitive with or antagonistic to the pathogen.

Evidence is available that there is a correlation between the rhizosphere flora and resistance to some soil-borne pathogens. Thus, varieties of flax susceptible to the wilt caused by *Fusarium oxysporum* f. *lini* possess a greater number of bacteria, actinomycetes, and fungi per unit weight of rhizosphere soil than wilt-resistant varieties. Likewise, tobacco varieties susceptible to *Thielaviopsis basicola* root-rot support a larger number of bacteria, actinomycetes, and fungi in their root zones than resistant varieties (table 3). Qualitatively, the susceptible flax and tobacco plants have in their rhizospheres a greater relative abundance of bacteria requiring amino acids and B vitamins than is found in disease-resistant varieties. Spore-forming bacteria and coccoid rods are more numerous in the rhizosphere of the resistant flax and tobacco while the short, gram negative rods constitute a large per cent of the bacterial flora in the disease-susceptible plants (15). Analogous qualitative and quantitative changes among the bacteria have been found in varieties of other agricultural crops. Because the root population is often related to disease resistance, programs designed to control soil-borne pathogens not succumbing to conventional treatments should take into account not only the pathogen but also the normal root microflora.

In this light, the rhizosphere may be considered as a microbiological buffer zone in which the microflora serves to protect the plant from the attack of the pathogen. The mechanism of the buffering

TABLE 3

The Population in the Rhizosphere of Plant Varieties Resistant and Susceptible to Disease (16)

Plant Variety	Organisms/g of Soil $\times 10^3$		
	Bacteria	Actinomycetes	Fungi
Flax			
Wilt resistant	13,100	2,100	48.5
Wilt susceptible	18,100	3,000	75.6
Tobacco			
Rot resistant	269,600	31,900	239.5
Rot susceptible	505,400	155,200	939.7

action is unknown. Antibiotic production by the root microflora is often cited, but rarely is there a correlation between the numbers or types of antagonists and the disease resistance of the variety. Other possible microbiological interactions have been discussed in the previous chapter. However, regardless of the explanation, the importance of non-pathogenic soil inhabitants to plant disease has been well established. Future developments will no doubt help resolve the problem.

REFERENCES

Reviews

Clark, F. E. 1949. Soil microorganisms and plant roots. *Adv. Agron.*, 1:241–288.

Katznelson, H., A. G. Lochhead, and M. I. Timonin. 1948. Soil microorganisms and the rhizosphere. *Botan. Rev.*, 14:543–587.

Starkey, R. L. 1958. Interrelations between microorganisms and plant roots in the rhizosphere. *Bacteriol. Rev.*, 22:154–172.

Literature cited

1. Agnihothrudu, V. 1955. *Naturwissenschaften*, 42:515–516.
2. Bartholomew, W. V., and F. E. Clark. 1950. *Trans. 4th Intl. Cong. Soil Sci.*, 2:112–113.
3. Barton, R. 1957. *Nature*, 180:613–614.
4. Clark, F. E., and D. H. Smith. 1949. *Soil Sci. Soc. Am., Proc.*, 14:199–202.
5. Coley-Smith, J. R., and C. J. Hickman. 1957. *Nature*, 180:445.

6. Fred, E. B., and A. R. C. Haas. 1919. *J. Gen. Physiol.*, 1:631–638.
7. Goring, C. A. I., and F. E. Clark. 1948. *Soil Sci. Soc. Am., Proc.*, 13:261–266.
8. Harris, J. R. 1953. *Nature*, 172:507–508.
9. Katznelson, H. 1946. *Soil Sci.*, 62:343–354.
10. Katznelson, H., and J. W. Rouatt. 1957. *Canad. J. Microbiol.*, 3:265–269.
11. Katznelson, H., J. W. Rouatt, and T. M. B. Payne. 1955. *Plant and Soil*, 7:35–48.
12. Krasilnikov, N. A. 1934. *Mikrobiologiya*, 3:343–359.
13. Krasilnikov, N. A., A. E. Kriss, and M. A. Litvinov. 1936. *Mikrobiologiya*, 5:87–98.
14. Linford, M. B. 1942. *Soil Sci.*, 53:93–103.
15. Lochhead, A. G. 1940. *Canad. J. Research*, C, 18:42–53.
16. Lochhead, A. G., M. I. Timonin, and P. M. West. 1940. *Sci. Agric.*, 20:414–418.
17. Nilsson, P. E. 1957. *Lantbruks-Hogskol. Ann.*, 23:175–218.
18. Nowotny-Mieczynska, A., and J. Golebiowska. 1956. *Acta Microbiol. Polon.*, 5:129–132.
19. Roberts, J. L., and E. Roberts. 1939. *Soil Sci.*, 48:135–139.
20. Rouatt, J. W., and H. Katznelson. 1957. *Canad. J. Microbiol.*, 3:271–275.
21. Rovira, A. D. 1956. *Plant and Soil*, 7:195–208.
22. Rovira, A. D. 1956. *Plant and Soil*, 7:209–217.
23. Smaly, V. T., and O. I. Bershova. 1957. *Mikrobiologiya*, 26:526–532.
24. Smith, N. R. 1928. *J. Bacteriol.*, 15:20–21.
25. Sperber, J. I., and A. D. Rovira. 1959. *J. Applied Bacteriol.*, 22:85–95.
26. Starkey, R. L. 1929. *Soil Sci.*, 27:433–444.
27. Starkey, R. L. 1939. *Proc. 3rd Intl. Cong. Microbiol.*, New York, pp. 686–687.
28. Steinberg, R. A. 1947. *J. Agric. Research*, 75:199–206.
29. Timonin, M. I. 1940. *Canad. J. Research*, C, 18:307–317.
30. Timonin, M. I., and A. G. Lochhead. 1948. *Trans. Royal Soc. Canada*, Ser. III, Sec. 5, 42:175–181.
31. Voroshilova, E. A. 1956. *Mikrobiologiya*, 25:697–699.
32. Wallace, R. H., and A. G. Lochhead. 1949. *Soil Sci.*, 67:63–69.

Index

461